The Empowered Laboratory Team

**A Survival Kit for
Supervisors, Team Leaders, and
Team Professionals**

Practical Laboratory Management Series

The Practical Laboratory Management Series

I Developing Performance Standards for Hospital Personnel
II The Customer-Oriented Laboratory
III Implementing Quality Assurance
IV Coping With Difficult People in the Health Care Setting
V Systematic Quality Management
VI The Empowered Laboratory Team
VII The Customer-Oriented Laboratory, 2nd Edition

The Empowered Laboratory Team

A Survival Kit for Supervisors, Team Leaders, and Team Professionals

William O. Umiker, MD
Adjunct Professor of Clinical Pathology
Hershey Medical Center
Penn State University
Hershey, Pennsylvania

American Society of Clinical Pathologists
Chicago

Notice

Trade names and equipment and supplies described herein are included as suggestions only. In no way does their inclusion constitute an endorsement or preference by the American Society of Clinical Pathologists. The ASCP did not test the equipment, supplies, or procedures and, therefore, urges all readers to read and follow all manufacturers' instructions and package insert warnings concerning the proper and safe use of products.

Library of Congress Cataloging-in-Publication Data

Umiker, William O.
   The empowered laboratory team: a survival kit for supervisors, team leaders, and team professionals / William O. Umiker
     p. cm. — (The practical laboratory management series)
   Includes bibliographical references and index.
   ISBN 0-89189-384-9
   1. Medical laboratories—Management. I. Title. II. Series.
RB36.3.F5545 1996
616.07'56'068—dc20

95-39084
CIP

Printed in the United States of America.

00 99 98 97 96   5 4 3 2 1

This book is dedicated to Stacey Bailey

Contents

Preface ix

Acknowledgments xii

1 Introduction 1

I Prelude to Team Building 11

2 Risk Taking: A Team Imperative 13

3 Adjusting to Change and Transition 21

4 Delegation and Succession Planning: Keys to Empowerment 33

5 Empowerment: The Engine of Participative Management 47

6 Participative Management: Group Empowerment 59

7 Introduction to Teams and Building Interdependence 71

8 Establishing Self-Directed Teams 83

II The New Team and Its Leaders 93

9 Supervisor-in-Transition: The Coach 95

10 The Leader of the Self-Directed Work Team 107

11 The Members of the Team 115

12 Principles of Coping With Difficult People 127

13 The Underperformers 137

14 Unpleasant Colleagues and Superiors 147

III Systems and Culture 159

15 Recognition and Reward Systems 161

16 Organizational Culture and Cultural Diversity 173

17 Principles of Project Management and Process Reengineering 181

18 Practical Aspects of Process Reengineering 195

19 Union-Management Partnership in Team Building 205

IV Training of Team Members 215

20 Training Team Members 217

21 Power Communication: The Foundation of Team 229

22 Decision Making and Problem Solving 239

23 Team Meetings That Work 251

24 Persuasion and Negotiating Skills 261

25 Financial Management 271

26 Networks, Mentors, and Organizational Politics 279

27 Innovation, Creativity, and Entrepreneurship 291

28 Time Management for Individuals and Teams 297

Index 309

Preface

I began this book by envisioning a laboratory in which customer satisfaction was the top priority and employees were not only satisfied with their roles but actually looked forward to the next day—a facility in which no one says, "I don't want to go to work today."

In my vision, employees believe that what is good for them is also good for the organization, and the entrepreneurial spirit thrives. The empowered employees feel and act like owners of the organization. They do not hesitate to voice their opinions and are willing to make decisions and take calculated career risks.

They accept challenges, welcome opportunities to expand their range of competencies, and respect their teammates. They know that their rewards and compensation are based on customer satisfaction, applied technical or professional expertise, and performance results, not on length of service, title, or the number and kinds of letters after their names.

Personnel empowerment, participative management, and team building provide the blueprint for making my vision come true. This is what this book is all about.

The book's goal is to enable organizations to move toward this vision. The objectives for reaching this goal include delegation, empowerment, participative management, coaching skills, leadership, power communication, effective training, increasing innovation, and team building. Other objectives are the induction of change and risk and the prevention or resolution of dysfunctional behavior on the part of group members.

Employers expect—or at least hope—that their employees will assume more responsibility for the success of their enterprises. Most employers strive to replace bureaucracy with entrepreneurial spirit, and they are taking intense second looks at how their organizational practices and politics affect this new paradigm.

Employers and executives will appreciate the thorough overview of the transition to participative management and team building. They will note the practical value to their managers and workers of the pages loaded with suggestions for empowerment, team building and functioning, and training. They will approve at least some of the ideas for formal, informal, and one-on-one reward and recognition systems. I hope they share their copies of the book and make others available to teams and individuals.

Supervisors and other front-line care providers are my primary target audience. This book's strength lies in its ability to serve as a launching pad for supervisors and others who are contemplating involvement in initiatives such as delegation, empowerment, and team building. I visualize the successful supervisors as change specialists who can eliminate the fear and apprehension of operational changes, and who create a work environment in which innovation and customer service thrive.

These front-line managers will learn how to switch from a parental leadership style to a situational and participative one by delegating and empowering more effectively. They will lay the groundwork for team building not only by shifting accountability and authority but also by eliminating the roadblocks to effective teamwork by vigorously addressing the dysfunctional behavior of employees who have difficulty adjusting to the team concept.

Many supervisors who are learning how to turn over their tasks to work teams have not been told what is in store for them when this has been accomplished. Unfortunately, some of them will be out of a job unless they can prove that they will be of value to the organization in a new role. Reading this book may prevent such undesirable end games.

I encourage supervisors and team leaders to make full use of the talents of each member of their work group, to make their daily routines more bearable, and to rekindle the creative spirit that resides in each of us.

I help supervisors learn how to build successful teams and to train new team members. As their role changes from boss to coach, facilitator, and trainer, these managers will become increasingly aware of the opportunities they will have to pursue opportunities that they did not have the time for when they were overly busy discharging their duties as bosses. This book will help them to make the important decision whether they should stay on as a group leader elected by their team or move up the managerial hierarchy, perhaps becoming facilitators for multiple teams.

Personnel problems in the workplace are magnified when people are molded into collaborative work situations. From the abundant literature dealing with behavioral problems, I have selected the most common kinds of problems encountered in team functions.

I also kept the team members in mind when I wrote this book. When management embarks on employee empowerment, participative management, or the molding of self-directed teams, extensive training of everyone involved is essential. In the traditional work situation, technical and professional employees spend most of their time applying the expertise of their specialty. They work independently to a large extent, rather than in coherent teams. Now they must learn two additional sets of activities— teamwork and the many functions that previously had been carried out by their supervisors. Often employees' tasks become more general and less specialized.

Most of these professionals will require intensive training in interpersonal skills, including better communication, conflict resolution, and adjusting to change. Their training in administrative skills must be on a par with that received by their former supervisors. Some of these players will serve as team leaders, either on a rotating or a semipermanent basis.

What's Different About This Book?
Many excellent books are available on participative management and self-directed teams. This one is different in the following aspects:

- The ambiance is that of a clinical laboratory.
- The supervisor-in-transition is featured. This is the first-line manager who is responsible for developing a semiautonomous work group.
- Just about everything that a team member needs to learn is presented, and not only what should be done but how to do it.
- Team members who want to prepare themselves for team leadership roles will find practical, hands-on advice.
- The book can be used as a training manual for any organization that is introducing participative management or team building.
- Although the main thrust is on the development of self-directed teams, much valuable information is presented for those managers and professionals in organizations that are not instituting self-directed teams.

Acknowledgments

My Virtual Network of Authors

This book would not have been possible without tapping into the writings of a host of authors. The names of the following writers will be found sprinkled throughout: P. Block, W.C. Byham, M.E. Douglass and D.N. Douglass, R.J. Doyle and P.I. Doyle, K. Fisher, D. Harrington-Mackin, C.R. McConnell, D.Q. Mills, J.D. Orsburn, T.L. Quick, R.S. Wellins, and J.H. Zenger.

The following writers made significant contributions to the indicated chapters:

Chapter 5.	P. Block
Chapter 6.	L.C. Plunkett, K. Fisher, and G. Milite
Chapter 7.	J. Gordon
Chapter 9.	K. Fisher
Chapter 14.	H. Geneen
Chapter 15.	R.L. Hale and R.F. Maehling
Chapter 16.	S.M. Ketchum, B. Bloch, and B.B. Karp
Chapter 17.	M. Hammer
Chapter 19.	C.R. McConnell and T. Haimann
Chapter 20.	R.S. Wellins and W.C. Byham
Chapter 22.	C.H. Kepner
Chapter 24.	K. Albrecht and S. Albrecht
Chapter 25.	J. Sattler
Chapter 26.	P. Block
Chapter 27.	E.O. Teisberg
Chapter 28.	M.E. Douglass and D.N. Douglass

My Local Team

I am beholden to a great nurse leader, Betsy McIntyre, who patiently explained the functioning of the new nursing team concept at St. Joseph Medical Center in Lancaster, PA.

Herb Kruger, our audiovisual wizard, always stood ready to answer my distress calls when my computer took advantage of my naiveté.

Pat Miller, a magnificent medical librarian, has been indispensable in finding references for me for a number of years. I thank her again for her help in making this book possible.

My Midwest and Far East Mentor

Joshua Weikersheimer, Director of the ASCP Press, has, as always, been patient and supportive.

1. Introduction

FROM A BROAD perspective, businesses are being impelled toward nontraditional management by three forces. The first is today's business environment with its demand for quick responsiveness to customers and cost control. The second is the sudden availability of technology. The third is the desire of employees for greater involvement in their work.[1]

D. Quinn Mills

CHAPTER OBJECTIVES

- To review the challenges faced by health care employers and their responses to these challenges
- To delineate the prerequisites to successful shared governance
- To describe the employee empowerment concept
- To provide a brief overview of participative management
- To characterize the features of true work teams
- To depict the new roles of supervisors and team leaders
- To sum up the new responsibilities of team members and note potential problem members
- To discuss the significance of systems and culture
- To propose a comprehensive training program for team members
- To focus on some barriers to shared governance initiatives

THE CHALLENGES FACED BY HEALTH CARE EMPLOYERS

Although the shared governance paradigm has taken the world by storm, for many employers it has remained an elusive dream.[2] Health care employers face the challenges of uncertainty: changing markets; new technologies; demands of patients, physicians, and third-party payers; greater expectations of employees; new regulatory demands; and shifting alliances among physicians, hospitals, and third-party payers.

Hospitals struggle to get inpatients—many beds are empty. Surgicenters and medical clinics take many of their outpatients by offering faster service, more convenient locations, and better parking. Physician groups install their own diagnostic and therapeutic facilities. Former hospital employees, such as physical therapists, set up in private practice. Sales representatives of commercial laboratories try to divert physicians from sending specimens to hospital laboratories.

Physicians demand faster turnaround times. Surgeons want the latest and most expensive gadgets. Nursing services must negotiate daily with employment registries for the services of nurses to fill gaps in some specialties.

In many organizations, the percentage of employees who provide hands-on medical care plummets, while administrative and clerical staffs increase. Furthermore, the acuity of the average inpatient has increased because less ill patients are not admitted and patients are discharged sooner. Patients are more medically knowledgeable and more demanding.

Managers must now accommodate new employees who are mentally or physically challenged. Their staffs include more people who speak little or no English or who have disparate cultural practices. They must train entry-level employees who can barely read or write.

Employees request expanded benefits. Union organizers wait in the wings to respond to any signs of employee dissatisfaction.

THE RESPONSES OF MANAGEMENT TO THE CHALLENGES

Health care executives strive for improved customer service, greater efficiency, and competitive advantage—or at least survival. To achieve these goals they reduce staffs, modify operational systems and processes, and market new services such as industrial medicine, wellness clinics, and home care. They buy more efficient equipment, apply economies of scale, and update their recognition and reward systems.

Many executives practice "management by best-seller."[3] They hire consultants to help them embark on shared management enterprises. To be successful, these actions require multitiered coordination and collaboration, new work groups, new facilities, and greater flexibility and adaptability.

THE AWAKENING

It finally dawned on the people in the executive suites that to be successful they must make maximum use of the current and the potential capabilities of every employee. They also realized that to expand these capabilities, much time and thorough education and training are required.

Many administrators were pleasantly surprised to find that their front-line caregivers possess common sense, are capable of handling much more responsibility, have great ideas about how things can be improved, and can make better decisions than many of the consultants and highly paid MBAs sitting in the front offices. They also found that when these power shifts take place, morale rises, turnover and absenteeism decrease, and productivity may soar.

To take full advantage of this people power, health care executives try to switch from paternalistic leadership aimed at control, consistency, and predictability to democratic leadership that features empowerment, participative management, and self-directed teams.

CEOs are flattening their organizational charts by eliminating layers of management or by replacing pyramidal charts with matrix configurations. The most progressive among them turn their charts upside-down, with customers and front-line care providers at the top and senior officials in lower supporting roles. A few have installed "open book" management in which they not only provide their employees with the same data they give to their governing boards but also teach their workers how to interpret the financial reports.

Unfortunately, many employers have not succeeded in decreasing the power, privileges, and rewards that are concentrated at the top. Many have at least eliminated the trappings of privilege, such as reserved parking and executive dining rooms.

Adaptive CEOs know the new ways of using old teams and new teams. They have learned that empowerment, the introduction of self-directed teams, and gain-sharing reward systems beget employees' sense of ownership and commitment. Their authoritarian colleagues try to accomplish this by persuading, manipulating, or demanding.[4]

Laboratory and other health care managers are also faced with challenges that exceed any they encountered in previous years. They are expected to accomplish more with smaller staffs and to roll back costs at a time when everything they must purchase is more expensive. Accrediting agencies, such as the Joint Commission on the Accreditation of Healthcare Organizations (JCAHO), mandate more, and governmental laws and regulations bury them in red tape.

Managers are being told that they must delegate more, practice participative leadership, and develop semiautonomous work teams that are to assume some or all of the administrative and supervisory responsibilities of first-line managers.

PART I: PRELUDE TO TEAM BUILDING

The first prerequisite to any form of shared governance is the ability of leaders to take career risks and to encourage their employees to do likewise. The kinds of risks include willingness to voice opinions, make decisions, and accept challenging assignments (Chapter 2).

The second prerequisite is the ability of individuals and groups to adjust to the many changes that participative management demands (Chapter 3).

The third prerequisite is the ability and willingness of managers at all levels to delegate authority and responsibility to the people who report to them. Without delegation, participative management cannot exist (Chapter 4).

Empowerment: The Engine of Participation

Empowerment is the engine of continuous quality improvement (CQI), participative management, delegation, quality circles, self-directed work teams, creativity, entrepreneurship, time management, and succession planning. Delegation of authority and other modalities of empowerment are vital to serious attempts to compete in today's health care market.

To get employees to accept a culture of total quality management (TQM), take ownership of their jobs, and develop personal interest in improving their performance, they must be trained and empowered. How else can managers get employees thinking every day about ways to improve quality; to increase output, quality, and customer service; and to stimulate and focus their creative juices?[5] Empowerment reduces workers' feelings of helplessness. The more people are in control of their work, the greater their enthusiasm, optimism, self-confidence, and energy.

The chief beneficiary of employee empowerment is the customer. External customers find that the quality and speed of service increases. Internal customers note better coordination and cooperation among departments and services (Chapter 5).

Participative Management

The participative style of management enjoys current popularity. It enables organizations to respond better to changing customer needs and improve quality, productivity, cost savings, and employee morale. Autocratic, bureaucratic, and manipulative leadership are anathema to advocates of participative management.

Participative management is predicated on three assumptions[6]:

1. People who are closest to the work know best how to perform and improve their jobs. Participative management demands that organizational decision making be made at the lowest appropriate level.

2. Most employees want to feel that they "own" their jobs and are making meaningful contributions to the effectiveness of their organizations.
3. Teams provide possibilities for empowerment that are not available to individual employees.

The quality circle is an example of a kind of participative management technique that has lost much of its luster. Developed in Japan in 1962, it reached its peak popularity in the early 1980s. For many organizations, quality circles represented the first application of worker participatory groups. A variation of the quality circle is the task force in which a single problem is addressed.

Effective application of shared governance does not always require semiautonomous work teams, but these do showcase participative leadership and provide benchmarks for leaders who want to enhance teamwork.

In a true participatory system, the relationships among employees and between employees and their superiors are profoundly altered. The meaning of participatory leadership gets subverted when employees treat their superiors as their most important customers or when they cannot function effectively without the control and support of superiors.

The implementation of full participation by workers mandates that the scope of education and training programs be broadened to include team building skills as well as enhancement of technical and professional capabilities. Rotation of tasks and cross-functional activities are becoming the initiatives of the 1990s. When leaders fail to provide full and complete support, their efforts are more cosmetic than enduring (Chapter 6).

The True Work Team

The team concept has always received lip service in most organizations. One still hears traditional managers talking about "teamwork" and "being a team player." Teamwork is usually a characteristic included on the rating lists of performance appraisal forms. However, most people have not actually had a sustained true team experience at work. Employees can work in the same department for years, serve on committees, meet in management groups regularly, and still not be a part of a true team. For example, surgical teams require great teamwork, but they are not self-directed teams. In fact, they are autocratic, with the surgeon in the patriarchal role.

What then is a true team? We define a team as a highly interactive group of people who share a common goal and who work together to achieve that goal. Semiautonomous teams represent the ultimate in terms of employee participation. The significance of the team movement has been equated with that of the scientific management principles enunciated by Frederick Taylor at the turn of the century. These principles led to scientifically designed jobs that reduced the required skill of blue-collar workers. Participative management, empowerment, delegation, and self-directed teams represent movement in the opposite direction.[7]

Self-Directed Teams

Self-directed (autonomous or empowered) teams are empowered to control the work they do without a formal first-line manager. Each team has a leader who usually comes from the ranks of the workers on the team. Most such teams plan and schedule their work, make operational and personnel decisions, solve problems, set priorities, determine who does what, organize vacation leave and other time off, and share leadership responsibilities.

Hundreds of recent books and articles have been written about team dynamics, group cohesiveness, and high-performance teams.[6] However, the concept of self-directed teams is not a recent development. Coal miners in England had such teams in 1949. Others have been in existence for years in Sweden and in a few progressive companies in the United States.[8] For a number of years, the 3M Corporation has used small groups of employees called "Skunk Works" that take an idea, do some quick experimentation to test feasibility, and take it forward if it has potential or drop it quickly if not.[9]

Self-directed teams are essential to the development of a TQM culture.[7] The concept of quality improvement has been the motivating force for team building paradigms such as quality circles, brainstorming groups, and work simplification teams.

Unfortunately, in some organizations team building consists solely of teaching group meeting skills to new work groups. For executives looking for a quick and easy fix, jumping into the team building strategy is a quick and painful experience. Supervisors and managers who accept the concept without understanding what they are getting into are also in for a rude awakening.

The building of self-directed teams does not have to start as a pervasive massive management wave. It can begin as a pilot study or as the result of the initiative of a departmental chief. A paradigm shift can spring up anywhere (Chapters 7 and 8).

PART II: THE NEW TEAM AND ITS LEADERS

Supervisors-in-Transition

True self-directed work teams do not have supervisors and subordinates; they have coaches or facilitators and associates or colleagues. The supervisors-in-transition are the key to successful team building. Without their cooperation and support, team building will fail. These supervisors-in-transition are expected to turn over most or all of their authority and responsibility to their work groups—now called teams. For supervisors who have been in control for years, this is not easy. For those who are die-hard autocrats who cannot or will not share their power or delegate administrative responsibilities, this transition is all but impossible.

These power shifts offer supervisors new opportunities to do important things that they never had the time to do before (Chapter 9).

Team Leaders

Team leaders are usually selected from the team members and by those members, either on a rotating or a permanent basis. In a few instances these leaders had been the group's supervisor. The team leader can be deposed at any time by the other team members.

The team leaders do not have the full range of responsibilities carried by supervisors-in-transition. They promote teamwork, fill in for absent team members, help to develop people skills and commitment, answer general questions addressed to the team, and represent the team at meetings. They strive to improve safety, enhance morale, and minimize errors (Chapter 10).

Team Members

Team members must adjust to team member roles. In the past, they spent all of their time performing technical or professional duties—often in a specialist role. Now they are expected to coordinate their tasks more closely with other members of the team, learn enough new tasks to qualify as generalists, and perform administrative duties such as making operational decisions, helping select and evaluate new employees, assuming responsibility for purchases and inventory control, cross-training colleagues, and sometimes evaluating the performances of their coworkers.

Some employees are unable or unwilling to make the necessary role adjustments. Some of these will resign or be reassigned to units that do not have self-directed teams. Others will remain and cause interpersonal problems that must be confronted by the supervisors-in-transition or the team leader (Chapters 11 through 14).

PART III: SYSTEMS AND CULTURE

"To realize gains in quality, productivity, efficiency, and competitive edge, health care providers must deploy proven methods such as work redesign, team-based structures, and empowered workforces."[10]

Recognition and Reward Systems

The focus in Part II is on people and the adjustments they must make. Successful participative management also necessitates taking a second look at systems, processes, values, and cultures. Major changes in these are often needed for successful team-building initiatives. Take, for instance, recognition/reward systems.

When team building begins, intrinsic motivations alone may provide sufficient enthusiasm. Later, employees begin to look for payoffs for accepting all the additional accountability and undergoing the extensive training. Sustained team function requires both financial and nonfinancial incentives.[11] People respond favorably to operational changes when they find that appropriate behavior and results are recognized and rewarded. Therefore, new recognition and reward systems are essential. Team efforts must be rewarded as much as individual efforts (Chapter 15).

Culture in the Workplace

Organizational observers need not remind us that the composition of our work force is changing rapidly and radically. Many employees speak little or no English, creating veritable Towers of Babel. Special consideration must now also be shown to mentally and physically challenged individuals.

Cultural, racial, and gender differences can create major communication and interpersonal problems if they are not handled with care. The Japanese find it easier to implement initiatives that involve worker participation because their culture has long fostered worker identity with the organization, commitment to consensus decision making by groups, and concern over employee welfare.[11] The American culture, on the other hand, is built on individualism, which runs counter to teams (Chapter 16).[2]

Process Reengineering and Project Management

"We are in a process of rethinking and reconfiguring every aspect of our operation, not just specific departments. In short, no aspect of our operation will go unexamined."[12]

It has become apparent that most inefficiencies at the work stations are not the fault of employees but are attributable to bad operational systems or processes. To improve efficiency and quality while reducing costs, extensive process and system reengineering are needed. This also requires cross-functional training to break down interdepartmental walls that traditional management created around departments when work was divided into functional units, such as laboratory, radiology, and the like. When major operational changes are contemplated, processes must be reengineered and often special projects must be structured (Chapters 17 and 18).

Unions and Teams

Many hospitals and nursing facilities are unionized, and more will be in the future if unions continue their current efforts and employers fail to live up to the lofty mission statements that adorn their reception areas. Supervisors and other managers must learn to work with union representatives and avoid the legal pitfalls that can get them into trouble with the National Labor

Relations Board (NLRB) when work teams make the mistake of discussing work factors that are the province of the union (Chapter 19).

PART IV: TRAINING OF TEAM MEMBERS

"A company that has hired people of very limited educational and social skills will not be able to convert them to highly productive employees just by offering them greater involvement in their work."[1]

Every writer and consultant who has studied shared governance enterprises warns that much time and resources must be devoted to the education and training of managers and team members. Supervisors learn how to transfer power. Team members learn how to interact in teams; how to perform technical or professional tasks that they had not previously done; and how to handle administrative, training, and supervisory responsibilities that had been performed by their supervisor.

To ensure understanding and collaboration, team members are taught communication skills. They learn how to cope with conflict, persuade people, negotiate, and enhance team and individual power by enlarging their networks. Special skills include managing time and finances and improving creativity and innovativeness. This training is so essential that we have devoted the last 9 chapters to it (Chapters 20 through 28).

BARRIERS TO SHARED GOVERNANCE

Generations of patriarchal management make it difficult for some older managers to become disciples of democratic or delegative leadership. Empowerment and team building are not easy, and, like most management waves, they take years to develop.[8] In 1976, Timm[13] gave a speech in Pinehurst, NC, in which he described the concept of MBWA—Management by Walking Around, but the concept was not popularized until the mid-1980s.

In addition to conceptualizing, planning, and operational implementation, extensive training is required. Technical or professional skills, administrative skills, and interpersonal skills must all be mastered.

Many managers are reluctant to give up much of their power or fear the loss of their jobs so they stonewall the plans. Even when they try to switch to participatory governance, managers who on Monday are implementing democratic systems spend Tuesday instituting more controls.

Poor planning, inadequate training, and reward systems that are inadequate or that encourage individual rather than team efforts all take their toll.

Not all employees want to, or can, participate, and some get discouraged when they realize that extensive training is required. Their persistent dependency on others rests on the belief that there are people in power who know what is best.[4]

Another factor is the difficulty of maintaining enthusiasm for any new management initiative. When was the last time you attended a seminar on management-by-objectives or management-by-motivation? The success of quality circles in Fortune 1000 companies dropped from 67% in 1987 to 52% in 1990 according to Lawler and his group of investigators.[14] With diminishing returns on investment, a drop in interest always occurs on the part of both managers and workers.

Pitfalls include misunderstanding the concepts of all-out participative management. Misconceptions include regarding the initiatives as temporary cures, limited endeavors, or one-problem solutions or limiting teams to those involving only the workers and not the upper levels of management.

REFERENCES

1. Mills DQ. *Rebirth of the Corporation*. New York, NY: John Wiley & Sons; 1991.

2. Fisher K. *Leading Self-Directed Work Teams: A Guide to Developing New Team Leadership Skills*. New York, NY: McGraw-Hill; 1993.

3. Goodale JG. Effective teamwork and productivity conferences. *Clin Lab Manage Rev*. 1994;8:241-243.

4. Block P. *The Empowered Manager: Positive Political Skills at Work*. San Francisco, Calif: Jossey-Bass; 1987.

5. Byham WC. *Zapp!: The Lightning of Empowerment*. New York, NY: Harmony Books; 1988.

6. Wellins RS, Byham WC, Wilson JM. *Empowered Teams: Creating Self-Directed Work Groups That Improve Quality, Productivity, and Participation*. San Francisco, Calif: Jossey-Bass; 1991.

7. Lee C. Beyond teamwork. *Training*. 1990;27:25-32.

8. Orsburn JD, Moran L, Musselwhite E, Zenger JH. *Self-Directed Work Teams: The New American Challenge*. Homewood, Ill: Business One Irwin; 1990.

9. Hastings C, Bixby P, Chaudry-Lawton R. *The Superteam Solution*. Hants, Great Britain: Gower; 1986.

10. Montebello AR. Teamwork in health care: opportunities for gains in quality, productivity, and competitive advantage. *Clin Lab Manage Rev*. 1994;8:91-105.

11. Thompson PC. *Quality Circles: How to Make Them Work in America*. New York, NY: AMACOM; 1982.

12. Lyons JE. *St. Joseph Hospital Directions*. 1994;1:1.

13. Timm PR. *Managerial Communication: A Finger on the Pulse*. Englewood Cliffs, NJ: Prentice-Hall, Inc; 1986.

14. Lawler E III, Albers-Mohrman S, Ledford G Jr. *Employee Involvement and Total Quality Management Practices and Results in Fortune 1,000 Companies*. San Francisco, Calif: Jossey-Bass; 1993.

PART I
Prelude to Team Building

2. Risk Taking: A Team Imperative

THOSE WHO PLAY it safe may survive in the organization, but who'll know they're there?[1]
    Norman Metzger

CHAPTER OBJECTIVES

- To stress the importance of risk taking at work
- To describe the characteristics of risk avoiders and risk takers and postulate reasons why people eschew risk taking
- To provide suggestions for minimizing the risk in risk taking
- To help you to encourage others to take more calculated risks

The word "risk" sends shock waves up and down the hierarchical spine of health care institutions because much time and expense are allocated to reducing risk. They have credentialing, certification, equipment maintenance, preventive medicine, safety policies, infection surveillance, environmental testing, zero-order error missions, and quality assurance—all to minimize risk. Risk managers scurry about trying to avert possible medicolegal problems.

While all this risk aversion is receiving homage, organizational theorists and pundits correctly advise that if we want to be members of winning teams, we must be risk takers, and that we should also espouse risk taking by our associates.

The risks addressed here are not those that pose threats to patients' well being or to employee safety.

The risks in this chapter relate to operational decisions, career choices, and organizational initiatives.

Kindler[2] defines risk as "...a course of action or inaction, taken under conditions of uncertainty, which exposes one to possible loss, in order to reach a desired outcome." Some readers may be more comfortable if I substitute accepting responsibility for taking risks.

Risk is omnipresent. Every time we make a decision, undertake a change, or express an opinion, some risk is involved. The issue is not whether to take risks, but when and how to take reasonable risks. The goal of this chapter is to help you and your team handle risk with more awareness, skill, and assurance.

Risk taking adds zest to our lives, adds challenge to our work, and provides the opportunity for competitive advantage and personal development. Risk avoidance guarantees boredom, frustration, and stagnation.[3] Heroes and people we admire are usually the ones who take risks.[2]

Risk taking is like competitive diving—there are different degrees of difficulty, but the greater the difficulty, the greater the rewards when the endeavors are successful.

THE IMPORTANCE OF RISK TAKING

Risk and Decision Making

In even the simplest of decision-making situations, at least two choices are available: to decide or to not decide. To not decide may be riskier than making a poor selection. For example, a chemistry team could not reach a consensus on which automated analyzer to recommend. The result was that the item was stricken from the budget.

Because there is no such thing as perfect information, elements of risk are present in most decision-making situations. For instance, when selecting new employees, a team may find it difficult to decide between a promising but untested neophyte and an experienced marginal performer.

Risk and Delegation

Both the delegator and the delegatee assume some risk when responsibility and authority are transferred. Empowerment injects risk. Employee motivation and commitment may be increased when delegation and empowerment are successful, but considerable stress may be involved along the way, and the end result may be unsatisfactory.

Risk and Customer Service

Taking risks is essential to providing effective and efficient customer service.[4] For example, if Dr. Smith requests a laboratory test that is not on the Sunday menu, may the medical technologist on duty tell him whether or

Table I
Supervisory Activities That Involve Large Risks

Selecting candidates for employment or promotion
Delegating and assigning
Making proposals or requests
Disagreeing with superiors, especially in public
"Whistle-blowing"
Accepting or not accepting delegated accountabilities
Making demands
Playing the role of devil's advocate
Introducing major change
Making unpopular decisions
Preparing and defending budgets
Negotiating
Disciplining, especially firing

not the test can be done, or must the technologist either refuse to perform the test or hold up action while trying to contact a supervisor?

Risk and Career

Risk taking and autonomy are essential if one wants to advance. Even sitting pat involves risk because a job may become obsolete. Preparing for the future forces many decisions, some of which involve considerable time, expense, and sacrifice.

Our values play an important role in our willingness to take risks. Some values are subject to frequent change. For example, single people are often more willing to take vocational risks than are married people with families.

In some highly competitive organizations, risk avoiders may encourage their competing colleagues to take risks, then try to make the risk takers look stupid.

Personal development requires moving beyond our comfort zones into the unknown. Table I presents a partial list of supervisory activities that involve considerable risk.

RISK AVOIDERS

In a few stable organizations, such as government agencies and educational institutions, the people who get ahead are those who are the most cautious. Risk avoiders resist making decisions until they have explored every nook and cranny for bugs. They won't walk the high wire of decision making without the safety nets of equivocation and procrastination. They always need more data or to "pass it by the boss."

Risk avoiders are also hesitant to commit themselves to new objectives and plans and are resistant to change. They tend to be passive or introverted. As managers, they are highly bureaucratic and ineffective—often being held in contempt.

Risk avoiders do have a useful role. Sometimes resistance may be beneficial. It may represent a cautious, meticulous, and thorough approach—a strength to be put to good use.[5] They make great devil's advocates. You can spot these people quickly by paying attention to some of their comments:

- "You didn't give me the go-ahead."

- "That's not in my position description."

- "That's not what I'm paid to do."

- "We never did it that way."

- "You've got to be kidding."

- "I don't have the authority to do that."

Why People Avoid Risks

We all have a tendency to avoid risks because failure hurts. Avoidance of risk may be based on previous negative experience, having been falsely blamed, or simply a lack of trust of one's superiors. Assigned risky tasks may be perceived as threats.

The more fears we have, the less willing we are to take risks—and we have plenty of fears. Loss of job, physical harm, failure, change, and being sued are just a few of these.

Individuals vary markedly in their willingness to take risks. Bureaucrats avoid risks like the plague. When things go sour, they can always find other people or policies to blame. Howard[6] claims that managers are reluctant to encourage risk taking by their employees because costly mistakes by subordinates are difficult to explain to results-oriented senior managers.

Women are thought by some to be less willing to take risks. Hegerty[7] claims that women executives often regret not having taken more risks.

Kindler[2] discusses the impact of being pressured to make decisions. External pressures come from schedules, group expectations, and aggressive competitors. These pressures can force us to make decisions that we would otherwise avoid or delay. He offers as an example the reluctant decision of the space shuttle contractors to give the go-ahead on the launching of the ill-fated *Challenger*.

Internal or self-generated pressure is expressed as anxiety and fear, producing such behaviors as perfectionism, procrastination, and dysfunctional decision making. Lack of confidence magnifies such pressures. We all have a subconscious inner critical voice or voice of judgment—probably derived from parental influence—that tries to keep us from making mistakes or accepting risk.[8]

Risk Takers

Winners look for the rewards of success. Losers worry about the penalties of failure.
      Unknown author

Autocratic leaders, by making all the important decisions and shunning input from others, assume complete responsibility for their actions, and thereby accept one kind of risk. Delegative and empowering leaders accept risks knowing that they are still accountable for the performance of their employees.

Sharpshooters take calculated risks. They appraise the alternatives and then act. Their theme is ready, aim, fire. The fast-draw artists may shoot themselves in the foot by making decisions before evaluating the situation sufficiently. Their theme is ready, fire, aim. Procrastinators always seem to need more data or advice. Their theme is ready, ready, ready.

Characteristics of Risk Takers

- They strive for achievement and to be the best they can.
- They have less concern about security. They take risks without even seeing the risks as risky.[8]
- They show the flexibility needed to cope with change.
- They have high self-esteem and self-confidence.
- They are enthusiastic and optimistic.
- They regard mistakes as learning experiences.

Group Risk Taking

Psychological research shows that groups make riskier decisions than those that the individuals who make up the groups would have recommended separately. Apparently, sharing accountability reduces personal risk in the participants' minds. What is everybody's responsibility is nobody's responsibility.[5] Janis[9] found a common thread that he termed "groupthink," which describes the social pressure close-knit groups generate that tends to short-circuit consideration of alternatives.

Table II
Questions That Assist in Making Major Decisions

What is my goal or objective?
What are the best and the worst outcomes?
What additional information do I need?
What are the alternative strategies or tactics?
What are the relative rewards and risks of each alternative?
How can I increase the reward or reduce the risk?
What barriers must be overcome?
What support is available?
How will delay affect the rewards and risks?
Is a pilot study possible?
How will the results be monitored?
If things fail to work, what contingency plan is available?

HOW TO MINIMIZE THE RISK IN RISKS

- Establish a support system through networking. Include at least one mentor. Risk taking is difficult without someone to turn to for support.[7]
- Do not take a lot of risks for others. Learn to say no.
- Learn from the mistakes of others.
- Weigh potential problems and losses against potential gains.
- Relax, enjoy, and learn from your risks.
- Delineate the problem before jumping to solutions.
- Pay attention to intuitive warnings.
- Avoid making the same mistake twice.
- Get other people involved in sharing risks.
- Have backup strategies and alternatives.
- Minimize risks by minimizing potential losses, eg, find a new job before resigning from the present one.
- Risk your ego. Admit your errors. Do not overreact.
- If your boss will not let you take risks, it may be time to look for a new boss.[7]

A practical approach to avoid excessive risk when making a major decision can be assisted by answering the questions listed in Table II.

When comparing the relative risk of alternatives, the probability and seriousness factors can be determined and compared. See chapters on planning and decision making for more on this.

ENCOURAGING OTHERS TO TAKE RISKS

Converting hand wringers into risk takers does not come easy. It takes time and patience. It is easier to encourage risk taking when the risks concern objectives that are obviously achievable. When the chance for success is less than 50/50, the objective becomes frustrating, even incapacitating.

Support risk taking by helping colleagues, supporting the implementation of initiatives, being patient, and allowing sufficient time. You can enable teammates to recognize their capabilities and limitationsand how the latter can be minimized.[6]

Show employees how to avoid foolish risks, and do not tolerate repeats of the same errors. Give them all the information they need; people are more willing to take risks when they know as much as possible about what is involved. Also, let them know which actions are reversible and which are not. A decision believed to be irreversible (like a position change) takes at least twice as long to make as one that can be changed.[10]

Permit employees some leeway to be wrong and to realize that intelligent mistakes are part of the price one pays for personal and departmental growth and progress. We all must face up to our mistakes, examine them, and go on with our work. The only real mistake is being afraid to make a mistake.[11]

When people goof, have them criticize their work first. This encourages them to look at action from a variety of angles, and it sharpens their risk-taking skills for the next time.

Tips for Encouraging Risk Taking

- Include "willingness to take risks" among qualifications described in position descriptions.
- Emphasize innovativeness and resourcefulness when orienting new employees.
- Teach the skills necessary for intelligent risk taking.
- Talk openly about errors that you have made.
- Ensure early and quick successes at the beginning. Early successes encourage more risk taking. Reluctant risk takers need to taste success.
- Place minimal restrictions on delegated authority.
- Take risks yourself. A good risk taker inspires others to do likewise.
- Get upset when you hear employees tell clients "I can't do anything about that" or "I'll have to check with my supervisor."

- Do not be too cautious or overly protective.
- Reward risk taking, not risk avoidance.
- Help people express disparate views.
- Do not express your opinion until they have expressed theirs.

REFERENCES

1. Metzger N. *Handbook of Health Care Human Resources Management*. Gaithersburg, Md: Aspen Publishers; 1981.
2. Kindler HS. *Risk Taking: A Guide for Decision Makers*. Los Altos, Calif: Crisp Publishers; 1990.
3. LeBoeuf M. *The Greatest Management Principle in the World*. New York, NY: Berkley Books; 1985.
4. Davidow WH, Uttal BK. *Total Customer Service: The Ultimate Weapon*. New York, NY: Harper & Row; 1988.
5. Giegold WC. *Practical Management Skills for Engineers and Scientists*. Belmont, Calif: Lifetime Learning Publications; 1982.
6. Howard JP. Moderate risk: Key to professional success. *Supervis Manage*. 1990;35:1-2.
7. Hegarty C. *How to Manage Your Boss*. Mill Valley, Calif: Whatever Publishing Co; 1982.
8. Ray M, Myers R. *Creativity in Business*. Garden City, NY: Doubleday & Co; 1986.
9. Janis IL. *Victims of Group Think*. Boston, Mass: Houghton Mifflin; 1972.
10. Kirby T. *The Can-do Manager*. New York, NY: AMACOM; 1989.
11. Geneen H. *Managing*. New York, NY: Avon Books; 1984.

3. Adjusting to Change and Transition

ny significant change requires effort, is disruptive, and takes time away from the daily job.[1]
    Clay Carr

CHAPTER OBJECTIVES

- To emphasize the impact of technical and organizational change on clinical laboratories and other health care facilities
- To describe the various kinds of changes taking place
- To list the indicators for change
- To outline the responses that change requires
- To characterize the stages of change and the kinds of employee responses
- To portray the role of leaders
- To depict goals, objectives, and planning involved
- To help you cope with resisters and cynics

Have you experienced any work changes in the past five years? the past year? last month? yesterday? Health professionals and managers are continually faced with change. Every year they are inundated with volumes of new governmental regulations and revised standards promulgated by accrediting and licensing agencies. Technologic advances and medical breakthroughs are reported almost daily. Threats of new and old competitors challenge hospitals like never before. Acquisitions, reductions in force, mergers, reorganizations, and alliances cause tremors throughout health care institutions.

Pritchett[2] highlights the frequency and importance of change by pointing out that from a roster of the 100 largest U.S. companies at the end of the 1800s, only 16 are still in existence. Moreover, during the decade of the 1980s, a total of 230 companies—46%—disappeared from the Fortune 500.

Many positions have been eliminated and even more new ones added. In addition, every few years another "revolutionary" management concept appears: Theory X,Y, and Z; One-Minute Managing; Management-by-Objectives (or by-Results, or by-Walking-Around); Total Quality Management; Participative Management; Empowerment of Employees; Team Building; and Process Reengineering. Today's health care leaders are rethinking and reconfiguring every aspect of their operations to achieve improvements in performance, cost efficiency, and quality of care.

In a continual cycle of learning, unlearning, and relearning, employees must master new technologies, adapt to new organizational processes or systems, and generate new ideas.

New areas of specialization spring up, and older ones phase out. When hospitals offer new and complex services—such as advanced trauma care or open heart surgery—employees who previously had only been vaguely aware of each other now find themselves on cross-functional work teams or special task forces.

While we cannot change the winds of change, we can learn to make the necessary adjustments to stay on course.

THE COMPETITIVE EDGE

The competitive edge often follows a chronologic sequence. A new service provides a jump start ("We have it, they don't"). When rivals catch up, the advantage goes to the one with better quality ("Take a look at our statistics"). Later, when differences in quality are slight, it is the customer's cost that drives the market ("Why pay more?"). When these three factors balance out, the sales pitch focuses on customer service: "We care."

To field a flexible, responsible, and adaptive team that can meet the competition, it is mandatory that changes be quick and effective.

KINDS OF CHANGE

McConnell[3] describes three general kinds of changes:

1. Organizational changes in which departments are altered, interdepartmental relationships or management/reporting relationships are changed, or a new management takes over.
2. New methods, procedures, or equipment are introduced.
3. Jobs are restructured.

INDICATORS FOR CHANGE

Listed below are some of the more common changes with which managers and teams must learn to cope:

1. Changes in laws, policies, and practices

    Medicare and Medicaid rules

    Private insurance changes

    DRGs (diagnosis-related groups)

    HMOs (health maintenance organizations) and other forms of managed care

    Billing practices

    Continuous quality improvement and new leadership initiatives, such as empowerment and team building

    The never-ending governmental requirements, such as the Americans With Disabilities Act and the Clinical Laboratory Improvement Amendments of 1988

2. Customer demands or expectations

    Increased productivity, quality, or safety

    New services

    Greater availability of product or service

    More information for patients

    Choice of health care providers

    Charges and ease of interpreting them

    Satellite stations and outpatient services

3. New competitors or new challenges from old competitors

    Surgicenters and Urgicenters

    Physician clinics and groups

    Private and commercial laboratories

    Independent practitioners of physical therapy and other specialties

    Home care

4. Changes in the workforce

    Increased education (so-called "knowledge workers" now outnumber blue-collar workers)

    Lower personnel retention (average Americans change their jobs every $2\frac{1}{2}$ years)

    Demands for quality of work life

Union activities (the National Labor Relations Board [NLRB] now permits up to eight separate union bargaining units for each health care institution)

Problems of recruitment, staffing, morale, or employee retention

WHAT CHANGE REQUIRES

1. Change essentials. These are the desire and determination to make the change, the pervasive belief that it can be done, the availability of resources, and the taking of the necessary actions.

2. Creativity and entrepreneurship. Change efforts must mobilize people and often must add to what is not yet known. Intuition, brainstorming, and creative thinking are often needed. Change also requires power skills and power sources to turn ideas into innovation.

3. Employee commitment and ownership. Employees must "buy in" to the change. As their input increases, they acquire more ownership of, and commitment to, decisions about change. They want to see their ideas flourish. However, before employees buy in, they must trust their leaders and have faith in their leaders' integrity.

4. Adaptability, flexibility, and willingness to take risk. Adaptability and flexibility must be manifested at all hierarchical levels. Relearning and retraining are the orders of the day. Thus, today's health care managers must be change specialists and trainers.

   Motivating people to change is one of the major challenges of leadership. Managers must understand why people resist change. They must persuade employees to view change as normal, and they must know how to introduce innovations. A culture of pride encourages the willingness to risk change. Such a culture is nurtured when organizations are successful, people are made to feel important, many promotions are made from within, and managers seek ideas first from internal audiences.

5. Stability of workforce. Stability requires high personnel retention, lots of patience, and strong support from management. Stability also requires a high expectancy of job security. Workers appreciate the reassurance that their jobs or their teams will not be altered. Employees whose positions are in jeopardy can often be offered new positions, retraining opportunities, early retirement, help in finding other positions, or assurances that their jobs will be eliminated only by attrition.

   Changes that require revamping of operational procedures or threaten unit integrity, such as developing cross-functional teams, are much more likely to encounter resistance.

6. Time and patience. Major changes take time, patience, and persistence. Even though the first official warnings from the Surgeon

General about smoking were issued in 1954, this threat to health persists. Even minor changes often take longer than expected. Many people learn slowly and forget easily. Almost always a few individuals drag their feet or must be carried along despite screaming protests.

7. Rewards. The people who are affected by change must see some payoff (WIIFM—What's In It For Me?). Change requires a system that rewards the people who must implement the changes as well as the people who must make the decisions. Money has limited and transient motivational force, and the lack of a fair reward system is a strong demotivator. Promotions are powerful motivators, but managers usually have limited powers in this area. Dual technical and management promotion ladders are highly recommended. Most employees are satisfied if they perceive that the change will enable them to get their work done faster, more easily, or more enjoyably. The change may help them solve their work problems or communicate more easily with others.

THE ROLE OF THE SUPERVISOR OR TEAM LEADER

Supervisors are involved in changes to a greater extent than are top managers. While major changes are promulgated from the executive suites, it is up to department heads, supervisors, or self-directed teams to implement most of these initiatives. Also, for every company-wide innovation, hundreds of changes originate within departments or smaller work units. In these instances, the team leaders must direct the change process. The activator must apply the principles of change, train, support, and monitor results.

GOALS AND OBJECTIVES OF IMPLEMENTING CHANGE

A well-defined goal is a prerequisite for productive action and arches over four critical objectives: the selection of the right people, preparing and motivating people to change, obtaining the necessary resources, and implementing the change. Team members must be able to vividly visualize the goal toward which they are moving. Goal appreciation is enhanced when visits are made to institutions in which the change has been highly successful. For example, enthusiasm for a change to self-directed teams builds when potential teams have an opportunity to talk to members of experienced teams.

THE PLANNING PROCESS

To plan for the change, gather information from past experiences. Focus on activities that were instrumental to success and those that were barriers. Assess the compatibility of the proposed change with the current organizational culture and goals. Be certain that the change does not violate organizational or societal cultural norms.

Strategies have limited impact unless they are rooted in specific activities that individuals perform. Detail the training that is needed to help prepare employees for the change. Consider contingencies for displaced workers.

Successful changes start with answering the following "W" questions:

Who wants the change? Why? Who will benefit? Who will be affected adversely? Who will resist? Who will support?

When should planning start? Will we have enough time? By what date must official approval be obtained? When should the implementation start and when should it be completed?

Where will we find the space, funds, and people?

What will it cost? What do we hope to achieve? What are the risks, constraints, and barriers? What additional data are needed? What resources are essential? What did we do wrong last time? What additional training will be necessary?

Will the benefits of the change appear quickly? (The longer a change takes, the hazier its payoff will appear and the more it will seem a burden.) Will the change provide an opportunity to utilize available skills better? Will people have more autonomy over how they do their work? Will the changes make employees' jobs (and yours) easier or harder? Will the change increase or decrease profit, motivation, morale, quality, and productivity)?

ENLISTING HELP FROM YOUR TEAM

1. Change always starts with communication.
   a) Changes promulgated from above. Keep tuned in to the formal and informal communication systems of your organization to learn about pending changes. Through networking, find out as much as you can about such changes, but avoid putting anyone in the position of having to confirm or deny a rumor. Pay close attention to what is said after meetings as well as in discussions during the sessions.
   b) Changes you want to initiate. Discuss the need for change with a few close associates, including people who would be involved in, or affected by, the changes.

2. If you are the originator of the change, prepare a mission statement and goal(s). If successful, how would the change improve the situation as it currently exists?

3. Prepare a list of alternative strategies for accomplishing the goal. Document possible benefits and disadvantages of each alternative.

4. Talk it over with your entire team. Establish the urgency to change, but do not overdo it. Do it without destroying self-efficacy (the belief that the actions one takes will have positive effects). Encourage complete discussion, including criticism. Invite additional alternatives or modifications of those already offered. Ensure that everyone knows what is in the offing, why the change is necessary, and how each of them will be affected.

5. Select an alternative, if possible by consensus, and try to get everyone's pledge of support.

6. Formulate and document a plan and get its approval from your team and your superiors.

7. Provide reassurance to those who may be concerned about the change. Listen carefully and encourage full expression of their apprehensions.

8. Assign responsibilities. As much as possible, get people to volunteer. Modify position descriptions where appropriate.

9. Prepare and publicize the agenda and timetable.

10. Implement the change and follow-up. Recognize individual and group contributions as your plan is carried out. Do not wait for the change to be completed before giving praise and recognition.

TIPS FOR AGENTS OF CHANGE

An Atlanta consulting firm offers the following suggestions[4]:

■ Realize what people affected by the change are experiencing. Don't argue with them about their feelings or be surprised by strong reactions. Expect grief, confusion, and anger.

■ Hold one-on-one discussions with each person affected by the change.

■ Help to create a vision to enable people to anticipate what things will be like when all the changes have been implemented.

■ Expect resistance.

STAGES OF EMPLOYEE RESPONSES TO CHANGE

1. Anticipation. Rumors of possible change threaten the status quo. Like the calm before the storm, this stage may be lengthy or brief. All employees experience some anxiety when change is mentioned. Many ignore the rumors at first, hoping that the change will not take place. If the change is a major one, such as a reorganization that involves relocations and disrupted work groups, people talk about early retirement or job change.

2. Immediate response. This is also called the denial stage. After the surprise and shock comes denial ("It won't affect me"), followed by anger ("Why us?") or a feeling of being betrayed. They talk a lot about the past—the good old days.

   Sometimes when new equipment shows up, when new employees move into old offices, and when familiar employees are let go, the remaining employees experience varying degrees of shock, anger, sadness, or depression. Some people attempt to bargain with management in attempts to preserve their employment. Often heard are statements such as "I'll be darned if I'm going to learn to operate that monster." However, when employees have been properly prepared or when the changes are ones that they had proposed, this phase becomes one of joy and celebration.

When people believe they will be unaffected, they become amused bystanders, sometimes taunting the people who are trying to cope with something new. These snide remarks should not be tolerated.

3. Resistance. Most employees will show a degree of support, others will take a wait-and-see attitude, and some will actively reject the process. Absenteeism, turnover, and grievance filing may be increased. Hostility, moodiness, and slowed output may result. Subtle sabotage is expressed in a myriad of ways: "forgetting" to do things, inciting resistance, doing exactly what is ordered knowing that such action is wrong, and setting up roadblocks.[5]

4. Acceptance. Sadness or depression gradually gives way to acceptance by those who remain on board. This acceptance starts with an exploratory phase in which employees voice concern about details, express confusion, and try to figure out the details of their role. It may be an exciting time often characterized by confusion, creativity, energy, and rebonding with associates.

As people find that they can cope with the situation, their attitudes become more positive. They begin to see why the change was needed and how it may actually improve their job.

Fortunately, most employees will settle down and accept the change. Later, they will fight to prevent any return to the old system. A computer breakdown that requires a temporary return to the old manual system causes consternation in the ranks.

WHY DO PEOPLE RESIST CHANGE?

At the very least, change is uncomfortable for everyone. Put down this book and cross your arms in front of you. Now cross them with a different arm on top—how did it feel? Some people thrive on change, but the majority of us do not.

1. Fear of the unknown. Employees are not just being obstinate or uncooperative, they fear the unknown and how it may affect them and their work group. Change shakes up their comfortable and predictable daily routines. The more a change affects established habits and relationships, the more complaining will result.

2. Loss of control. Reactions are more negative and intense when changes reduce employee control. One CEO was disappointed and

chagrined to find that the new expensive air conditioner that was installed only led to protests when employees learned that they could not fiddle with the thermostat.

"The more that a change conforms to the existing power and status structure, the less likely it is to be opposed by entrenched powers."[1] Many employees worked hard to achieve power and status. They are likely to oppose, overtly or covertly, any threat to this authority.

3. Mindsets. Changes can be perceived as threats or opportunities. A pervasive perception may be that the change is either impossible or not practical, or the team members may lack confidence in their leadership, especially if they have witnessed previous failures. Resistance is highest in organizations ensconced in bureaucratic tradition,

4. Others. People with low self-esteem and a great need for basic security often resist making the commitment to change. Others balk because they receive too little information or are omitted from the planning process.

Even changes that individuals had been hoping for can be psychologically upsetting. A promotion elicits mixed feelings. The pride and paycheck are nice, but the altered relationships with former coworkers may be upsetting. A new instrument you purchased may not live up to your expectations or the promises of the supplier.

A caveat: Managers and team leaders often mistake the lack of overt opposition for support—particularly when people go through the motions of supporting the change. In fact, the opposition may never surface because the change effort may have died. These covert opponents may actually bemoan its failure and point out how vigorously they had supported it.

How to Overcome Resistance

Successful change is achieved only when commitment is obtained from the people who must implement the change or who are affected by it. This commitment should be sought as early as possible when a change is contemplated. It will not be obtained if rational and emotional concerns are ignored. Concerns are minimal when employees have been involved in the planning right from the beginning. Preventing resistance is much better than trying to overcome it. Employees are relieved when their concerns are addressed head-on and they are told that their concerns are normal and will pass.

Communication is essential. Do not let the information filter down through third parties. Sending and receiving are equally important. Explain the need for change in pragmatic terms. Listen to employees blow off steam without reacting adversely.

Extensive and lengthy changes are usually best introduced by pilot projects using highly motivated teams. This increases the likelihood that quick and favorable results will be obtained.

Table I
Questions Employees Want Answered When Faced With Change

What is the change?
Why is it needed?
Who will be affected?
How is it to be accomplished?
How will jobs be affected?
When does it start?
How will each employee be affected?
How will I be affected?
What's in it for me?
Can I handle it?
Will they train me?
How will it change my daily routine?
How will my work group be affected?
Will this really improve things or solve the problem?

Encourage team participation and involvement. Instead of training everyone at the same time and covering all the material before opportunities exist to utilize the training, provide the training just before it is needed and to those who are going to use it first. Make training manuals and other instructional materials available, and give people enough time to get acquainted with them. Provide progress reports. Answer all the questions in Table I.

WHEN RESISTANCE IS ENCOUNTERED

When diversity of opinion is the principal resistance, it may be time to negotiate. Discuss all aspects of the change and try to understand other points of view. Seek consensus or win/win outcomes, but be willing to compromise.

Although autocratic management tends to increase resistance to change, sometimes it is necessary. For example, when OSHA comes up with inconvenient new safety measures that your employees feel are unnecessary and inconvenient, you have no choice but to enforce the new regulations. Coupling coercion with education and communication may mitigate some of the threatening aspects of a change.[5]

When you must champion a change you feel is inappropriate, avoid making remarks about "the idiots upstairs" who issued the orders. This only increases the resentment, lowers morale, and delays implementation. Your prestige is not enhanced by such exhibitions of disloyalty. Do your best to explain the purpose or need. You may need to get more information about the reason for the change or what is involved.

COPING WITH CYNICS

Tap into your grapevine and keep tuned to your network. When you hear grumbling in the background, investigate the problem and address it without delay. Since one highly vocal cynic can infect an entire team, it is hazardous to ignore critics or naysayers unless the team's enthusiasm overwhelms these negativists.

The cynic often has some truth to support pessimism. Failures may have occurred in the past. Upper management may have abandoned previous initiatives. Formidable barriers may lie ahead.

It helps to have some team members discuss their initial successes during the early phases of the change. Occasionally the critics can be converted simply by giving them more of the action or involving them more in the decision process.

Block[6] offers sage advice for handling cynics. He advises against trying to argue or persuade these negativists. Rational arguments seldom have the desired effect, such as pointing out that this change is unlike previous initiatives that failed or that we are really committed this time. Instead of trying to convert the cynic, our goal should be that of damage control—to limit the influence of the cynic on other members of the team.

Block's strategy is to replace coercion and persuasion with invitation. Managers should acknowledge their feelings and doubts, even admit that they too have some of the same feelings but have made the choice to take the risk and go ahead with the change. Encourage the cynic to make the same choice.

USE YOUR REWARD SYSTEM EFFECTIVELY

Focus attention on vision-supporting behaviors. Be a credible role model. Expect, measure, and reward those who use the vision. Measure only what you really want. Keep it simple.

Autonomy is a powerful reward. Delegate authority to those who demonstrate using the vision. For real achievers who relish challenges, the strongest reward may be to get involved in another change—maybe a bigger or more difficult one. Watch pinball machine addicts. Their only reward is winning the opportunity to play another game.

Preferred work assignments, expanded turf, opportunities to meet the top brass, a new title, opportunities to get away from the immediate work site, being given more responsibility and authority, or simply spending more time with you or with others are all strong rewards. Instead of taking credit for the implementation of the change, lionize others.

A list of additional helpful suggestions is presented in Table II.

Table II
How to Achieve Smooth and Effective Change

Fully explain why change is needed.

Show sincere consideration for employees' feelings.

Refer to the changes as opportunities or challenges.

Give employees as much control as possible.

Be patient. Tolerate some failures.

Reward with praise, recognition, opportunities for additional participation, and great performance evaluations.

If there is a payoff for people, tell them about it.

If people are adversely affected, do not try to conceal that information.

Express confidence in your team.

Follow through on as many of a person's suggestions as possible.

Create a supportive environment that encourages innovation.

Serve as a support and resource center.

Encourage small changes, especially at first.

Make certain everyone knows the goals and standards.

Avoid making a change until everyone knows what to expect and can voice his or her concerns.

Prepare yourself for setbacks or temporary failures.

Chalk these experiences up to learning experiences.

REFERENCES

1. Carr C. Seven keys to successful change. *Training.* 1994;31:55-60.
2. Pritchett P. *New Work Habits for a Radically Changing World.* Dallas, Tex: Pritchett & Associates; 1994.
3. McConnell CR. *The Effective Health Care Supervisor.* 2nd ed. Rockville, Md: Aspen Publishers; 1988.
4. QualTeam Inc. Tips for aspiring change agents. *Training.* 1994;31:14-15.
5. Boe GP, Hudson CG. Managing change in troublous times. *MLO.* 1991;23:24-27.
6. Block P. *Stewardship: Choosing Service Over Self-Interest.* San Francisco, Calif: Berrett-Koehler Publishers; 1993.

RECOMMENDED READINGS

Belasco J. *Teaching the Elephant to Dance.* New York, NY: Crown Publishers; 1990.

Dalziel MM, Schoonover SC. *Changing Ways: A Practical Tool for Implementing Change Within Organizations.* New York, NY: AMACOM Book Division; 1988.

Kanter RM. *Change Masters.* New York, NY: Simon and Schuster; 1983.

Plunkett LC, Fournier R. *Participative Management: Implementing Empowerment.* New York, NY: John Wiley & Sons, Inc; 1991.

4. Delegation and Succession Planning: Keys to Empowerment

FTER THE NEW superior settles in, the first test of his leadership is apt to center about how he delegates.[1]
Herbert M. Engel

CHAPTER OBJECTIVES

- To provide an overview of the benefits of delegation
- To reflect on why some leaders fail to delegate
- To discuss common problems related to the delegative process
- To relate how to avoid "dumping," upward delegation, and "hopscotch" delegation
- To describe four techniques for selecting what to delegate
- To disclose three major categories of responsibilities that should not be delegated and six others that should either not be delegated or be delegated with caution
- To describe how to select and obtain acceptance from delegates
- To outline the four steps of the assigning process
- To delineate the follow-up activities
- To provide advice on coping with a failed delegation
- To discuss the importance of and technique for succession planning

Delegation is the first step in the march toward shared governance. Delegation and self-directed work teams or participative management are closely linked. In delegation, a superior turns over some of his or her responsibilities and authority to individual subordinates. In the case of a self-directed team, a spectrum of functions is transferred to a work group. In participative management, a universal attempt is made to delegate at all levels.

Delegation is an art and can be good or bad. Careers can be ruined or stalled, not only by failure to delegate but also because of amateurish delegative execution. Management texts often fail to mention that motivation is achieved only when delegation is handled skillfully.

BENEFITS OF DELEGATION

To delegates
   Job enrichment
   Increased expertise, promotability, marketability
   Full advantage taken of abilities and potential
   Increased self-esteem because confidence is shown publicly in their abilities
   Greater comprehension by the delegate of the manager's job

To organization
   Delegation is the cornerstone of team building
   Greater flexibility and capability of workers
   Improved morale, attendance, and productivity
   Earlier identification of potential leaders
   More in-house promotions

To delegators
   Motivated employees
   More time to do more important or neglected tasks
   Enjoying time away from work and vacations with fewer interruptions
   Satisfaction of developing subordinates (What better tool do we have to find out if a person has the ability to relieve you or become your successor?)
   Become more promotable since you are no longer indispensable in your current job

WHY LEADERS FAIL TO DELEGATE

The failure to delegate is often cited as the most frequent reason why supervisors fail in their jobs. Nevertheless, many supervisors neglect this vital function for many of the following reasons:

   They are workaholics or perfectionists.
   They are insecure.
   They are afraid that the delegate will fail.

They are afraid that they will be accused of dumping.

They don't like to turn over what they enjoy doing.

They don't think their staffers are ready or willing.

They have had unpleasant previous experiences with delegation.

They don't know how to go about it.

Things you hear reluctant managers say:

"I don't have the time."

"You want to know what happened when I tried that?"

"If you want it done right, do it yourself."

"I can do it faster and better."

"When I try to delegate, they say that it is not in their position description."

"When I try to delegate, they ask what's in it for them."

The willingness of employees to be delegates is determined by:

Whether they think they are qualified

Whether previous efforts have succeeded or failed

What their teammates may say or think

Whether they think they have the time

Whether they like what is delegated or see some reward in it

Whether they think that they will have enough authority

How much confidence they have that the delegator will support them

Whether they think they are being manipulated or dumped on

PROBLEMS WITH DELEGATION

Delegation is a two-edged sword. It can be the key to increased productivity, time management, and motivation or it can be a wet blanket that squelches initiative and lowers morale.

"Dumping"

Dumping is when you shovel onto people repetitive, mundane work of little value to the organization or to the employees' growth.[2] Because dumping is often done on the spur of the moment, the recipient feels like an errand runner.

The bottom line is that the persons selected feel resentment over having to do the task. Rather than viewing it as an opportunity, they perceive it as being dumped on. Dumping is most likely to be perceived when delegates (1) have a poor relationship with their bosses; (2) have been dumped on in the past; (3) know that others have refused to do the same task; (4) fail to see any personal advantage in carrying out the assignment; (5) have not been told that occasionally they will be asked to do things that are not in their position descriptions; and (6) see the delegator wasting time while they are performing the delegated work.

If you have good rapport with a subordinate and seldom take advantage of your authority, that person will not mind some dumped work. When a task is being discussed and an employee says, "How come I never get asked?" that is delegation. When the employee says "How come I always get asked?" that is probably dumping.

Upward (Reverse) Delegation

Upward delegation is the art of people passing along to their superiors what they cannot do or do not want to do. They are often successful because their bosses just cannot say no. Managers who seldom delegate are especially susceptible to upward delegation.

"Every subordinate is good at delegating upstairs. It's hard to resist because it's very flattering. They imply, 'You know so much better than I do, do my job' and you do. You must learn to say no."[3]

Reverse delegation often follows attempts by a manager to delegate. The delegates reluctantly accept a task, then at the first obstacle they throw up their hands and try to pass the buck back to the manager, who then becomes the reluctant delegate.

Sometimes upward delegation is necessary. For example, a person is so overloaded with delegated assignments that routine work cannot be finished. It is then up to the delegator to take back some of the work, to establish priorities, or to permit the delegate to transfer work to another person.

"Hopscotch" Delegation

"Hopscotch" delegation is when your boss gives assignments directly to your subordinates. To correct this, it helps to know your boss's temperament and have good rapport.

If you confront the boss in a belligerent mode, you may get something like "Well, you're never around when something must be done." If this bypass of authority happens infrequently or only under special circumstances, it is probably best to ignore it.

If confrontation with your boss seems indicated, take a positive approach by downplaying the issue of authority, and focus on the advantages of your knowing what the boss wants done and how your staffers get confused and frustrated when they get conflicting or multiple orders.

If you cannot get action through your boss, you may be successful by acting through your staffers. When the requests are not urgent, tell them to hold up action until they have informed you. Another strategy is to have your associates politely ask your boss to please make the request directly to you because they are working on a priority item of yours.

Inept Delegation

Failure to delegate authority or instructions results in the delegate constantly running into the delegator's office with problems.

Table I
Delegative Task Selection Chart

Column 1	Column 2		Column 3		Column 4	Task
A	1	+	4	=	5	Maintain QC records
A	4	+	7	=	11	Monitor inventory
B	5	+	5	=	10	Schedule personnel
B	8	+	1	=	8	Service cost analysis
A	2	+	2	=	4	Teach benchwork

Step 1. List 10 of your tasks in the last column. Do not list any task or responsibility that may not or should not be delegated.

Step 2. In column 1, place an A opposite tasks that can be assumed by someone right now or a B for tasks that can be learned by a delegate.

Step 3. In column 2, prioritize each A and B task according to how much time you would save by delegating the task (eg, 1 for the most time saved, 10 for the least time saved).

Step 4. In column 3, prioritize according to how much the delegation would benefit the delegate or how acceptable it would be to the person.

Step 5. In column 4, place the sum of the figures from columns 2 and 3.

Interpretation:
  Delegate the tasks in the sequence of the numbers in column 4, addressing the lowest numbers first. In the example, the first task would be to teach benchwork.

SELECTING WHAT TO DELEGATE

Picking what to delegate can be accomplished in four simple ways:

1. As you go about your daily routine, just before you tackle a task ask yourself if this is something that someone else could do.

2. When you return from a vacation, list the duties that your subordinates took care of while you were away. Some of these temporary assignments could become permanent.

3. At the time of performance reviews when you discuss future plans with your associates, ask them if they would like to take over some of your responsibilities.

4. Select the tasks from those listed in your position description (see Table I).

What May Not Be Delegated

1. Accountability: Delegators are still accountable to their bosses for the work that has been transferred. They must not abandon the delegate.
2. Powers other than authority: Only formal power—authority—can be delegated. The powers of intellect, experience, knowledge, skill, leadership, persuasiveness, and physical intimidation cannot be delegated.
3. Functions forbidden by law, regulation, or policy: Licensure, certification, special training, qualifications, or education are required for some duties.

What Should Not Be Delegated or Is Delegated With Caution

1. Sensitive or high-leverage activities dealing with people:
   Interviewing, selecting, and orienting new employees
   Approving new hires
   Coaching, counseling, and disciplining
   Evaluating employee performance
   Recommending for promotion, special awards, or merit pay
   Resolving personal conflicts, complaints, or grievances
2. Activities that involve too great a risk for delegator or delegate
3. Activities that are perceived by delegate as "dumping"
4. Special administrative responsibilities:
   Formulation of mission statements, goals, objectives, strategies, and plans
   Making, publicizing, explaining, and enforcing policies
   Presiding over important meetings
   Preparing or approving budgets and reviewing fiscal variances
5. Tasks assigned by superiors for their personal attention
6. A few functions that provide lots of pleasure to you

SELECTING THE DELEGATE

Select a delegate who has the necessary competence and willingness. Evaluate employee interests, attitudes, abilities, and motivation. The most qualified person for a particular assignment may not be the one who will benefit from it most and often is not the most motivated.[4]

Be careful about delegating a majority of tasks to the same person. You may send the message that you think the person does not have enough to do or that his or her regular work is less important.[5]

If the person lacks expertise, provide it. In all instances tell delegates the following:

> Why you decided on the transfer
>
> Why you picked him or her
>
> Whether or not the change is voluntary
>
> What you expect
>
> What resources and authority are available
>
> What you are going to tell the others
>
> Any changes in current assignments
>
> The checkpoints and timetable

People are more willing to take risks if they know as much as possible about what is involved. Individuals are sometimes reluctant because in the past they took a small step and Pandora's box opened. Tell them exactly what they are getting into and see the limits they can accept. Give them possible outs.

Employees often do not want the responsibility and authority, especially if it affects their peer relationships. They prefer remaining one of the gang or having the safety of little responsibility.[1]

Get Acceptance From the Delegate

Seek cooperation, not sullen compliance. Consciously or unconsciously, delegates ask themselves, "What is in it for me?" If the answer is a negative one, the delegation starts out in trouble. Be very wary if you hear the following:

> "Is that an order?"
>
> "Do I have to?"
>
> "That's not in my position description."

Documenting important delegations prevents later problems, but this should be preceded by face-to-face discussions. When delegating in writing, keep the memos informal and friendly. A formal memorandum can be perceived as a cold directive and its impact is doubled when copies are sent to the individual's superiors.[5]

THE ASSIGNING PROCESS

1. Start with small responsibilities that relate directly to the delegate's current assignments or with simple parts of a complex task.
2. If this is a major change, get permission from your boss. Discuss it with other people who will be affected.
3. Establish specific standards and timetables.
4. Listen to their ideas on how to get it done.

THE FOLLOW-UP

Sharing responsibility does not mean abandoning the delegates. Supervisors still must know what is going on, step in and make decisions the delegate cannot, and assess performance.

To ensure that the progress is on course, set up well-chosen checkpoints ahead of time. For example, if a large report is part of the task, have the delegate submit a preliminary rough draft. Another advantage of establishing checkpoints is that it gives you an opportunity to award some pats on the back.

Every so often stop by and ask how things are going, just as you do in your routine managing-by-walking-around for the rest of your staff. Avoid constantly looking over shoulders or asking too many questions. Questions should reflect your interest in their approaches rather than exhibiting nervousness you may have about their ability to finish the job.

Be patient and tolerant. Avoid statements like "Don't worry," "You should have..." or "I wish you had...." Avoid the temptation to abandon ship when problems occur. Allowing people to make some mistakes is the best way to encourage meaningful growth.

You should seldom have to take over the job, but there are exceptions. For example, in complicated assignments or when the delegate was reluctant and needed reassurance, you may want to promise to share some of the work or agree to take it back if things don't work out.

HORIZONTAL DELEGATION

The movement toward self-directed teams makes horizontal delegation as important as vertical delegation. Horizontal delegation is delegating to colleagues or others over whom you have no formal authority.[6] Cross-functional health care teams depend largely on horizontal delegation. It takes place at every committee or team meeting at which assignments are given and accepted by members of that group.

Truly skilled delegators have the ability to delegate to people over whom they have no authority, such as colleagues or volunteers. The likelihood of success depends largely on factors such as persuasiveness, influence, interpersonal skills, rapport, degree of teamwork, past favors for the other person, the strength of one's network, available rewards, and especially, expressed appreciation and past cooperation.

WHEN A DELEGATION FAILS

Remember that when your delegate fails, you too have failed. When employees have done their best but failed, have them do a balance sheet. Ask them to identify what went well and what were the shortcomings. Always let them criticize themselves first. Ask how you could have helped more. When performance review time rolls around, do not hold a failed delegation against the employee's record, especially if you had to do some arm-twisting to get acceptance in the first place.

WHAT TO DO AND WHAT NOT TO DO WHEN DELEGATING

Do

Pick the right task and the right delegate.

Delegate entire tasks, not fragments of that task.

Evaluate the impact on the employee's regular assignments.

Explain exactly what it is that you want.

Inform others who are affected, especially if they must take direction from the delegate.

Make yourself available as a resource.

Tolerate mistakes.

Reward the delegate, at least with praise and appreciation.

Establish specific standards and timetables.

Do not

Confuse delegating with dumping.

Delegate involuntarily unless you absolutely must.

Delegate to punish.

Take it back without good reason.

Penalize those delegates who fail.

Delegate without telling delegates what is in it for them.

Apologize for your selection of the delegate.

SUCCESSION PLANNING: ONCE A LUXURY, NOW AN IMPERATIVE

If you haven't prepared someone to step into your shoes, you're not ready to take a successful step upward.[7]

M. Feinberg

Maxine, the chief medical technologist of the General Hospital, was a superstar. She had the laboratory running like a well-oiled machine. Morale and productivity were high, and the medical staff had nothing but kudos for the department. Suddenly, however, Maxine and her family moved to another state. The laboratory literally fell apart because no one could replace indispensable Maxine, and she had never considered developing a backup.

Ask Yourself These Questions

In today's uncertain times with all sorts of upheavals and major changes, the need for succession planning is more vital than ever. Everyone who is in charge of a work unit must ask questions such as:

"If my services are suddenly not available, who will step into my shoes?"

"How long would it take to find and train my replacement?"

"Who is on board right now who could take over?"

"What have I done to prepare a successor?"

The Benefits of Succession Planning

The strength and adaptability of an organization are linked to how fully it has developed the talents of its personnel. This development depends largely on the willingness and capability of supervisors to share their expertise with potential successors.[8]

After you have mastered your job and are looking for advancement within your organization, make yourself dispensable. Not to do so may freeze you into your present position because your superiors will regard you as indispensable.

Moreover, the supervisor who develops a backup can be absent from the work scene with the assurance that the department will function smoothly. The supervisor will not have to call in daily to check on how things are going.

Yes, Risks Are Involved in Picking and Training a Successor

A risk of picking a lemon is always present, but remember that the only people who never fall down are those who never leave their chairs. Every leader worthy of that title has made poor decisions and choices. Regard such mistakes as learning experiences.

A more common risk is that your protégé will be promoted out from under you or enticed away by a competitor. While this always elicits pangs of disappointment proportional to the effort you made in developing the individual, you still get several benefits: a reputation as a career builder, the gratitude of the person you trained, having a supporter (your former protégé) in other units or organizations, and the ability to repeat the process with greater competency.

Finally, there may be an insecure feeling that when a subordinate can perform up to your standards, your job may be on the line. However, the frequency of that happening is low. Having a trained backup means that more time is available for you to do the things you couldn't get around to do before, which usually increases your value to the organization.

Your Selection and Training Plan

Finding the appropriate understudy can be simple or complicated. If you already have an assistant and are satisfied with that person's potential capability for taking over your job, you don't have to look far.

If you don't have an assistant and must choose from several employees who seem to have about the same potential, this can be a more delicate matter. Don't take for granted that members of your unit are interested in your job. This is something you should find out during formal performance reviews or when counseling employees. Don't waste your time preparing a reluctant successor unless that person has impressive leadership talents. Don't be in a hurry to move a single candidate into the position of assistant. The moment you name a person as your assistant, others stop striving for the job.[9]

When you have several prospects, treat them as equals. Delegate to each. Assign parts of your job to several individuals and see how they handle the added responsibilities. Rotate leadership roles. For example, let them take turns moderating staff meetings or representing you at interdepartmental or task force meetings. When you go on vacations, appoint substitutes on a monthly rotation.

Pay close attention to how they handle these situations. Does the work get done? Do they try to do everything themselves or do they get the cooperation of other team members? How did their fellow workers perceive their performance?

Any effective program of supervisory development begins with an appraisal of a person's strengths, weaknesses, and potential. It sets attainable development goals and charts a course of practical on-the-job coaching and experience, formal education, and reading that will lead the person toward those goals. It ends with a review of the person's development successes to date.[8]

The planning database includes the situational analysis of work demand and identifies the major job performance outputs required for the position. Table II shows an educational database for succession planning.

Grooming Your Successor

How you go about preparing the chosen successor is very important. The process consists largely, but not exclusively, of a series of delegations and special assignments. Ensure that the successor does each of these tasks often enough to become competent and comfortable. Make certain that you give the successor enough time to handle his or her own daily responsibilities.

Besides these delegations and assignments, enable the successor to accompany you to meetings, to sit in on interviews you hold, and to accompany you as you manage-by-walking-around. Work together on things such as budgets or plans.

Table II
Database of Supervisory Training Needs

Professional or Technical Development
1. Informed of new professional/technical developments
2. Up to date on supervisory/administrative techniques
3. Active participation in professional society
4. Balance between people and task orientation
5. Documented goals and career development program

Planning and Organizing
1. Efficient and effective use of time and resources
2. Emphasis on planning of all important activities
3. Competency in interviewing and selecting new employees
4. Exemplary job descriptions and performance standards
5. Work and vacation schedules fair, acceptable, and posted well in advance

Communication
1. Most effective and cost-effective use of communication channels
2. Keep everyone well informed
3. Empathetic listener
4. Good facilitator, moderator, or chairperson at meetings
5. Good relations with other work teams and units

Controlling
1. Establish just-in-time inventory control
2. Policies, procedures, and rules are clear and acceptable
3. Performance appraisals improve performance and morale
4. Practice managing by walking around
5. Mediate, arbitrate, persuade, or negotiate effectively

Motivating
1. Associates feel valued and important
2. Praise often, criticize seldom
3. Establish work ambiance that improves creativity
4. Associates are enthusiastic and energetic
5. Recognition and reward techniques are effective

Developing
1. Good coach and career developer
2. Excellent teamwork within unit
3. Active cross-training and work station rotation
4. Supportive of training and development programs
5. Active delegator. Rarely "dumps"

Getting Results
1. High level of productivity and quality service of team
2. Low rate of employee turnover and absenteeism
3. Great customer service
4. Cost effective
5. Change master

Table III
Action Plan for Skill Enhancement

Subject:	Skill to be enhanced
Purpose:	Why this is important
Objectives:	How success will be measured
Resources:	Funds and other materials needed
Obstacles:	How they can be removed
Implementation:	List in sequence the steps to bring about the desired change (if possible, assign target dates)

Developing a successor involves lots of mentoring. Provide opportunities for meeting senior managers and important customers. The latter include internal customers—other units that serve or are served by your department. Provide visibility by letting the successor give reports to the bigwigs and chair or moderate meetings of various sorts.

When your chosen succesor does something worthy of mention, let your boss know about it. When you submit performance appraisals, make sure that you use phrases such as "shows much leadership ability" or "is developing into an excellent facilitator."

Worthy protégés will do most of the planning and energizing on their own. They will decide what seminars to attend, what courses and workshops to take, what books to study, and what periodicals to read. They will set goals and develop action plans. They will make the extra effort needed to work on career development while still discharging daily responsibilities. Table III provides an example of an outline for a training plan.

Monitoring

The true test of managerial potential is not just what the person knows how to do, but also how they perform when they do not know what to do. Progress should be evaluated at periodic joint meetings as well as at formal performance reviews.

REFERENCES

1. Engel HM. *How to Delegate*. Houston, Tex: Gulf Publishing Co; 1983.
2. Werther WB Jr. *"Dear Boss."* New York, NY: Meadowbrook Press; 1989.
3. Drucker P, Flower J. Being effective. *Healthcare Forum J*. 1991;24: 52-57.

4. Yate M. *Keeping the Best*. Holbrook, Mass: Bob Adams Inc; 1991.

5. Noel RT, Parker T. What you say to your employees when you delegate. *Supervis Manage*. 1993;38:13.

6. Douglass ME, Douglass DN. *Time Management for Teams*. New York, NY: AMACOM; 1992.

7. Feinberg M. *Wall Street Journal*. November 12, 1990:A14.

8. Meyer HD, Margolis BL, Fifield WM. *The Manager's Guide to Developing Subordinate Managers*. New York, NY: AMA Management Brief-ings; 1980.

9. Belker LB. *The First-Time Manager*. 2nd ed. New York, NY: AMACOM; 1986.

5. Empowerment: The Engine of Participative Management

HE WAVE OF the future is empowerment of employees and maximization of their skills.[1]
Tess Kirby

CHAPTER OBJECTIVES

- To define empowerment
- To present the benefits of empowerment
- To delineate the importance of feelings of powerlessness and to list their causes
- To portray the characteristics of powerless people
- To outline the risks, barriers, and pitfalls of empowerment
- To describe the role of leaders in empowerment initiatives
- To offer 12 empiric empowering actions
- To focus on the empowering of work groups

WHAT IS EMPOWERMENT?

Conger and Kanungo[2] define empowerment as a process of enhancing feelings of self-efficacy; the belief that one's actions can produce positive results by removing conditions that foster powerlessness.

Block[3] states that empowerment is also a state of mind that causes people to believe they can cope effectively with situations and people.

Bardwick[4] writes, "Empowerment means giving

everyone—not just people with certain positions or certain job titles—the legitimate right to make judgments, form conclusions, reach decisions, and then act."

Mills[5] defines empowerment as "the liberation of those who do the work from rigid oversight and direction."

According to *Webster's Dictionary*, to empower is to authorize or to enable. Empowerment has three major enabling purposes:

1. To enable employees to discharge their duties more effectively
2. To enable employees to expand their expertise and qualifications
3. To enable supervisors and managers to delegate some or all of their current responsibilities to their empowered employees

To feel empowered, we must take responsibility for the services we provide.

BENEFITS OF EMPOWERMENT TO THE ORGANIZATION

Fisher[6] writes that empowerment is potentially as important for contemporary organizations as the first industrial revolution was at the turn of the century.

Continuous quality improvement (CQI) presupposes the empowerment of individuals, where front-line employees have knowledge of customers' needs and how to meet them. The implementation of CQI with concomitant empowerment lessens the need for supervision and eliminates the need for micromanaging.[7]

Empowerment is also an essential component of participative management, process reengineering, delegation, quality circles, self-directed work teams, creativity, entrepreneurship, time management, and succession planning.

The increased willingness of staff to contribute and take risks maximizes worker motivation, initiative, productivity, and reliability.[8] Leaders can mobilize stronger forces when responding to crises with less risk of chaos. They can set higher performance goals and standards.[2]

Workers focus more on the customer's needs and less on their bosses. In traditional organizations, the real objective of employees is to keep the boss happy.

Other benefits include:

- Greater personnel retention and decreased absenteeism
- Improved teamwork because a "can-do" attitude prevails
- More skilled workforce with greater flexibility
- Cost effectiveness, improved service, and increased revenue

BENEFITS OF EMPOWERMENT TO EMPLOYEES

Empowerment reduces or eliminates feelings of helplessness and raises self-efficacy. The more people are in control of their work, the greater their enthusiasm, optimism, self-confidence, and energy. Empowered people believe their actions mean something and produce positive results.

Building an adequate self-image is recognized today as a necessary strategy in the empowerment of individuals. Employees' self-esteem and feelings regarding their personal efficacy are strengthened when they know the following:

- They are technically or professionally competent.
- Their performances are as good as or better than those of their colleagues or competitors.
- They will receive positive feedback from superiors and associates.

Empowerment enables skill enhancement and professional growth that increase employee marketability, job security, and promotability. Work becomes more interesting and satisfying because it is more meaningful. The quality of work life (QWL) and stress resistance increase. Byham[9] claims that empowerment provides psychological energy that activates us and motivates us to improve.

Our perceptions of being empowered are as important as our empowerment as perceived by others and are essential in overcoming our feelings of powerlessness. Feeling empowered is feeling valued. Self-empowered people perform at their fullest potential, have high self-esteem, and are willing to assume responsibility and take risks.

Other benefits include feelings of being valued, a sense of trust, freedom for creativity, a strong sense of contribution, and elimination of the victim complex.

BENEFITS OF EMPOWERMENT TO CUSTOMERS

Empowered people, free from bureaucratic restraints, will act quickly at the customer's behest.[5]
    D. Quinn Mills

The most important beneficiary of employee empowerment is the customer. Employees, being closer to the customer, can recognize and satisfy the customers' needs, wants, and expectations and address complaints better and faster. Being closer to the services being rendered, they can spot problems and make recommendations for improving services and systems.

The result is that external customers find that the quality and speed of service increase. Internal customers note better coordination and cooperation between departments and services.

Feelings of Powerlessness

Removal of real or perceived powerlessness is probably the most important thrust of empowerment. The issues of powerlessness of minority groups, such as women, nonwhites, elderly, and the physically or mentally challenged, have been addressed more vigorously than has the issue of the powerlessness of the average American employee. Union efforts have not helped much because they focus primarily on reward systems and work environment.

Effects of Powerlessness

When employees lack confidence in their ability or feel that external forces control them, their self-esteem plummets and they feel helpless. Powerlessness reinforces feelings of low self-esteem and lack of control over one's work life. Powerless employees feel like puppets, with many people or other outside forces pulling the strings.

The sensation of lack of control increases susceptibility to stress and burnout. When powerlessness results in a victim mindset, the "victims" seek sympathy and divorce themselves from work-related responsibilities.

Individuals who suffer from a pervasive feeling of powerlessness are poor risk takers. They are often chronic complainers or negativists. Powerless people sometimes do not get angry, they get even. They slow things down and engage in subtle sabotage.

Causal Factors

Four categories of contextual factors relate to powerlessness.[2]

1. Organizational factors include rapid changes, under- or over-staffing, inadequate space or resources, faulty communication systems or practices, and outdated or overly restrictive policies or rules.
2. Job design factors include lack of goals, inadequate position descriptions and work standards, lack of authority, overdependence on others, and dead-end jobs.
3. Leadership style factors include autocratic or manipulative leadership, favoritism or discrimination, lack of positive performance feedback or recognition, emphasis on criticism and other negative feedback, lack of delegation, or delegation of responsibility without transfer of authority.
4. Employee development factors include inadequate orientation of new hires, lack of continuous education and training programs, little or no encouragement for career development, and no opportunities for cross-training or work station rotation.

Characteristics of Powerless People

Block[3] describes three major characteristics of people who feel powerless.

1. Feeling of lack of control. All decisions are made by a boss and attempts to bypass the boss are signs of disloyalty.
2. Denial of self-expression. People refrain from discussing issues during formal meetings but spend much time doing so in the hallways.

3. A sense of sacrifice instead of a sense of commitment. Workers do what is expected rather than what they believe in.

Powerlessness can occur in individuals or in groups. Group powerlessness is an intrinsic part of the health care setting in which professionals respond to life-threatening situations. Some degree of powerlessness is accepted as part of being a care provider. Health care workers are also required to do more with less, especially less time and help. Powerlessness is increased when employees are overwhelmed with work or unrealistic time demands.[10] When we hear "It's all politics around here" or "What do you expect in this bureaucratic organization?" we are hearing statements that suggest lack of empowerment and feelings of powerlessness.

THE RISKS OF EMPOWERMENT

Empowerment does involve risks. Any transfer of authority involves risk. Some empowered employees erupt with streams of worthless ideas, and some take inappropriate actions. Overconfidence may result in poor judgment. A few empowered individuals, the "loose cannons," abuse their influence or have difficulty defining the limits of their authority.

BARRIERS TO EMPOWERMENT

Some People Eschew Empowerment

Empowerment involves change, and change introduces all kinds of employee fears (see Chapter 3). Not everyone is comfortable with more power, especially nonassertive people or those with bureaucratic or victim mindsets. For example, in a hospital blood bank, the manager wanted the night supervisor to assume the responsibility for releasing blood to other hospitals. The supervisor balked because he did not want to be accountable for a possible inventory shortage on the next day.

Many workers want dependency and entitlement, not more responsibility.[11] They seek an almost child-parent relationship. These people feel they are entitled to a permanent job, automatic pay increases, and a wide range of benefits. They prefer conformity and safety to entrepreneurship and risk.

Stanton[12] found that the following characteristics of employees strongly indicate a lack of interest in or responsiveness to attempts to empower:

- The person does not seek fulfillment through work.
- The person lacks the requisite qualifications.
- The person is reluctant to take on additional responsibilities.
- The person requires a structured, clearly defined work environment.
- The person needs close supervision or support.

- The person fails to identify sufficiently with the goals of the organization and department.

Employees Lack Confidence in Their Leaders

Employees who have seen leadership fads come and go are inclined to regard empowerment as just another passing fancy of management. They do not want to put lots of energy into a change only to watch it be replaced quickly by another gimmick, as their new power flows back upstairs. Their past experience may lead them to believe that the change will only end up with additional unrewarding work.

Employees may feel that management is exploiting them. They may protest with remarks such as "That's your job" or "I'm not getting paid for that." Others see the change as an attempt to get them to work harder without raising their pay.

Managers Do Not Want to Share Their Power

Some managers are loath to empower because they fear the more power others have, the less they will retain. They may feel they have worked hard to earn the power they have and are reluctant to give up any part of it.

All too often, managers either refuse to give up control to others or they abandon all decision making to unprepared delegates who are left twisting in the wind. Other leaders exploit or manipulate their employees.

Institutions must weed out managers who are unwilling or unable to make the necessary adjustments.

THE ROLE OF LEADERS

The challenge of leaders is to back off and let people do their work in a new way. Traditional teaching guides list planning, organizing, coordinating, directing, and controlling as the five responsibilities of managers. Today's challenges require another—empowering or enabling.

EMPIRIC EMPOWERING ACTIONS

Responses to the following 12 questions keep you on the right track:

1. What do the shareholders want?

   To enhance employee self-efficacy and to provide whatever it takes to help empower people, find out what they want or need. At their next performance review, ask:

   What do we do that helps you do your job?

   What do we do that gets in your way?

   What additional information do you need?

   What resources do you need?

Would you like more input into activities such as work assignments; schedules; selection of new employees, instruments, or procedures; chairing meetings; or getting involved in any other organizational functions?

2. What performance is already possible?

The empowering of individuals starts with an analysis of individual authority and qualifications. This is facilitated by the use of special employee evaluation worksheets.[13] List only the tasks, authority, and responsibility related to the key areas of empowerment. Include items such as skills, strengths, and potential qualifications (eg, "experienced in using Lotus 1-2-3"); current levels of authority (eg, "unrestricted access to..."); new responsibility (eg, "chair quality circle on..."); and additional training or experience needed (eg, "attend supplier's training program on...").

3. What is your new role?

Change your role from boss to coach, teacher, supporter, resource person, consultant, mentor, and facilitator.

4. How do you get employees involved?

Involve your staffers in one or more of the following activities:

■ Improved customer service.

■ Quality improvement.

■ Responsibilities currently held by you, such as scheduling, budget preparation, new employee selection, supplier contacts, and selection of methods and instruments.

■ Goal setting with the participation of the people who will work to achieve them. These goals may be for the leader, the group members, or the work team. The principles of management by objectives may be invoked.

■ Decision making. The more a program or change affects employees, the more input they should have in the decision-making process. Three types of organizational decisions have been defined.[14]

a) Decisions made independently by individuals during the course of daily work, eg, how to respond to an unusual service request or complaint from a physician.

b) Group or individual decisions that are overturned by managers. In pure participative leadership practices, these reversals should be infrequent.

c) Decisions that do not require approval or review by management. Such team decisions are customarily limited to issues that affect team actions and results, such as work or vacation scheduling, training, goal setting, performance evaluation of colleagues, or other issues relating to the operation. Teams may

- **Problem solving.** The greater the possibility of employee resistance to an action, the greater the need for participation in problem solving. Problem solving requires more empowerment than does decision making; the latter deals only with selecting alternative actions or solutions, while the former includes the formulation of alternatives as well as selecting the best one. Competent problem solving also involves more than practical experience. It requires information-gathering techniques, use of planning tools, and learning skills such as brainstorming and negotiating.

- **Operational changes.** Smooth transitions and the acceptance of change require involvement of people who are affected by the change. Ideally this involvement is initiated during the planning phase and continues throughout the preparation and implementation phases. See Chapter 17 for more on process reengineering.

5. **Do employees know what they are working for?**

   Workers should know the purpose—the mission—of their jobs. This should be stated in their position descriptions and stressed during their training. Clarify the job and your expectations of their performance. Lay it on the line: "Here is what I want from you; tell me what you want from me." Positive expectations on the part of managers will decrease manipulative attempts by employees who respond to requests for increased production with plaintive and repetitive cries of "We can't do all that." Managers who are perceived as tentative or uncertain will be more susceptible to such negative reactions.[10]

6. **Do you know what they do now?**

   Become more familiar with what each of your employees does. Have them draw up detailed flow charts describing what they do. Review each step with them, asking "Could this be eliminated?" "Does this improve service?" and "How could we do this better?"

7. **Is your training program adequate?**

   Institute a cross-training and job rotation program so more people become aware of customer questions and problems and can provide immediate answers and solutions. Teach your employees how to cope with complaints and angry customers. Refrain from penalizing staffers for exceeding their authority when trying to satisfy a customer. When policies interfere with good customer service, get the policy changed.

   I cannot overemphasize the importance of education and training to enable workers to reach their full potential—to be winners. They must be told why they are asked to do things, especially in relation to customer satisfaction. Leaders and trainers should be heard saying, "The reason we do this is...." Expose employees to advanced training in professional/technical skills, assertiveness, time management, stress relief, problem solving, negotiating skills, and planning techniques.

8. Can you make their tasks more interesting or challenging?

   Make employees responsible for complete, not fragmented, tasks. Assign them progressively more difficult tasks starting with ones that ensure success.

9. Can you delegate more?

   Encourage autonomy (lack of dependency) and control over employees' work. They should have ownership of their jobs and feel like their jobs really belong to them. They should be expected to solve their own problems and to become more self-reliant. Demonstrate trust and confidence in their competency. Give them a greater voice in work decisions and permit more freedom in how they carry out their tasks. Encourage assertiveness. Let them "fail forward" by turning failures into learning opportunities. (See also Chapter 4 on delegation.)

10. Are you providing enough support?

    Provide the support employees need, but no more. Protect them from hostile outsiders. Support includes approval, endorsing, and sponsoring. Eliminate bureaucracy by modeling nonbureaucratic behavior, issuing fewer memos, eliminating nitpicking rules, condensing procedure manuals, and encouraging verbal disagreements as well as agreements.

    Establish an environment that has a positive effect on motivation. Reinforce the behavior you want through praise and recognition. Use criticism sparingly and diplomatically. Be the team cheerleader. Ask them for advice and take it.

11. Is your emphasis on commitment rather than conformity?

    Demand commitment but not sacrifice or excessive conformity. People who feel they are constantly making sacrifices for their employer are either constantly looking for rewards or are building a victim mindset.

12. Are you involving them in decision making and planning?

    Prepare action plans jointly—you and the person to be empowered—in which the empowering actions are spelled out after reviewing the options described earlier in this chapter. (See Chapter 17 on project management.)

THE EMPOWERING OF WORK GROUPS

Empowerment extends to teams as well as to individuals. Group power is power *with* people, not power *over* people. Within hospitals, various departments have different perceptions of the amount of power they have. In a study by Norville,[16] the departments of finance, public relations, marketing, planning, and human resources felt they had much influence, while the departments of social work and pharmacy felt they had little influence.

To help empower work groups, list the key functions or responsibilities of the group. Evaluate each function on the basis of time invested, costs of quality product or service, and, most significantly, the importance to customers. Obtain customer input by multiple means: comment logs, feedback from front-line service providers, focus groups, and visits from customers or visits to customers.

Select a critical function that needs improvement. Prepare flow charts relating to that function and identify steps or tasks that can be eliminated or improved. Employees identify tasks that involve them. Brainstorm for solutions. Assign responsibilities and prepare time schedules. Assigning can be facilitated by using a worksheet that includes answers to these questions: What is the title of the assignment? Why is this being undertaken? Who are the people who will participate? What funds, facilities, or other resources are available?

PROBLEMS AND PITFALLS

- Expectations are unrealistic.
- Employees are not involved in the planning process.
- Staffers reject the changes outright, threaten to resign, or challenge all your ideas.[17]
- Productivity and morale suffer initially.
- Withdrawal of authority or dilution of empowerment may lead to ultimate failure.
- Training, resources, or support are not sufficient.
- Work suffers because employees spend too much time thinking up ideas.[17]
- Managers use participative management to avoid taking responsibility for decisions and actions.[17]
- Communication failures of all types occur, including faulty perceptions or assumptions, vague or nonfactual messages, and poor listening skill.

REFERENCES

1. Kirby T. *The Can-do Manager.* New York, NY: AMACOM; 1989.

2. Conger JA, Kanungo RN. The empowerment process: integrating theory and practice. *Acad Manage Rev.* 1988;13:471-482.

3. Block P. *The Empowered Manager: Positive Political Skills at Work.* San Francisco, Calif: Jossey-Bass; 1987.

4. Bardwick J. *Danger in the Comfort Zone.* New York, NY: AMACOM; 1991.

5. Mills DQ. *Rebirth of the Corporation.* New York, NY: John Wiley & Sons; 1991.

6. Fisher K. *Leading Self-Directed Work Teams: A Guide to Developing New Team Leadership Skills.* New York, NY: McGraw-Hill; 1993.

7. Lewis A. Too many managers: major threat to CQI in hospitals. *Qual Rev Bull.* 1993;19:95-101.

8. Pfeiffer IL, Dunlap JB. Increasing productivity through empowerment. *Supervis Manage.* 1990;35:11-12.

9. Byham WC. *Zapp! The Lightning of Empowerment.* New York, NY: Harmony Books; 1988.

10. Davidhizar R, Bowen M. When the manager encounters "We can't do it!" *Health Care Supervis.* 1992;11:27-32.

11. Block P. Stewardship: *Choosing Service Over Self-Interest.* San Francisco, Calif: Bard-Koehler; 1993.

12. Stanton ES. Employee participation: a critical evaluation and suggestions for management practice. *SAM Adv Manage J.* 1993;58:18-23.

13. Benson LP, Pattillo ME. *The Power of Empowerment.* A four-part television series distributed via the Health & Sciences Television Network (HSTN) by Westcott Communications, Inc; 1993.

14. Plunkett LC, Fournier R. *Participative Management: Implementing Empowerment.* New York, NY: John Wiley & Sons; 1991.

15. Quick TL. *Successful Team Building.* New York, NY: AMACOM; 1992.

16. Norville JL, Begun JW. Building departmental influence in healthcare organizations. *Health Care Supervis.* 1990;9:43-51.

17. Milite G. Participative management: pros and cons. *Supervis Manage.* 1992;39:10.

6. Participative Management: Group Empowerment

T HE INTENT IS to redesign our organizations so that service is the centerpiece and ownership and responsibility are strongly felt among those close to or doing the work and contacting customers.[1]
Peter Block

CHAPTER OBJECTIVES

- To define what participative management is and is not
- To delineate the benefits of participative management
- To characterize the skeptics and recommend how to handle them
- To describe employees' responses to participative management
- To outline the prerequisites for successful implementation
- To present the problems and pitfalls involved
- To provide examples of successful and unsuccessful applications of participative management

WHAT PARTICIPATIVE MANAGEMENT IS AND WHAT IT IS NOT

Participative management is a form of shared governance. Sashkin[2] states that participative management is "...a system in which subordinates are involved in making decisions with guidance from their supervisors." Plunkett and Fournier[3] define it as "...a philosophy that demands that organizational decision making be made in a way that input and responsibility are extended to the lowest level appropriate to the decision being made."

Participative management represents a culture change process that involves a job-specific development strategy.[4] This governance strategy shifts from parenting or patriarchy to partnership and participation.[1]

Participative management is not laissez-faire management based on the premise that no interference is best. Participative managers do not abdicate their responsibilities in the decision-making process since they usually have information or experience that their employees do not.[3]

Autonomous work teams and quality circles provide excellent examples of participative management in action, but team efforts are not always needed. Managers can achieve participation by interacting with individuals or with work groups that do not qualify as teams because they lack employee interdependency.

Autocratic, bureaucratic, paternalistic, and manipulative leadership as well as management-by-crisis are anathema to advocates of participative management.

Managing-by-walking-around is participative when the leader is walking around soliciting opinions and suggestions, promoting innovation, and granting greater license to act. It is not participative management when the walks are to inspect, correct, criticize, or nitpick.

Managing-by-objectives is participative when the workers have real input into the selection of objectives; develop their own action plans; have the resources, time, and authority to implement their plans; and receive minimal mandated direction from higher authorities.

Participation involves managing-by-principle rather than by policy.[5] For example, a manager who practices managing-by-policy might issue the following memo:

> "Under no circumstances shall children younger than the age of 12 years be permitted in the department after working hours."

On the other hand, a manager who manages by principle would permit more judgment on the part of professionals by issuing the following:

> "Personnel who are recalled after working hours should be aware of the risks of having children in the department without supervision."

Participative Management Is Not a Recent Leadership Concept

Many employers have practiced some form of participative management for years. Sashkin[2] found this ancient gem from a Roman landowner.

> "Nowadays I make it a practice to call them into consultation on any new work.... I observe that they are more willing to set about a piece of work on which their opinions have been asked and their advice followed."
>
> *Columella On Agriculture I*, around 100 AD

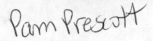

In 1961, Likert[6] reported that participative leadership was one of the four major leadership types (authoritarian, paternalistic, and consultative were the other three).

Quality circles, a relatively early form of participative management, were endorsed enthusiastically at first, but like so many other management initiatives, lost much of their former popularity.

When layers of management are stripped away, the surviving managers must assume a larger spectrum of responsibilities and more people to direct. They must delegate. The ripple effect of this downward transfer of responsibility forces a degree of participative management.

Other examples of limited employee participation include suggestion boxes, rewards for innovative ideas, support for entrepreneurial efforts, focus groups, and problem-solving committees or task forces.

THE BENEFITS OF PARTICIPATIVE MANAGEMENT

Sashkin,[2] a powerful advocate of participative management, states that participative management responds to three basic human needs: increased autonomy, increased meaningfulness of work, and decreased isolation from fellow employees. Participative management makes possible the many benefits listed in the chapter on empowerment. Anecdotal reports claim that participative management reduces employees' feelings of powerlessness, increases commitment by individuals and work groups, promotes pride in workmanship and accomplishments, provides challenge, and makes self-actualization more feasible. Other purported advantages over directive leadership styles include higher morale and personnel retention and more innovation. Staff members develop harmony, assume greater ownership of their work, and have more opportunities to attain common goals.

THE DISBELIEVERS

Most of the available literature on the subject is anecdotal rather than empirical. Skeptics question the desire and ability of the average employee to function in a participative work environment. These agnostics note the lack of controlled experimental design that can withstand rigorous scrutiny.[7]

Hurst and associates[8] warn about the risks of noncompliance, staff confusion or stress, unpredictability, and large variances. Employees may potentially abuse power, and laissez-faire leadership may be encouraged. Stanton[7] cautions that participative leadership sometimes creates unrealistic expectations, may generate poor decisions, and may confuse accountability. Conventional wisdom postulates that the switch from authoritarian leadership to participative leadership is time consuming and involves some risk.

EMPLOYEE RESPONSES TO PARTICIPATIVE INITIATIVES

In the initial stages, some employees show enthusiasm, others take a wait-and-see attitude, and the rest actively resist the change.[3] Individuals in this third group say things like, "Here we go again, another management quick fix" or "They're trying to keep us happy without giving us more money."

Employee attitude surveys are important and valuable, provided that leaders act on their findings. Stanton[7] recommends using a list of pertinent questions that can help to predict whether participative management will be successful in an organization:

> What is the level of employee competence?
>
> How great is management's confidence in subordinates?
>
> Do employees seem eager to participate?
>
> Is the organizational culture conducive to this change?
>
> Do all layers of management support the change, especially at the supervisory level?
>
> Are we willing to spend the necessary time and resources?

PARTICIPATIVE MANAGEMENT PREREQUISITES

1. The feeling of ownership by participants.

   The paradigm of empowerment is that of seeking commitment rather than compliance, power sharing rather than authority building, encouraging thoughtful disagreement rather than encouraging agreement. Successful empowering efforts can be achieved only when the work paradigm shifts from control to commitment.[5]

   We do not seek 100% commitment. Universal acceptance is not desirable because some differences lead to healthy and creative tension while "complete" commitment usually indicates suppressed conflict. An organization and a team are best served by employees who are willing and able to express differences and reservations.

   Ownership and responsibility have to be felt strongly at every level for participative management to succeed.[1] Ownership is achieved when people at all levels have more control over how changes take place. Miller[9] claims that the greatest single barrier to the psychology of ownership is the maintenance of the two-class system: management and labor.

   Empowerment requires the mindset of self-efficacy, but this mental status cannot be acquired simply by reading inspirational messages about positive thinking or by attending seminars. It requires organizational changes that remove real and perceived feelings of powerlessness. Ownership is not adopted unless the shareholders share the employer's vision.

2. Commitment by management.

Unless a serious long-term commitment is made by employers to change the organization's culture in radical ways, it may be better to avoid the change altogether because empowerment is a slow, gradual process requiring much time and energy. When an organization pays lip service to the ideals of empowerment but fails to nurture an environment that supports empowered behavior, employees become cynical.

Commitment requires putting information, resources, and power into the hands of the people closest to the customer or customer service.[1] "The meaning of service gets subverted when it is defined as treating your boss as your most important customer. This is what creates bureaucracy."[1] The goal of management is to replace bureaucracy with entrepreneurial spirit, helplessness with participative leadership.

Employers and their top managers are responsible for the strategies and actions needed to empower. The principles of empowerment are expressed in vision statements. A vision is like a lighthouse, it gives direction but not a specific destination. It expresses what is and what can be and incorporates the values of the organization. A typical segment from a vision statement might be: "Our decisions will be made where the work gets done."

A vision statement differs from a mission statement. The latter is simply a statement of the reason for the existence of your organization (eg, "To provide one-day surgical services").

The following executive actions help to achieve goals and visions:

a) Keep employees informed. Management support is lacking when managers withhold information or distort the truth. Absolute honesty and full disclosures are musts. If financial information is withheld from a "partner," no participative management is apparent. All too often the only information that employees receive is what pertains to their own unit or what they can glean from gossip and newsprint. This information should include items such as how the organization is doing financially, what restructuring or cutbacks are contemplated, and who the competitors are and how they are doing. Manipulation often starts when information is massaged, such as when cutbacks are necessary or projects must be discontinued.

Shareholders also need data concerning customers and their wants; new technologies; laws, requirements of accrediting agencies, impact of operations on the environment; such as the discharge of contaminated materials; relationships with suppliers; and budgetary information, such as revenues and operational costs.

b) Alter structures, culture, policies, and operations. Enlightened CEOs have turned the organizational pyramid upside down, with the customers and front-line service providers now at the top and everyone else in a lower supportive role. They have flattened the pyramid by removing layers of management.[1] Simply reducing the number of managers forces nonmanagerial employees to assume more responsibility. The CEOs provide the necessary resources—personnel, facilities, equipment, tools, and education. They minimize red tape, manipulation, and exploitation—the trappings of bureaucracy. They eliminate or modify restrictive policies, rules, and procedures, while instituting policies and rewards that emphasize the acceptance of greater responsibility.

As health care organizations become more complex, specialization leads to communication problems. What begins as a lack of understanding and cooperation easily escalates to serious and often hostile competition.[10] Leaders must strive for cross-functional communication and cooperation. Employees who are engaged in true participative management can and do communicate with whomever they want.

c) Augment team activities and employee participation. The formation of problem-solving groups, quality circles, task forces, focus groups, or self-directed work teams is encouraged.

d) Provide recognition, rewards, and celebrations. In the early stages, participation in and of itself can be rewarding, but when the novelty wears off, more tangible rewards must be given. Reward and recognition systems will be discussed in greater depth in Chapter 15.

e) Permit employees to write up performance evaluations of their superiors. This information can also be obtained indirectly through employee surveys.

3. Commitment by supervisors.

Supervisors are the empowerment gatekeepers. They must be prepared to change from bosses to facilitators or consultants. To become a convert to the empowerment movement, leaders must abandon theory X thinking—that people are lazy and need to be watched and controlled.[5] The management tenet that successful leadership requires a delicate balance between the ability to get the job done and the ability to work with people is especially true in management-by-empowerment.

During the empowering process and when building self-directed work teams, effective leaders adopt a situational leadership style. Situational leadership utilizes a directive style in the early phases of employment when employees lack the necessary competence or are not yet aware of their limitations of knowledge and skill. At this point, empowerment should be minimal. Counseling is added during the phase when the employees require more psychological than technical support—they have become aware of their limited qualifications. Again, empowering should be minimal at this time. When employees have matured and possess the prerequisite skills—the participative or delegative phase—the empowering process can be introduced.

Essential Leadership Traits

The first essential characteristic is credibility. Trust must exist between team leaders and team members, and this takes time, especially if the previous leadership had been bureaucratic, directive, or manipulative. Managers must trust their associates before participation and empowerment can occur. Development of trust may involve a radical paradigm shift for some.

Communication skill is vital. It must go up, down, and across. Sharing is essential along each of these channels. Managers share knowledge, information, responsibilities, authority, decision making, and planning. Supervisors share ideas, experiences, and feedback about initiatives. Criticism must be offered diplomatically.

Patience and diplomacy are important. Leaders must offer support and encouragement and anticipate temporary setbacks. Leaders must become skilled at steering participants in the right direction without taking over the responsibilities. While leaders should be hesitant to take back the reins, they must know when to step in to avoid a disaster. Ill-conceived suggestions from others are to be expected and never ridiculed.

Facilitating skills are involved. Leaders educate and train. Employees are trained and empowered to solve problems of customer service, instrument malfunction, and safety risks. They receive all the information and resources needed to discharge these functions.[5] Facilitating support demands that employees have the right to say no on occasion and always have the right to express disagreement.

IMPLEMENTATION OF THE INITIATIVE

The first action after vision, mission, and value statements have been enunciated is to test the water—to determine employee interest, adaptability, and competence. Participative management takes time, and the participants must perceive the extra time and effort to be worthwhile and to produce something tangible and visible.

This will be a major change for most participating employees, and major change induces apprehension and fear. Much reassurance and handholding is needed at this stage. Since employees will be expected to spend considerable time engaged in new activities, one of their major questions will be "Who is going to do what I used to do?" or "What activities can I stop doing?"

It is also important to learn the workers' perceptions of personal power and the degree to which they would like that power increased. This informa-

Table I
Participative Management Planning Matrix

Time	Jan-Feb	Mar-April	May-June	July-Aug	Sept-Oct	Nov-Dec
Executive Actions	Vision; employee survey	Initiate program	Attend meetings	Monitor and modify	Reward	Employee survey
Executive Training	Planning	Leadership	Empowerment	Diversity, culture, ADA	Process improvement	Managing change
Team Skill Training	Introduction	Communication skills	Meeting	Decision making	Customer service	Conflict resolution
Technical Training	Safety, TQM	Schedules	Budget, supplies, equipment	Suppliers, inventory	Equipment maintenance	Process improvement
Delegated Tasks	None	Safety monitoring	Prepare schedules	Recommend purchases, budget	Equipment maintenance	Process improvement

ADA, Americans with Disabilities Act.

tion can be obtained best via a comprehensive employee attitude survey. Exit interviews and other one-on-one interviews by members of the human resources department can also be useful. Proceed slowly so as not to disrupt operations and cause distress.

Planning

As in all major changes, strategic planning is essential. Sometimes it is best to start at the top of the organization and work down; other times it is best to work up by picking a good work group and using it in a pilot study.

Pilot studies are strongly recommended. Select a work group that you know has the interest and skills necessary for quick early successes. Enthusiasm and small victories can have a profound positive effect on the nonparticipants.

Holpp[4] emphasizes the value of successive approximation in which implementation takes place unit by unit.

The plan should select the functions to be activated, eg, decision making and problem solving. Start with one of these and move on to another when the first initiative is successful. Of all the functions to be learned, none are more important than decision making, for the real power is in the ability to make decisions. See Table I for an example of a planning matrix.

The principal categories of actions are the executive actions, the training of managers and participating teams, and the delegation of new responsibilities to individuals and groups. The employee training has two components: the learning of team skills and the acquisition of new professional and technical knowledge pertaining either to new duties or to updating old ones. Cross-training and job rotation have the added advantage of utilizing employees to train each other.

A fully developed plan is not without cost. The preparation and implementation is often expensive, including the cost of training employees, supervisors, and managers; the cost of holding meetings and addressing issues that previously were handled by one or two people; the cost of time for building and honing participatory skills; and the cost of the organizational development or human resource functions to provide coaching and facilitation to increase the effectiveness of the process.[3]

Organizing

The organizing issues include providing good tools, technology, and systems; establishing a structure for participation and teamwork; and ensuring decision making at the proper level.[10]

Monitoring and Evaluation

As in the case of any major change, monitoring should take place throughout the implementation process. Bottom-line results are documented, and a final (or periodic) employee attitude survey is used to evaluate how shareholders have responded. Customer satisfaction and recommendations should be checked frequently.

PROBLEMS AND PITFALLS

- Autocratic organizations that attempt to preserve a culture of leadership, consistency, control, and predictability when trying to implement participative management paradigms will fail.[1]
- Failure to redistribute power, purpose, or privilege will produce no real improvement.[1]
- Premature transfer of responsibilities. Employees must be ready to assume new responsibilities, which requires training and testing.
- People lack time to tackle new duties and still perform their old ones.
- Supervisors fail to achieve mutual respect among the workers they supervise.
- The future role of supervisors is unclear or threatened (see Chapter 9).
- New rules, policies, and practices are unclear.

Possible Infringement of Union Rights

The National Labor Relations Board (NLRB) has rules that some employee involvement programs violate. Employees must be free of management influence or pressure when they meet in discussion groups. Meetings must steer clear of labor-management topics such as pay practices, grievances, working conditions, or hours of employment, which are considered by the NLRB as collective bargaining topics.[11]

EXAMPLES OF SUCCESSFUL APPLICATIONS OF PARTICIPATIVE MANAGEMENT

1. With the assistance of a consultant, the nursing staff of a 750-bed community hospital in Ohio implemented the concepts of shared governance over a 2-year period. A major factor was the development of a 26-member Nursing Council. Communication, both within nursing and between departments, improved.[12]

2. Lawler[13] worked with groups of nighttime janitorial workers in a study of the design of their own incentive program. Some of the groups used a participatory approach, while others had no choice in the incentive program selection. Although the plans developed were essentially similar, the attendance of the participatory group improved dramatically.

3. Cummings[14] reported marked improvement in attitudes and perceptions toward performance appraisals when employees participated more actively in that process.

4. Heckert[15] identified two similar nursing departments in a community hospital in which the leadership style of the head nurse of Department A was authoritarian and that of the head nurse of Department B was participative. Department B had a lower rate of turnover and absenteeism.

EXAMPLES OF FAILURES OF PARTICIPATORY SYSTEMS

Examples of failures are not as easy to find in the literature because few people like to report their inability to achieve success. A striking exception is the report of failure of shared governance in a Norwegian shoe factory, which was attributed to the values and expectations of the workers.[16] Plunkett and Fournier[3] suggest that high failure rates are likely when participatory management is introduced into an organization that has a history of directive leadership or that experiments with every management gimmick that appears on the scene.

REFERENCES

1. Block P. *Stewardship: Choosing Service Over Self-Interest*. San Francisco, Calif: Berrett-Koehler; 1993.

2. Sashkin M. A manager's guide to participative management. *AMA Management Briefing*. New York, NY: American Management Association Membership Publication Division; 1982.

3. Plunkett LC, Fournier R. *Participative Management: Implementing Empowerment*. New York, NY: John Wiley & Sons; 1991.

4. Holpp L. Applied empowerment. *Training*. 1994;31:39-44.

5. Fisher K. *Leading Self-Directed Work Teams: A Guide to Developing New Team Leadership Skills*. New York, NY: McGraw-Hill; 1993.

6. Likert R. *New Patterns of Management*. New York, NY: McGraw-Hill; 1961.

7. Stanton ES. Employee participation: a critical evaluation and suggestions for management practice. *SAM Adv Manage J*. 1993;58:18-23.

8. Hurst J, Keenan M, Sipp R. Total quality management: a matter of quality, polarity analysis, and management. *Health Care Supervis*. 1993;11:1-11.

9. Miller LM. Creating the new high-commitment culture. *Supervis Manage*. 1985;30:21-28.

10. Doyle RJ, Doyle PI. *Gain Management: A Process for Building Teamwork, Productivity, and Profitability Throughout Your Organization*. New York, NY: AMACOM; 1992.

11. Milite G. Participative management: pros and cons. *Supervis Manage*. 1992;39:10.

12. Anderson R. Voyage to shared governance. *Nurs Manage*. 1992;23:65-67.

13. Lawler EE III. *Pay and Organization Development*. Reading, Mass: Addison-Wesley; 1981.

14. Cummings LL. A field experimental study of the effects of two performance appraisal systems. *Personnel Psych*. 1973;26:489-502.

15. Heckert R. Hospital managerial styles examined: authoritarian versus participative. Personal communication, July 1993.

16. French JRP Jr, Israel J, As D. An experiment on participation in a Norwegian shoe factory. *Hum Relations*. 1960;13:3-19.

7. Introduction to Teams and Building Interdependence

W ELL-DEVELOPED TEAMS can substantially outproduce the sum of their individual members working independently.[1]
Robert J. Doyle

CHAPTER OBJECTIVES

- To explore the need for more teamwork in health care
- To define the team concept
- To classify the various kinds of teams
- To compare and contrast traditional work groups and self-directed teams
- To describe the benefits and the disadvantages of team building
- To outline the major prerequisites to successful team building
- To characterize effective self-directed teams
- To elucidate the reasons why some teams fail

As enterprises become more complex, they depend more on the effectiveness of group effort. In today's health care environment, few individuals function as solo practitioners. In the old days, an emergency department was staffed by a physician and a nurse. Now that suite features dozens of professional, technical, and clerical people representing diverse skills and experience and working as a team to save lives. Cross-functional processes are the order of the day.

Other needs for teamwork and cross-functional activities include setting up a satellite facility, introducing a new computer system, developing a new service, implementing changes to comply with mandated governmental or regulatory requirements, adjusting to cultural diversity, and establishing departmental and interdepartmental quality improvement.

A work challenge or urgent need is more likely to stimulate team building than any "off-the-shelf" team-building exercise or the transient fancy of a CEO. In other words, self-developed work teams (SDWT) are best introduced when there is a perceived need for improvement to satisfy updated visions, goals, values, or bottom-line results.

DEFINITIONS OF SELF-DIRECTED TEAM

In this book I am not discussing hospital patient teams that provide specialized service to individual patients (eg, the combined efforts of a surgeon, internist, respiratory therapist, and nurse to look after Mrs. Smith in room 330B). My paradigm focuses on employee groups that work together within traditional configurations or in special projects or task forces.

A true team is a highly interactive functional group of people who share a common goals and the responsibility for a unit of service. Self-directed (autonomous or empowered) work teams are small teams that have the authority to control the work they do without a formal first-line manager. Although they may not have a formal leader, these teams are not undirected but simply directed differently.

In traditional management, managers let employees take the position that as long as they do as instructed, they have met their obligations. The managers retain accountability for the final results. In a self-directed team, every person accepts individual accountability for the group effort. In this sense, team members become true professionals, whatever the nature of the work being performed.[2]

Most SDWTs have 2 to 15 people, usually fewer than 10. Typically they plan, schedule, implement, and control their work processes, make operational and personnel decisions, solve problems, and share leadership responsibilities. These teams integrate the managing of work with doing the work. This requires the merging of individual accountability with mutual accountability.

An effective team makes optimum use of the talents and experience of each person and works in congruence with the unit's vision, mission statement, values, and goals. Members possess a variety of professional or technical skills, have been trained to be multiskilled, and are capable of performing each other's tasks.

TYPES OF TEAMS

Many teams serve in an advisory capacity and could be called committees. They solve problems or recommend operational or fiscal improvements. These

Table I
Responsibilities That May Be Assigned to Self-Directed Teams, but Seldom to Traditional Work Groups

Set group and individual goals.

Assume responsibility for productivity, cost, and quality.

Plan, schedule, control, and inspect their own work.

Prepare their own budgets and accept responsibility for complying with the terms of those budgets.

Select suppliers.

Interview and hire new people.

Coach and counsel teammates.

Evaluate the performance of team members. They may have disciplinary powers.

Monitor and control quality and safety.

Make major changes in their work systems or processes.

Order supplies, maintain inventories, and recommend new equipment.

Plan their own training and assume responsibility for orienting and training new hires.

Perform routine repairs, maintenance, housekeeping, and trouble-shooting services.

Deal directly with people at all levels of the organization.

PAM

include quality circles, project teams, process reengineering teams, focus groups, and various types of task forces. When such groups cross the boundaries of departments or other units, they are called cross-functional teams.

Policy-making teams or quality councils recommend or establish policies or rules dealing with quality, safety, customer service, laws, or requirements of accrediting agencies.

One department may have several SDWTs, and an employee may be a member of several teams. In hospitals, many SDWTs are cross-functional, especially teams devoted to process reengineering.

TRADITIONAL WORK GROUPS VS SELF-DIRECTED TEAMS

A key element in the difference between a traditional work group and a self-directed team is interdependence. Traditional groups take responsibility only for results derived from individual efforts, so the group's end product represents only the sum total of individual efforts. An SDWT demands both individual and mutual accountability, which requires common commitment. In the team, each person accepts a broader range of duties than were encompassed in the old job structure. A list of SDWT functions or responsibilities seldom assigned to traditional work groups is presented in Table I.

ADVANTAGES OF THE TEAM CONCEPT

Working in teams can benefit team members, team leaders, and their organizations.

Team Members

Team members report greater personal pride, increased competency, and greater feelings of ownership, empowerment, fellowship, and mutual support. Because the members participate in finding solutions and decisions are by consensus, they have more commitment to carrying out decisions.

They usually have higher morale as the motivational needs of affiliation, achievement, and personal control are satisfied. Increased collegiality and togetherness is noted.

Team members are exhilarated by their new experiences, expanded skills, improved communication, and coordination. They gain confidence by overcoming barriers, and they report a new feeling of looking forward to coming to work each day. Most of them welcome the increased challenges. Many report that for the first time they see the "big picture" and have a greater appreciation for their role in it.

Opportunity still exists for outstanding performance by individuals, and they are entitled to any recognition that accompanies it.

Supervisors

Relieved of many mundane supervisory responsibilities, managers can spend more time developing strategy, formulating plans, and networking with external customers (patients, clinicians, and other clients), suppliers, and internal customers (other departments, trainees, support staffs, consultants, and subordinates). Some of these supervisors become facilitators or coordinators of multiple teams.

The Organization and Its Customers

Synergy may be the greatest benefit. Teamwork is multiplicative, not additive. Results of team efforts exceed those that would be achieved by each member acting independently. Because the team members are closer to the action, customer service and problem solving or decision making are improved.

Employers report improved quality, lower operational costs, increased productivity, greater employee commitment, and more innovation. Most observers note greater personnel retention and better attendance. Employees seem to be less prone to leave and more likely to show up when they are members of teams.

Scheduling flexibility is increased because there is less dependence on individuals when they are multiskilled, have been cross-trained, and are accustomed to station rotations.

Introduction of changes such as cost-cutting, quality improvement, or cultural diversity is facilitated. As team members perform a larger range of duties, they become generalists rather than specialists. Among the many benefits of this is a reduction in the number of different position descriptions.

DISADVANTAGES OF TEAMS

Let's be honest about all this. Teams are not the solution to everyone's problems. Many functions are handled as well or better by individuals. When quick action is needed, someone must take charge and get things rolling. When someone yells fire, that is not the time to call a team meeting. Persons who have unique professional or technical know-how or experience can deal with specific situations faster without consulting with others or requiring a series of approvals.

Only 17% of managers and team members surveyed in one study said that teamwork was working well for their companies.[3] A group of Ernst & Young investigators commented that forming teams resulted in measurable improvement most often in organizations that had not been functioning well and was sometimes detrimental in high-performing organizations.[4]

Most work groups require a lot of start-up time and grief, and have a tendency to become bureaucratic. When an enthusiastic focus group or task force turns into a standing committee, the topics often become repetitious and boring.

PREREQUISITES TO SUCCESSFUL TEAM BUILDING

There is more to team building than designating a group of workers as a team and telling supervisors that they must share their authority and responsibilities with that group. Here are some powerful forces that may be involved.

Flattening the hierarchical pyramid. Team building has a much greater chance for success when the organizational pyramid has been flattened by the elimination of layers of management, thus forcing more downward sharing of power. For even better results, the pyramid has been turned upside-down with customers and first-line care providers (or the people who serve these providers) now at the top while everyone else plays a supporting role.

If a team is composed of members from three different departments or units, the team should report to someone who has the authority over all three of these functional units.[5]

The work environment. A nonthreatening work ambiance provides openness, fairness, mutual trust, and mutual respect as well as safety and security, opportunities for growth, and respect for individuality. Union and management must cooperate with each other.

No group will ever become a team without a clear sense that this is who we are and this is what we do.[6]
J.H. Zenger

The mission. Success derives from three elements: the mission, the leadership, and the people who make it work. Everyone must be clear about the team's purpose and to whom it reports. The mission gets team members moving in the same direction. It must be clearly expressed in one paragraph or less and in clear language. It must be believable to every team member.

Visions and goals. Team building is a process like creating an orchestra from a group of individual musicians. Unlike a goal, a vision is an endless process. Visions and mission statements must be translated into specific and measurable goals (eg, "to have a mobile laboratory unit in operation by the end of the year").

Team values. Teamwork demands a set of values that encourage listening and responding constructively to views expressed by others, providing support, and sharing knowledge.

Team accountability. The lines of authority within and outside the team must be unambiguous. Team members need a clear understanding of rules, responsibilities, and who makes the decisions.

The flow-chart paradigm. Fundamental to the concept of self-directed teams is the idea that work is a system, not a series of discrete tasks. Teams must perceive tasks as steps in operational flow charts.

CHARACTERISTICS OF EFFECTIVE SELF-DIRECTED TEAMS

Team Membership

The team is not limited to members from an isolated unit but may include vendors, customers, people from other units, and key staff personnel. It actively constructs formal and informal networks that include people who can help.

The critical issue that surfaces with team membership is inclusion and exclusion—who is or isn't on a team. Members on a team may flaunt their special status, and resentment grows.[7] Doyle and Doyle[1] point out that every organization has its "orphans"—employees who are seldom included on teams, such as secretaries, clerks, staff specialists, and janitors. All of these individuals should be assigned to teams and given full membership whenever possible.

Team members feel empowered and exhibit voluntary commitment that stems from feeling involved as a valued participant, from a sense of personal ownership in and control over what the team does, and in having a stake in the team's success. They have a shared sense of mission or common purpose and clearly defined goals that are congruent with those of the team. Participation is egalitarian, and decision making is by consensus. Individual members or cliques do not dominate. (For more on team members, see Chapter 11.)

Supervisors

The supervisors, or the persons in charge of the group before the team initiative has been undertaken, are enthusiastic or at least supportive of the change to self-directed teams. These supervisors normally progress from coaching and training to facilitating and serving as consultants as the team matures. (For more on supervisors-in-transition, see Chapter 9.)

Team Leaders

Most teams prefer leaders whom they select to those assigned by management. Rotation of leadership is recommended because effective teams do not have indispensable players, and that includes team leaders. No matter what kind of problem arises, more than one person should be capable of coping with it, which is also an essential for good customer service. Some teams elect a permanent leader from among team members. (For more on team leadership, see Chapter 10.)

Team Features

The team exhibits certain functional characteristics, such as those shown in Table II.

WHY TEAMS FAIL

1. Lack of top management support.

    A team-building initiative can be stopped cold in its tracks by the lack of persistent sponsorship and leadership at the top. If the CEO provides only lip service or quickly turns attention to other initiatives after getting the ball rolling, team building will probably wither and die or be limited to units where persuasive and energetic leaders pick up the baton. Equally bad is the situation in which the CEO rams the new concept down the throats of unwilling employees.[5]

    Some employers use the team rubric to extract more work from everyone, which is a gross misuse of the team concept. If the culture does not change from authoritarian to participative, the team concept will be an empty shell.

    Most organizations still prefer individual over group accountability. For example, many employers evaluate and reward results based entirely on individual performance.

    Other team killers attributable to poor leadership at the top are listed in Table III.

2. Attitude or incompetence of managers.

    The second major obstacle is sabotage by first-line managers who see their jobs being threatened and stonewall efforts to hand down

Table II
Functional Characteristics of a Successful Team

It constantly seeks ways to improve quality, productivity, and customer service. It strives to remove any factors that inhibit these objectives.

It studies successful teams but does not try to mimic them, recognizing that every team is different.

It welcomes innovation, new services, or techniques, and is willing to take risks.

It is democratic, with an absence of rank or formal authority.

It uses great multidirectional communication that features openness and candor. Consensus forms the basis for commitment, resolving conflict, promoting creativity, and making decisions.

Everyone has patience.

Team members feel free to ask for help, and work sessions are pleasant experiences.

The team's power is not based on formal authority, but on the team's credibility.

It minimizes conflict with other teams or nonteam employees through better collaboration, coordination, and cooperation.

It adheres to ethical and moral considerations.

It is enthusiastic and optimistic. It has fun.

It is adaptable and responsive. It can adjust to changes in services, systems, and procedures.

It is lean and caring.

Table III
Team Killers Attributable to Poor Top Leadership

Downsizing and restructuring

Paternalistic or bureaucratic leadership

CEO overwhelms staff with confusing array of leadership theories

Lack of goals or common purpose

Unrealistic expectations or mandates from upper management

Insufficient resources or understaffing

Low pay or adverse work environment.

Internal politics and favoritism

Pressure for conformity

Excessive paperwork

Lack of sufficient education and training of team members

Disapproval of, lack of action on, or delays in implementing team-building initiatives

Management fails to tell middle managers and supervisors what is to happen to their jobs power or to serve as effective facilitators. Supervisors often have the most to lose and therefore are likely to oppose team-building initiatives. They must be reassured that they will not lose their jobs. When job loss is by attrition rather than by layoffs, these fears can be alleviated. The advantage of forming teams during corporate growth spurts makes these promises easier. Supervisors also worry about what their friends and family will think about their title loss. They may spend too much time benchmarking or collecting data ("paralysis from analysis").

Leaders may incorrectly assume that team members already have the competencies needed by the team. They may delegate authority too quickly or too slowly. The training process may be incomplete or they may neglect making necessary changes in work guidelines, such as position descriptions, planning, scheduling, policies, and procedures. Process reengineering is almost always needed when team building is initiated.

Experienced team builders stress the importance of coping with the fears of employees. All too often leaders fail to help employees get over the grieving process they must go through when a major team-building program is instituted.

Communication problems of all sorts can deliver fatal blows to team-building efforts. For example, the team concept must be presented in such a way that people will be willing to take risks. Then, communication breakdowns may occur within or around teams. Customers, suppliers, and other outsiders may not know with whom they are to communicate when leadership is rotated. This can be overcome by the person in charge occupying a special desk or having his or her name posted on a bulletin board.[8]

Positive and negative feedback should also be directed to the team as a whole. Criticism and complaints are not swept under the rug but are discussed openly and fully at team meetings.

A list of potential supervisory deficiencies is seen in Table IV.

3. Resistant or incompetent team members.

The third major obstacle is unwillingness of employees to be more accountable or to develop new competencies. Individuals may be unwilling or unable to lay aside the selfish, political concerns of their own functional specialties in order to focus on the larger good of the enterprise. Equally troublesome are the situations in which people do take off their specialist hats but ignore their accountability for certain key functions in an effort to be good team members.[5]

Some workers are addicted to working alone, and they eschew all team efforts. Others go through a sort of permanent grieving process when the team process is implemented. This persistent emotional response can render an employee incapable of serving on the team. It is not surprising that some employees want to continue to work with people like themselves, failing to value diversity.

Table IV
Potential Supervisory Deficiencies

Supervisors cannot switch from paternalistic leadership to a participative style.

They do not alleviate employee fears of job loss or the inability to adjust to the new system. Workers must be reassured that increased productivity will not eliminate their jobs.

They fail to include union officials in the conversion process.

Seniority determines who gets the most desirable assignments or work stations.

Team members are trained poorly.

Replacement team members do not receive sufficient orientation or training.

They do not delegate sufficient authority to the team, or they withdraw it when setbacks are encountered.

Team meetings are held on members' personal time.

Team is not given sufficient time to adjust to new responsibilities.

The new team leader role is not well defined.

Supervisors do not know when to tolerate mistakes and when to intervene.

When experienced team members are selected to serve as leaders, they may develop an autocratic style and fail to take advantage of the skill and experience of other team members.

In most instances, employee problems are not the fault of the employees. When employees fail to perform up to expectations, the usual causes include poor employment selection, inadequate training, weak coaching, or bad work systems and processes. The greater the number of employees deemed unsatisfactory, the more likely it is that management at fault. A key question some teams face is what to do about the specialist who refuses to be a team player. In some instances provision can be made for that person to remain in the specialist role without participating in team activities. In other instances the person must be transferred or eliminated. (See Chapter 11 for more on team member deficiencies.)

4. Dysfunctional dynamics.

When something goes wrong, it is usually a system or a process that is at fault, not the people. For example, performance appraisal and reward systems that are based solely on individual performance and include merit pay incentives can be detrimental, even fatal, to team success.

Some team members burn out after months of intense activity. This can be avoided by rotating membership. However, turnover or rotation of membership can be detrimental. Not only are experi-

Table V
Examples of Dysfunctional Team Dynamics

Overemphasis on conformity. Members may struggle so hard to reach conformity and to avoid conflict that team decisions and judgments may be faulty.

Team leaders are ineffective.

Too much closeness and team spirit may shut team off from rest of the organization.

Teams suffer from lack of progress, failure to meet deadlines, setbacks, and bad results.

Teams suffer from internal politics, hidden agendas, or conformity pressures.

Interteam competition may be self-defeating or overall organizational goals are lost.

Expectations may be too high or goals are unrealistic.

Teams suffer from inadequate or ineffective policies, procedures, equipment, or environmental factors.

Because of the emphasis on becoming generalists, specialist expertise is less developed.

---

enced members lost, but new members must be brought up to speed. Rehashing and possibly resolving of old issues may ensue. This can be minimized by planned, overlapping substitutions.

Opportunities must exist for team leaders to emerge. Gordon[5] points out that even in children's playgrounds leaders will emerge.

Cross-training can reduce specialist skills and force some skilled people to assume roles for which they have neither aptitude nor interest. Creativity is sometimes smothered.

Other pitfalls are presented in Table V.

REFERENCES

1. Doyle RJ, Doyle PI. *Gain Management: A Process for Building Teamwork, Productivity, & Profitability Throughout Your Organization.* New York, NY: AMACOM; 1992.

2. Mills DQ. *Rebirth of the Corporation.* New York, NY: John Wiley & Sons; 1991.

3. *Boardroom Report.* July 15, 1993:10.

4. Zemke R. Rethinking the rush to team up. *Training.* 1993;30:55-61.

5. Gordon J. The team troubles that won't go away. *Training*. 1994; 31:25-34.

6. Zenger JH, Musselwhite E, Hurson K, Perrin C. *Leading Teams: Mastering the New Role*. Homewood, Ill: Business One Irwin; 1994.

7. Harrington-Mackin D. *The Team Building Tool Kit*. New York, NY: AMACOM; 1994.

8. Orsburn JD, Moran L, Musselwhite E, Zenger JH. *Self-Directed Work Teams: The New American Challenge*. Homewood, Ill: Business One Irwin; 1990.

8. Establishing Self-Directed Teams

Pᴇʀᴍᴀɴᴇɴᴛ ᴡᴏʀᴋ ᴛᴇᴀᴍs...are not outside the organizational structure, they are the organizational structure.[1]
Jack Zigon

Cʜᴀᴘᴛᴇʀ ᴏʙᴊᴇᴄᴛɪᴠᴇs

- To delineate the preimplementation phase of team building
- To describe preparatory activities
- To depict the norms of self-directed teams
- To detail the five stages of team maturation
- To recommend methods for evaluating team performance
- To provide examples of self-directed teams in hospitals

Supervisors and other managers who have become change specialists, are willing to take risks, and delegate effectively find team building to be relatively facile. Shared leadership techniques such as rotating meeting chairpersons and dividing up administrative responsibilities among members of a work group at times when the leader is absent lay the groundwork for a team-building enterprise.

When organizations embark on process reengineering, quality improvement, or shared governance initiatives, they find that team building is essential. Team building and process reengineering are interdependent. It takes team effort to implement reengineering, and without process reengineering, teams do not function effectively or efficiently.

THE PREIMPLEMENTATION PHASE OF TEAM BUILDING

While team building starts with a vision, the engine of team building is the action, not the talk, of upper management. Actions are based on values. The wise employer or CEO includes the values of customer service, respect for employees, search for new and better technologies, continuous education, and training at all levels. Insistence on quality improvement, cost control, work safety, good neighbor relations, and protection of the environment round out the registry of values. The supervisor-in-transition is the engineer of team-building initiatives. Top management provides the engine and fuel.

Information Collection

Information may be gathered from word-of-mouth, publications, seminars, and consultants. Senior officials or designated groups visit organizations that have reported team-building success—the process of benchmarking. Others prefer to bring in consultants. Many do both. If you are appointed to such a group, make sure that you prepare a list of questions to be asked at the time of the benchmarking visits.

The Steering Committee

Usually the CEO appoints a steering committee, although in some organizations managers at a lower level take the initiative with their own groups. If this local trial is successful, other units may follow suit, or administration may jump start similar programs throughout the entire organization. The steering committee usually performs the following tasks:

- Explores feasibility and makes recommendations.
- Makes multiple site visits.
- Forecasts costs and recommends time schedules.
- Tests the waters by getting answers to questions, such as the willingness of employees and managers to participate and take career risks. Internal employee surveys determine worker perceptions of the organization and its management, culture, goals, values, systems, and structures.
- Determines the technical competencies of the workers and the leadership abilities of the managers.
- Reviews the history of successes and failures of major changes.
- Makes decisions about where and how teams can be most effective.
- Prepares responses to the expected naysaying of critics and the challenges of reluctant participants.
- If the organization is unionized, considers the impact of this relationship and defines the role of the union officials.
- If the decision is to proceed, recommends employment of a consult-

ing group, the size and number of initial teams, the tentative composition of the teams, appropriate work sites, and problems to be addressed.[2]

- Initiates a pilot study. An effective steering committee will start with a work group that has already demonstrated the ability to adjust to change and has already exhibited signs of teamwork. The people work smoothly with each other, are enthusiastic about changes, and are willing to take risks.

- Participants in the pilot study are selected carefully, sufficient time and resources are made available, and trainers and facilitators are selected. Training course content, modalities, and duration are determined. Performance standards and criteria for evaluating results are established.

- Decisions are made concerning whether participation is to be voluntary or not and what will be done with employees who are unwilling to join the new teams.

- The committee describes major activities the team is expected to undertake; specific objectives to be achieved; strategies, practices, processes, and results expected; resources available; type and frequency of reporting; skills and abilities necessary; and the authority the team will have.[3]

- A new recognition and reward system should be installed that rewards team results as much or more than it rewards individual efforts. (See Chapter 15 for more on reward and recognition systems.)

- Training is featured among the committee's recommendations. (See Chapter 17 for more on training.)

In larger organizations, councils may be formed to spearhead the formation and activities of self-directed teams. For example, Beesley et al[4] reported on the successful use of quality councils in their blood bank and laboratory to coordinate the growing interest in quality improvement programs.

INITIAL TEAM ACTIVITY PLANS

Initially the team holds many meetings. The team plans and prioritizes its work. Members assume responsibility roles, coordinate with teammates, and consult with support groups, facilitators, or mentors. In addition to scheduling and assigning work, the group starts to solve technical, administrative, and interpersonal problems. Much time is spent learning from facilitators and engaging in cross-training.[2]

After the routine work has been organized, the team may engender annual group plans. Individual members formulate their own plans by partitioning the annual team plans. The individual plans may include objectives, work standards, training to be completed, and areas for improvement.

TEAM NORMS

Team norms are unwritten agreements about behavior that are carried over from former groups, modified by the new social ambiance and member interaction. These norms include ethical and moral considerations.

Unfortunately, not all group norms are beneficial to the organization or its customers. When the norms are functional, team members quickly defend them. When the norms are dysfunctional, the employees usually recognize this and claim that these norms have been imposed on them by management.

Some conflict is beneficial, even essential to effective problem solving. In fact, few improvements ensue in the absence of complaints or problems. Cohesion does not mean absence of differences of opinion, arguments, or disagreements. Members of great teams can frequently be heard heatedly debating among themselves.

STAGES IN TEAM MATURATION

Team building is a five-stage process that takes some time to complete. Progress is up and down, not in a straight line. Teams often fluctuate back and forth between stages.

Stage 1: Transition

The stage of transition or anticipation usually requires up to six months. It represents the transition from individual worker to team member, and participation is hesitant as members wonder what is expected of them.

During this stage, senior managers make presentations about mission and goals. Facilitators (coaches) get members to agree on the ground rules on how meetings and other activities will be conducted. Flow charts are developed to highlight change in processes (see Chapters 17 and 22). Schedules are prepared and modalities for progress checks are posited.

With the cooperation of team members, the supervisor submits a hand-off plan, which outlines the sequential transfer of tasks to team members as they become qualified to handle them. This list includes the tasks the team can take on now, those that can be transferred after some training, and those that can be eliminated. Training includes formal team skill training and much informal cross-training.

In some organizations, the employer attempts to increase interdependence by subjecting employees to team sports and outward-bound exercises such as mountain climbing, obstacle courses, wilderness survival, or sailboat cruises. These expensive and time-consuming exercises require high levels of communication, cooperation, and trust. An inexpensive substitute is having employees fall backward into the arms of coworkers or running a computer simulation of a laboratory.[5] While the jury is still out on the effectiveness of the expensive exercises, the suppliers and consultants who offer them are prospering, and employees enjoy the time away from the job with pay.

Early in this stage, everyone who has volunteered to participate is usually very polite and congenial—a sort of honeymoon phase. Team members gather impressions, form relationships, and establish patterns of behavior.[6] Suspicion, fear, anxiety, and low productivity are often manifested. The team leader may have different points of view from the members. Lots of talking tends to take place, but little listening. If the employees have been coerced into participation, no honeymoon takes place.

Team feedback: A questionnaire or direct verbal questioning[7] can elicit important feedback from members by asking questions such as:

Do you really understand what a self-directed team is?

Do you believe this concept will work in our unit?

Do you trust management to provide us with the necessary resources?

Do you think you can support the team approach and other members will do likewise?

Stage 2: Confusion

The stage of confusion, which is also termed bickering or dissatisfaction, may be permanent in poorly led groups. Members begin to see what kinds of roles they want to play. They still see themselves more as individual workers; not yet a true team, but rather a collection of persons brought together for a common purpose.

Dependence on formal leaders has decreased. Low productivity persists. Confusion still exists over roles, tasks, and leadership. The interactions between people reflect relationships, biases, perceptions, and antagonisms brought in from outside the group.[8]

The facilitator encourages, listens empathetically, and encourages people to vent. Team members are urged to solve their own problems. When they bring problems to their facilitator, they must also bring solutions—they soon realize that problem solving is now their responsibility.

Benchmarking visits are conducted, and training continues at a fast pace. The team gets better acquainted with individuals at the front end and the back end of the work process (suppliers and customers).

More time is spent discussing problems and celebrating progress. Some team members test the management support and the transfer of power; a few push the limits of their new authority.

Polarization occurs, with some members displaying negativity, hostility, or resistance, while others are overly zealous. This may lead to infighting, defensiveness, and competition. Some actively grieve over the loss of the old system, with anger and tears being common observations. Some workers want out. Members who do not have the big picture resist efforts to add or subtract members or to modify goals.[9]

Conflicts may occur between those who want to get the job done quickly and those who want to proceed more deliberately. Some people insist on applying solutions they used before they joined the team. Highly task-oriented members may be impatient with those who wish to abide by the group dynamics.

Team feedback: Appropriate questions for team members near the end of this phase include:

Do you think our goals are realistic?

Do you know what is expected of you and the team?

Do you know what responsibilities and authority will be transferred to you in the future?

Are you actively participating in scheduling, training, and other team activities?

Do you consider your colleagues competent and trustworthy?

Are your suggestions listened to and implemented?

Stage 3: Resolution

The stage of resolution, also called role clarification or normalization, requires a variable period to complete but usually spans several months. Leadership and task assignments are rotated, and the facilitator emphasizes creative thinking and problem solving. Productivity now proceeds at a moderate pace.

Group norms and roles emerge. Dissatisfaction and conflict diminish. A sense of cohesiveness develops, which depends on team members sharing a perception of interdependence and feeling responsible for the success of the team. Internal and external customer performance improves. Players start thinking of themselves as multiskilled generalists.

The group now practices consensus at meetings and accepts individual strengths and weaknesses. Relationships with other teams improve. At this point, the team will resent any member who fails to accept that responsibility.

Team feedback: Appropriate questions for the team members include:

How effective are meetings?

Do you know what is expected of each member?

Are information systems and management support adequate?

How well do the individual and team reward and recognition systems work?

Stage 4: Maturation or Unification

The maturation or unification stage usually requires from six months to more than one year. The team experiments with new roles, such as informal leadership.

The facilitator transfers more difficult administrative and supervisory responsibilities to the team and gradually withdraws from routine daily team activities as the team develops its own leadership, usually with rotating leaders.

Team members are now energetic and self-confident. Productivity is high, performance smooth. Cross-training is showing results with growing excitement over accomplishments.

Team members have developed insight into personal and interpersonal processes. They have learned how to resolve their differences and give each other constructive feedback. Team identity and pride grows, and they trust and respect each other. On the negative side, teams may be less open to innovation and challenges at this stage—little kingdoms may develop.

Team feedback: Feedback from team members should reveal that they are comfortable with rotating tasks, work well with other teams and departments, are able to reach consensus at meetings more often, meet most or all performance standards, meet regularly with their external and internal customers, are recognized and rewarded as a team more than as individuals, have frequent celebrations for accomplishments, and are constantly seeking new ways to improve.

Stage 5: Re-forming or Disbanding

During the reforming or disbanding stage, group enrollment starts to change. New members are added, and old ones leave. A project may be terminated or new dynamics introduced. Periodic reviews determine if the team is still needed. If the team's functions change, new goals or membership is indicated.

When a team re-forms or disbands, a formal meeting can achieve a sense of closure and satisfaction by tying up loose ends and highlighting necessary follow-up. If some people remain as a team, they need to know what their new assignments are.

When a new team is formed from the nucleus of the old one, the team will pass through the various stages much more quickly. Some members become facilitators of new teams.

EVALUATION OF TEAM PERFORMANCE

Since most performance appraisal systems were developed for individuals, not teams, they must be adapted to fit the particular requirements of teams. Teams are rated largely by their ability to operate systems or processes effectively and efficiently, to contain costs, and to maintain quality and safety. Team members are judged not only on their technical or professional expertise but also on their cooperation and teamwork.

Different teams require different approaches to measurement. A team of nurses and other care providers on a nursing floor will be evaluated largely on the basis of surveys of patient satisfaction. The performance of a laboratory team will be reflected in turnaround time and reliability of test results.

A common error is to try to measure everything using numbers. Work results can always be expressed using only words, not figures. However, the document must demonstrate validity—the key is verifiability.[1]

Who Should Do the Appraising?

Teams may be evaluated by their facilitators, with or without participation of team players. Individual performance is evaluated by team members when self-directed work teams are in place. In the early phases of team building, the supervisor may do the honors.

Zigon[1] points to reasons why performance appraisals of teams are not easy to modify. For one thing, most performance reviews were developed with only individual performers in mind, and rewards are still given chiefly to individuals. Second, it is often difficult to decide where the team leaves off and the individuals begin. Third, measuring team performance is somewhat difficult, especially when bottom-line data are hard to come by. Finally, different types of teams require different approaches to measurement. For example, a temporary project team that ends with a recommendation to higher management is measured differently from a permanent operational team.

Zigon[1] offers five keys to designing a system of team appraisal:
1. Tie team results to organizational goals.
2. Begin with the work process that deals with customer satisfaction.
3. Measure both team and individual performance and base the individual evaluations largely on team members' contribution to the team effort.
4. Verify not only by using numbers but also by comparing performance with work standards.
5. Train the team to create its own measures.

Peer Feedback

In effective teams, members benefit from feedback from their peers. Peer reviews are usually more accurate and acceptable and can help to reinforce the emphasis on collective responsibility. Such feedback is especially valuable because the persons being evaluated learn how their behavior affects the other members. Members may be surprised to learn that their perceptions of what the team regarded as most important differ from those expressed in the performance reviews.

Quick[8] recommends quarterly peer evaluations, with each team member completing an evaluation form for all other members. When one member's evaluation differs markedly from those of the rest of the group, this should become a group issue.

The downside of group peer evaluation is that a member who receives unfavorable evaluations, especially when these seem to lack objectivity, may feel threatened or aggrieved. The team leader must attempt to reverse these negative reactions by pointing out the positive aspects of the individual's performance and helping that person overcome the deficiency.

EXAMPLES OF TEAM BUILDING

- Werner and Pauley[10] improved the productivity of their chemical laboratory by increasing the number of rungs in their career ladder. Their initial staff in the 1970s consisted of one technical director, one supervisor, and 20 medical technologists. This evolved to their current structure of a technical manager, three supervisors, six senior medical technologists, and 16 medical technologists at three experience levels. Over the same time span, their work load increased from 600,000 tests to 2.5 million assays (obviously automation had also increased).

  The change created opportunities for duties such as continuing education, inventory control, method development, QC review, and instrument specialization to be shifted down the ladder. Each technologist enjoyed greater opportunities for advancement and more stimulating assignments.

  These authors also used the team approach by combining nine work stations that previously stood alone into three functional work circles organized and operated by teams of four technologists each with a coordinator. Added team responsibilities included organization, training of new members, advanced maintenance and troubleshooting, and QC and result review.

- In a 119-bed hospital, nurses learned to manage without a unit manager or supervisor. Each nurse had to be involved in at least one of 12 operational tasks in addition to her usual nursing duties. These tasks included scheduling, census management, quality improvement, mentoring, interviewing candidates, tracking supplies, performance review, and committee service.[11]

- The CEO of a 200-bed hospital (St. Joseph's Hospital, Lancaster, Pa) decided to combine the maternity and pediatric services. A nurse director was charged with the responsibility for combining the facilities and staffs of the delivery and postpartum suites, the newborn intensive care unit, the nursery, and the pediatric inpatient and outpatient services.

  A special team was appointed, comprising the nurse director and three clinical nurse managers from the original units. This team developed business and marketing plans, cross-trained the staff, set up a hospital-wide multidisciplinary team, and recruited a community advisory panel.

  The nurse leader assumed responsibility for strategic planning and implementation, marketing, fiscal management, and facility issues. The clinical managers handled the hiring, training, staffing, scheduling, and performance reviews for their individual units. They monitored departmental supplies and equipment. Day-to-day operations and problem solving were integral parts of their positions.

REFERENCES

1. Zigon J. Making performance appraisals work for teams. *Training*. 1994;31:58-63.

2. Orsburn JD, Moran L, Musselwhite E, Zenger JH. *Self-Directed Work Teams: The New American Challenge*. Homewood, Ill: Business One Irwin; 1990.

3. Harrington-Mackin D. *The Team Building Tool Kit*. New York, NY: AMACOM; 1994.

4. Beesley J, et al. Quality management series: how we implemented TQM in our laboratory and our blood bank. *Clin Lab Manage Rev*. 1993;7:217-227.

5. Gooddale JG. Effective teamwork and productivity conferences. *Clin Lab Manage Rev*. 1994;8:241-243.

6. Zenger JH, Musselwhite E, Hurson K, Perrin C. *Leading Teams: Mastering the New Role*. Homewood, Ill: Business One Irwin; 1994.

7. *Implementing Self-Directed Work Teams Workbook*. Boulder, Colo: CareerTrack Publications; 1993.

8. Quick TL. *Successful Team Building*. New York, NY: AMACOM; 1992.

9. Kaeter M. Reporting mature work teams. *Training*. 1994;31(suppl):4-6.

10. Werner M, Pauley C. Revamping the lab's staffing structure. *MLO*. 1994;26:44-49.

11. Jannota M, Maldonado T. Self-management for nurses. *J Nurs Admin*. 1992;22:59-63.

PART II
The New Team and Its Leaders

9. Supervisor-in-Transition: The Coach

Y OU GET PAID for what *they* do, not what *you* do.

CHAPTER OBJECTIVES

- To differentiate the supervisor-in-transition from the team leader
- To reflect on what happens to supervisors when self-directed teams have been developed
- To elaborate on the various key roles of the coach
- To detail the specific training for new coaches
- To provide advice to a coach who has just acquired a team

Top management authorizes team building, but the first-line managers—the supervisors—make it happen. Supervisors play the leading role in the training of a self-directed work team (SDWT), to which they eventually relinquish their authority. During this conversion, which may require many months or years, the supervisor continues to direct while serving as team builder. I will call these team builders "coaches." Other titles include facilitator, coordinator, or expediter.

COACHES AND TEAM LEADERS

The supervisor-coach is appointed by management and continues as a member of the management staff.

The team leader described in this book is not the supervisor or another member of management. Team leaders are usually selected by team members (although the first one may be appointed). Sometimes a supervisor may give up his or her management status and serve as a team leader.

A coach may serve several teams. A team leader usually serves one major team, although this person may be a member of several teams, especially cross-functional ones. Team leadership often rotates periodically. The coach continues to be accountable for the team, while the team leader shares responsibility with the other team members.

Team leaders may perform many routine team tasks; coaches usually do so only in emergency situations.

WHAT HAPPENS TO SUPERVISORS WHEN SDWTS TAKE OVER

When teams are ready to take off on their own, what is in store for their coaches (supervisors)? The answer to this question is very important—especially to the affected coaches. They must be convinced that although their roles will change radically, they will still have satisfactory employment. These new roles may be completely divorced from their former teams. If they do not get this reassurance, they will stonewall the power transfer, and the team-building program will come to a screeching halt because supervisors are the engines of the restructuring process.

Coaches who were uncomfortable in leadership roles may assume purely professional or technical functions on the team. Others may become members of management teams that function on the next higher level. Such teams may be called operational teams, and each member of one of these teams is responsible for several SDWTs.

Coaches may be promoted to management positions that are unrelated to teams. Others train new groups. Supervisors who cannot or will not adjust to the new concept may be transferred to units that maintain traditional operational systems. Some will resign or their jobs will be terminated. As much as possible, employers should permit supervisors to make their own decisions regarding role changes.

CHANGES DURING THE TRANSITION TO SDWTS

During the transition to SDWTs, supervisors devote more of their time to team training, indoctrinating new team members, and managing external forces that affect the team's success.

Training includes teaching team members how to assume supervisory and administrative functions, teaching team skills, and initiating job sharing and work station rotation. At a first glance, it appears that with the transfer of so many of their responsibilities, supervisors would have little to do. How-

However, Ambrose,[1] a team-building consultant, found that many clients were busier than ever preparing team members to assume new roles and responsibilities.

As they divest themselves of their controlling functions, supervisors are less likely to interfere in the daily routine of their teams—less likely to be bottlenecks. However, they remain available as resource persons.

New or Expanded Functions for the Coaches

The coach may check on competitors, visit customers and suppliers, investigate new technologies, redesign training programs, develop new products or services, address ways to improve work flow, remove barriers, and work with the leaders of other teams. The coach may become more involved in quality improvement, process reengineering, restructuring, and cost cutting, or may serve on cross-functional teams. The coach will have more contact with external and internal customers.

How the Duties of Coaches Differ from Those of Traditional Supervisors

In their best-seller, *Flight of the Buffalo*, Belasco and Stayer[2] point out that the old leadership paradigm was the equivalent of leading a herd of buffalo. Only the first buffalo in line could lead. When this buffalo was shot, the others milled around in chaos and became easy targets for hunters. The new leadership paradigm is like the leadership of a gaggle of geese. In flight, the leadership changes and every goose gets a chance to lead. This provides flexibility and continuity of direction—and prevents leadership fatigue.

A coach's responsibility differs from that of a traditional supervisor in that it focuses less on tasks and more on relationships. The traditional supervisor's responsibilities are to direct, control, solve problems, budget, select personnel, and schedule. The job descriptions of coaches emphasize ensuring availability of resources, advising, supporting, training, empowering, and representing teams. Supervisors are usually found within the confines of their units, while coaches spend much of their time with internal and external customers and other people involved in departmental input or output activities.

PAM

The Spectrum of Coaching Roles

Visionary

A vision describes how one hopes things will be, like President Kennedy's vision of having a man on the moon. Coaches create a vision around which people rally; managers marshal the resources to achieve the vision. The vision of top management must be broad enough that the visions of teams in the lower echelons of the organization fit within it.[3] For visions to be effective they must be clear and believable from the employees' viewpoint. Many vision statements are too vague or unrealistic.

Coaches must translate visions into mission statements—the reasons for the team's existence. Fisher,[3] who has had extensive hands-on experience with SDWTs, encourages the participation of employees in formulating vision and mission statements. He feels that this participation is just as important as the contents of these statements.

Here is a brief but succinct vision statement for a histopathology team:

> Our vision is to have a fully staffed, high-quality, committed work group that is efficient and effective in providing the highest-quality histopathology service in our community.

Customer Advocate

Coaches must know who their external and internal customers are, what these customers want or need, and how these expectations are best met. The best coaches learn how to surprise and delight their customers. Coaches must share that information with their teammates. All health care workers know that patients and physicians are customers, but how about internal customers such as nurses, students, and trainees and interacting departments? Relationships between nursing service and the departments of pharmacy, radiology, and laboratory are often adversarial rather than those of customer-provider. A provider-customer relationship exists at every interface of a work process. Carlzon[4] calls these interactions "moments of truth" because if any of these interfaces are negative, a customer becomes dissatisfied.

Customer service must be a prime consideration in the selection of employees, in orientation programs and staff meetings, and in employee performance rating and reward systems.

Persuader

Persuaders are the motivating force in any change or empowering initiative. Effective coaches persuade their teams to reach new heights of accomplishment. Power persuasion is not achieved through manipulation or charisma.

Communicator

Good coaches practice management-by-information. They specialize as diffusers of good news. There is not enough good news in health care these days, so coaches must make the most of what there is. On the other hand, they do not withhold bad news.

Coaches make certain that their teams have all the information they need to do their work and to understand why they are doing it. Technical information is up to date, forthcoming changes are discussed as quickly as information is up to date, forthcoming changes are discussed as quickly as they become known, and the team is kept informed about its progress toward goals.

Coaches exchange information by sharing reprints, handouts from seminars, and other technical or professional information. They solicit feedback from individual members—sometimes in private to ensure that "group think" is not unduly influencing individuals. They communicate anything that you would share with a business partner. This information is best delivered in person rather than via memos or computer printouts. Appropriate major topics include quality improvement, financial data, goal achievement progress, customer service, schedules, new technologies, and operational problems.[3] Other examples of important information include budget review, outside inspections, new policies, supplier information, staffing issues, new services, inventory control, work flow, safety, legislative news, and progress reports.

Coaches bolster communication between work shifts. When possible, these shifts overlap to permit personal interactions. When this is not possible, voice mail, electronic messages, and bulletin boards can be used. Coaches meet in person periodically with each shift or ensure that information discussed at meetings held during regular work hours gets to people who work evenings, nights, or weekends.

Coaches keep in touch with other work areas and units. They invite individual or small groups of team members to accompany them on visits to customers, outside similar facilities, suppliers, and management meetings. They encourage employees to deliver presentations at executive sessions.

In the early phases of team building, short daily operational meetings usually are held. As teams mature, the number and length of operational meetings decrease substantially. Lengthier meetings are needed for discussions of projects such as new services or systems; revised laws or regulations; and restructuring, downsizing, mergers, or major renovations.

Coaches strengthen their orientation programs. When orienting new team members, they emphasize customer satisfaction, quality standards, and relationships with other teams. Coaches update their organization charts, employee handbooks, and procedure manuals. They use memos, newsletters, and informational meetings skillfully.

Coaches encourage negative as well as positive feedback from the team members, especially information about quality improvement and customer satisfaction. They know how to give and take praise and criticism.

Facilitator

Facilitator is such a key role that coaches are often called *facilitators* or *external facilitators*. Facilitating is not doing the work for other people; it is showing them how, making it easier for them to get the job done, and learning how to solve their individual and team problems. Suggestions from coaches are offered as advice, not orders. Facilitating is expediting, responding to distress calls after hours, eliminating red tape, getting outside help, bending rules, and pitching in to help during emergencies.

Facilitators provide the necessary equipment, supplies, physical arrangements, and work processes, and they do all they can to make the work environment safe. Employees should have input into and control over each of these constructs. A lack of input and control can adversely affect such changes. For example, in one unit, a group of employees' delight when a more efficient air conditioner was installed changed to a grievance when the workers discovered that they had no control over the thermostat.

Facilitating is the avoidance of nitpicking, unduly interrupting work flow, or other devilish ways of wasting people's time. As facilitators, coaches do not surrender complete control. Occasionally, they must step in and intervene when things go awry.[5] When frequent interruptions are necessary, it may indicate that additional team training is needed. Facilitating involves MBWA (managing-by-walking-around), checking with team members to see how things are going and if they need any help.

In an organization with multiple SDWTs, a major function of facilitators is to ensure interteam communication and coordination. This fits into the current efforts of health care organizations to develop cross-functional systems. Facilitators may also serve as team representatives, voicing grievances or concerns for their team members, unless the organization is unionized.

Zenger and associates[6] list the following responsibilities of coaches:

- Urging team members to develop and use new skills
- Providing information that improves expertise
- Explaining how tasks relate to work goals
- Holding progress meetings
- Helping the team to identify expectations of customers
- Helping to obtain resources and information
- Debriefing the team on how well it performed a task
- Discussing what went well and what to do differently next time

An example of a list of shared responsibilities is presented in Table I.

Guide

Good coaches have a clear picture of what constitutes good performance for their teams and can communicate that picture so performers know what to emulate.[7]

Coaching is face-to-face leadership. It helps people get results by building on their strengths, developing their skills, providing encouragement, and increasing their self-esteem and confidence. To accomplish this requires identifying ways to enhance individual and team effectiveness, providing opportunities for skill enhancement, offering performance feedback, and preparing team members for new responsibilities.

The best coaches expect and demand the best from their team members.

Table I
Worksheet for Sharing Responsibilities

Responsibility	Team	Leader	Joint	Other
Troubleshooting instruments				
Recommending new equipment				
Working with vendors				
Hiring new employees				
Scheduling work				
Scheduling vacation				
Setting goals for team				
Determining training needs				
Cross-training employees				
Selecting new employees				
Orienting new employees				
Coping with customer expectations				
Meeting with internal customers				
Appraising colleague performance				
Addressing performance problems				
Recommending procedure changes				
Budgeting				
Enforcing safety				
Participating in TQM/CQI				

The best coaches expect and demand the best from their team members. Low expectations seldom result in high performance. Daily feedback and reinforcement are much more effective than periodic formal performance appraisals.

Effective coaches help employees adapt to change, meet new performance goals and quality standards, and be more innovative. They foster creativity by challenging, questioning old ways, and making demands, sometimes being a little difficult.[1]

Some coaching can be delegated to senior team members, but those "assistant coaches" should be selected with care. They should be willing and able and have both the time and the enthusiasm for the team-building initiative.

Liaison Agent

Coaches coordinate the activities of their teams with those of other teams and encourage collaboration and cooperation with those teams. They squelch arguments and ill-will between departments and avoid bilateral barrages of incident reports.[5]

Coaches also act as team publicist, ensuring that the teams get full credit for their accomplishments. They keep upper management informed of team progress, allow team members to make verbal reports, and invite upper managers to speak to the teams. They visit external and internal customers and seek feedback from them on how the teams can serve them better.

Change Agent

As change agents, coaches are committed to continuous improvement of customer service, quality, and safety. They minimize disruptions during change and motivate people to implement the systems. They foster creativity by challenging or questioning old ways. They are specific as to what workers should do differently, and they establish new goals and objectives.

The change agents create conditions that make people want to contribute and be committed. This requires lots of positive reinforcement, not only from the coach but also from upper management, customers, or anyone else whom workers respect. This reinforcement includes verbal comments, more freedom from control, financial rewards, and being acknowledged during rites and rituals. For more on this, see Chapter 15.

Defender

The coach defends the team from outside interference or pressure. Like a baseball manager, the coach protects players by stepping between them and outside antagonists.

Model

Coaches must "walk the talk." They should embody and symbolize the vision of the organization. Quality improvement and other initiatives are unlikely to succeed if coaches fail to back up their words.

Mentor

Mentors help team members develop political savvy, expand their networks, improve their expertise, satisfy their thirst for knowledge, and develop greater sensitivity to cultural and creative diversity.

EXAMPLES OF EXTRADEPARTMENTAL ACTIVITIES OF COACHES

- Serving on cross-functional teams and task forces
- Coordinating with other teams and departments
- Interacting with customers and suppliers
- Sponsoring joint supplier/team projects
- Solving problems between teams
- Monitoring competitors' activities and benchmarking (ie, studying how successful organizations do things)
- Investigating competitors' strategies

SUMMARY OF TEAM ACTIVITIES OF COACHES

- Mapping out new strategies
- Teaching team members technical, professional, and leadership skills
- Looking at new technologies
- Managing process reengineering
- Inviting suppliers to provide training
- Mediating or arbitrating personnel problems
- Developing work standards
- Counseling team members
- Coping with cultural diversity
- Referring incoming calls that coaches previously handled to appropriate team members
- Chairing some team meetings

- Planning special projects
- Anticipating technology shifts
- Investigating quality improvement and safety measures
- Preparing for inspections
- Obtaining resources or services from other parts of the organization
- Ensuring compliance with laws such as ADA and CLIA '88

THE TRAINING OF COACHES

The best coaches are enthusiastic and have a relaxed style. They know when to intervene in operational and personal problems. Most of this is not learned in seminars but comes from hands-on experience. However, some training of coaches is important. Most experts recommend training coaches as coaches just before they have opportunities to use these new skills—so-called "just-in-time learning"—because people learn faster and better when they have an immediate need to apply the things they are learning.

Training of coaches features meeting skills, principles of adult learning, group dynamics, problem solving, and conflict resolution. Meeting skills include the use of training tools such as overheads and flip charts. Coaches must be able to clarify, summarize, and integrate various points of view. They learn active listening skills, methods for collecting and analyzing data, basic charting methods, force-field analysis, and brainstorming techniques.[8] Coach trainees are reminded that adult learners have had experience and are more interested in the practical application of knowledge. They are cautioned never to talk down to the people they will train.

WHAT TO DO WHEN YOU ACQUIRE A TEAM

A team is like a wheel in which each member is a spoke. It is the team coach's responsibility to have enough spokes and to keep the spokes the same length.[9]

Keye Productivity Center

Review the team's record and examine its culture. If possible, talk to your predecessor. Identify and contact external and internal customers. Ask them how they can be served better.

Conduct a personnel resource audit. First, list all the areas of expertise that the team should possess right now or may need in the near future. Interview all members and probe their goals and expectations. Find out what they perceive as their strengths and improvement needs. Prepare a skill's inventory list of your team. (See Chapter 11 for an example of such a list.) Identify gaps in the sum total of the team's knowledge, experience, and motivation.

Sample the morale of team members by an employee attitude survey.

Evaluate material resources and determine immediate and long-range needs.

Articulate and translate your vision and update the team's mission statement or purpose. With your staff, define and prioritize team goals, develop strategies, and institute plans. Start with simple goals or projects to ensure a taste of success.

Clarify the roles and responsibilities of each team member. Avoid making major reassignments until you know team members better, then reassign according to their strengths and weaknesses. Prepare a chart that shows the sharing of responsibilities. Update this as delegation continues.
Develop a training program for team members.

Establish teamwork patterns, such as communication channels, meetings, procedures, policies, work reviews, schedules, and the like.

Start getting feedback and problem solving by attacking little problems. This is easier, is more acceptable to the team, and, if you goof, it is only a little mistake. Dawson[10] recommends gathering your team around and saying something like: "I'm new here and I don't know enough yet to help you with the big problems, but perhaps I can help you right away with some of the little ones. Who has something that's been bugging them?"

Establish credibility. When team members perceive their leaders as lacking credibility, they become cynical and fail to develop commitment toward their work and their employer. To earn credibility, coaches must demonstrate honesty, competency, and trustworthiness. They practice what they preach, demonstrate consistency between words and deeds, and demonstrate trust in others.

Fulfill your various roles.

Evaluate progress and goal achievement.

REFERENCES

1. Ambrose L. Coaching the self-directed team. *2000 Bulletin*. Perrone-Ambrose, Inc. 1993;3:1-3.

2. Belasco JA, Stayer RC. *Flight of the Buffalo: Soaring to Excellence, Learning to Let Employees Lead*. New York, NY: Warner Books Inc; 1993.

3. Fisher K. *Leading Self-Directed Work Teams: A Guide to Developing New Team Leadership Skills*. New York, NY: McGraw-Hill; 1993.

4. Carlzon J. *Moments of Truth*. Cambridge, Mass: Ballinger Publishing Co; 1987.

5. Quick TL. *Successful Team Building*. New York, NY: AMACOM; 1992.

6. Zenger JH, Musselwhite E, Hurson K, Perrin C. *Leading Teams: Mastering the New Role*. Homewood, Ill: Business One-Irwin; 1994.

7. Geber B. From manager into coach. *Training*. 1992;29:25-31.

8. Sisco R. What to teach team coaches. *Training*. 1993;30:62-67.

9. Keye Productivity Center. *How to Build a Better Team*. 2nd ed. Kansas City, Mo: Keye Productivity; 1991 (seminar manual).

10. Dawson R. Englewood Cliffs, NJ: Prentice-Hall; 1992.

10. The Leader of the Self-Directed Work Team

L EADERSHIP CANNOT REALLY be taught. It can only be learned.[1]
   Harold Geneen

CHAPTER OBJECTIVES

- To compare and contrast managers and leaders
- To define the four major responsibilities of team leaders
- To categorize the essential leadership skills or characteristics
- To discuss the barriers to team leadership
- To present a list of practical tips for team leaders

Team leadership includes not only actions that leaders take on behalf of their teams but also the actions by team members as they work with each other. Team leaders involve employees in the major decisions made about work processes and in the daily decisions about how to make the work safer, more productive, and satisfying.[2]

The leader of a self-directed work team is a team member, not a member of management. Team leaders may be elected by team members or may be appointed. Most work groups prefer a leader whom they select to one assigned by management, and leadership usually evolves during team building. Some management consultants are less than enthusiastic about allowing teams to select their leaders. One views the practice of permitting teams to choose their leaders as a major problem.[3] However, current literature does not seem to substantiate the concerns about teams selecting their own leaders.

Some groups select a permanent leader, others like to rotate leadership. The rate of rotation also varies, sometimes on a daily basis.[4] Organizations may not have designated team leaders but may install a system of shared leadership in which each team member has some leadership duties in addition to regular work. For example, one team member may be accountable for safety, another for quality improvement.[5] Team players usually receive a few "perks" when they serve as team leaders.

DIFFERENCES BETWEEN MANAGERS AND LEADERS

- People follow managers because they have to; they follow leaders because they want to.
- Managers often use people; leaders develop them.
- Managers direct; leaders guide.
- Managers like plans, facts, and logic; leaders rely much on visions and intuitive thinking.
- Managers' goals usually arise out of necessity; leaders' out of desires.
- Managers store practical knowledge; leaders may be impractical at times.
- Managers balance opposing views and act to limit choices; leaders open issues to new options.
- Managers seek to strengthen existing institutions; leaders seek to change them.
- Managers use hierarchy; leaders use networks.
- Managers are risk avoiders; leaders are risk takers.
- Managers often become indispensable; leaders are more likely to rise to the top.

(See Chapter 9 for differences between coaches and team leaders.)

THE FOUR MAJOR RESPONSIBILITIES OF TEAM LEADERS[2]

1. Building teams and promoting teamwork
2. Guiding work for productivity quality and safety
3. Developing people—skills, involvement, and commitment
4. Promoting goals for excellence

The first two responsibilities concern quality of work life (QWL), while the last two concern team productivity. A good team has a balanced concern for people and work, for quality of work life, and for productivity. Balance is the key to success.

Leadership Skills or Characteristics

- Respect and credibility. They earn the trust and confidence of their teams, colleagues, and superiors. This requires professional or technical competence plus leadership skills. They are fair, patient, and honest.
- Good communicators, great listeners. They provide empathetic feedback. They keep themselves available. They know the value of asking for the input of others.
- Caring attitude toward customers and staff. They model what they expect of others.
- High expectations of team performance while accepting individual differences.
- Flexible, proactive, enthusiastic, and optimistic.
- Effective facilitators at meetings and at the work stations.
- Ability to influence and persuade without pulling rank. They maintain control and resolve conflict quickly.
- Seek team commitment rather than compliance.
- Encourage change and innovation.
- Understand group dynamics.
- Provide a supportive environment for cultural diversity to flourish.
- Effective teachers and trainers.
- Act assertively and responsibly. They do not pamper the team members but demand excellence. Skilled team leaders set behavioral boundaries, of which team members are well aware.

Barriers to Team Leadership

Managers who believe that employees do not like to work and must be coerced into it, that employees shun responsibility, or that managers must be controlling, directive, and strict are not likely to show enthusiasm for the team concept. Situational leadership, as espoused by Hersey and Blanchard,[6] is essential. As team members mature and become more competent and confident, leaders shift from a highly directive style to one that is delegative or even hands-off.

Sometimes the responsibilities of the team leader are unclear. All too often they are told only the things that they must not do. They may receive little or no information about the construct of their new role—even when this is a brand new role for them. A common mistake is to think that a team leader or other team members can assume supervisory and administrative functions while still maintaining the same workload as before.

Some leaders have the false perception that their associates have the same knowledge and problem-solving skill that they have. They may praise too little and criticize too much because their expectations are too high. On the other hand, team members may underperform because their leader has only low expectations.

Lack of multidirectional communication is the most serious barrier. The leader may not be easily accessible or may not be able to provide insight as to why certain tasks are done or why they must be done in a certain way. At times leaders may be too impatient, while at other times they wait too long for workers to self-start.

Five Leadership Sins

- Isolation. Leaders who seldom leave their offices do not lead effectively. They don't know what's going on where the action is. They fail to build networks.
- Complacency. They avoid or delay changes and fail to keep up to date on their competencies.
- Passing the buck, procrastination, or showing indecisiveness.
- Lack of delegation of empowerment. They try to do everything themselves. They spend too much time doing what others could do and not enough time doing what only they can do.
- Disloyalty to their employer or to the people who report to them.

TIPS FOR TEAM LEADERS

Make customer service everybody's business. Get employees to feel like they own the company. Give the team maximum freedom and authority to do things their way. Permit team members to hold meetings without you. Ask for help in solving problems.

Serve as a good role model. Demonstrate a passion for work. Keep your commitments—underpromise and overdeliver. Earn their trust by being credible and respecting others. Be visible and available. Be honest and forthright.

Be predictable, like a vending machine rather than a slot machine. Take priorities seriously. Being predictable includes being consistent.

Visualize each team member as having two large badges. One says "MMFI" and the other "WIIFM." The MMFI badge signifies "Make Me Feel Important." This serves as a reminder to provide recognition and earned praise. The WIIFM badge is an often unexpressed question—"What's in it for me?"—that all of us have when we are on the receiving end of delegation.

Because that unexpressed question usually goes unanswered, delegation is often perceived as "dumping." This badge also serves as a reminder for team leaders to tell their delegates or assignees why what is asked for is important or can be beneficial to the person being directed.

Provide clear guidelines, expectations, and explanations. Improve efficiency and customer service by cutting through red tape. Avoid being a nitpicker or bottleneck. Provide opportunities for your team to meet with personnel of other teams involved in work flows.

Minimize turf battles by organizing your team around responsibilities rather than around titles. Make it clear that team members are accountable to the team.[7]

Be wary of negativists or individuals who demand a lot of attention.

Ensure that team members complement one another and that more than one member has competence in each critical area of responsibility.

Listen well and with empathy. Listen for feelings as well as content. Enhance self-esteem and self-confidence.

Provide negative feedback without eroding self-esteem.

Do not punish failures, but do not tolerate repeats of the same error or sloppy work.

Reinforce values by sharing anecdotes of success, solving problems, encouraging learning, and providing positive feedback.

Celebrate progress. Celebrations need not be elaborate. Occasional coffee and doughnuts or a simple Friday afternoon party will do just nicely.

Generate fun by welcoming it, laughing, joining in, and being cheerful.

Be knowledgeable about information technology and take advantage of new electronic wizardry.

How to Qualify as a Praise Master

Praise is our least expensive and most effective motivating force, yet for some people giving praise does not come easy. Although it can be overdone, especially if insincere, few of us make full use of this powerful tool.

Tager and Willard[8] described a hospital emergency department that was staffed by people who were highly competent but who did not get along. The solution was to make each one praise something a coworker did each day. They used a check-off board to keep the record.

To be effective, praise must be on target, earned, specific, and sincere. The praise master knows what, whom, when, and how to praise. Excessive, misdirected, or phony praise is manipulative and counterproductive. Specificity is important. The praisee should know exactly what is being praised, otherwise misunderstandings may arise. For example, leader Joan greets Steve with "Steve, your performance during that emergency last night was outstanding." Unless Joan clarifies what she was pleased with, Steve will not be clear about what it was that was outstanding. Maybe some of the things Steve did were much less than laudatory.

To praise effectively, leaders must know what is going on in their units. Those who try to manage from their offices are seldom able to specify what performance should be recognized or to select the person who merits the accolade—another advantage of managing by walking around and catching people doing something right.

Praising should usually be done in public, but not always. Some people are embarrassed by being the focus of attention, and sometimes they become the recipients of snide remarks from associates, especially those who do not think that the praise was earned. Some people are embarrassed by face-to-face compliments. When you notice this, praise them "behind their backs," that is, to third parties. The praise will get to the target, and the person being praised is more likely to believe that it is sincere. When it is delivered in person, it may be interpreted as flattery.

Be certain that you have picked the right person when you articulate accolades before a group of employees. Praising the team instead of an individual avoids this problem, but if one of the group feels that he or she did much more than the others, that person may feel slighted.

Many leaders acknowledge performance only when it is outstanding. To get the maximum benefits from your recognition system, do not limit your praising to the superstars. How about the marginal performer who shows improvement, the person who makes innovative suggestions, the ones who help solve problems, or the few who have the courage to bring you bad news?

Recognize the "light hitters" who are average performers but who always show up for work, do not make waves, or are usually willing to go the extra mile by substituting for a sick peer or accepting an unpleasant assignment.

The "One-Minute Praising" of Blanchard and Johnson[9]

This technique makes sense. Here is a slightly modified version:

1. Praise as soon as possible after the deed.
2. Be specific about what you are praising.
3. Tell the person how good you feel about what he or she did, or how it helps others or the organization.
4. Smile and shake hands.
5. Reaffirm your confidence in the person: "I knew you could do an exceptional job on that assignment, and you proved me right."

   Reinforce the verbal message in writing. This can be a thank-you note or memo. Put copies in the person's personnel file, and send duplicates to your boss. Try writing a brief thank-you note on a "Post-it" and stick it on a recipient's door. Watch how many people stop and look, and notice how long it stays there before the recipient removes it.

REFERENCES

1. Geneen H. *Managing*. New York, NY: Avon Books; 1984.
2. Doyle RJ, Doyle PI. *Gain Management: A Process for Building Teamwork, Productivity, & Profitability Throughout Your Organization*. New York, NY: AMACOM; 1992.
3. Brookes D. Four issues to address in using teams and groups. *Supervis Manage*. 1993;38:3.
4. Orsburn JD, Moran L, Musselwhite E, Zenger JH. *Self-Directed Work Teams: The New American Challenge*. Homewood, Ill: Business One Irwin; 1990.
5. Harper A, Harper B. *Skill-Building for Self-Directed Team Members*. Mohegan Lake, NY: MW Corp; 1992.
6. Hersey PE, Blanchard KH. *Management of Organizational Behavior*. 4th ed. Englewood Cliffs, NJ: Prentice-Hall; 1982.
7. O'Brian JD. Making work teams accountable. *Supervis Manage*. 1992;38:1-2.
8. Tager MJ, Willard S. *Transforming Stress Into Power*. Chicago, Ill: Great Performance, Inc, Audiotapes; 1988.
9. Blanchard K, Johnson S. *The One-Minute Manager*. New York, NY: Berkley Book Co; 1982.

11. The Members of the Team

I GIVE EVERYONE a t-shirt that has 'TEAM' on it in big letters, and 'ME' in small letters.[1]
Lou Holtz

CHAPTER OBJECTIVES

- To highlight the need for a broad spectrum of competencies
- To focus on followership styles and essentials
- To delineate team member norms
- To list and describe the characteristics of great team players
- To emphasize the importance of selecting potential winners
- To underscore the significance of team morale and present a simple form for an employee attitude survey
- To address the paradigm change in worker loyalty
- To offer a list of questions for new team members

Not everyone has what it takes to be an empowered team member. Everyone who joins a team should have certain competencies and the ability to develop more. According to Hughes,[2] as many as 30% of workers do not want more responsibility than they already have. Leaders should be reluctant to force unwilling employees into new teams, especially the first ones formed. However, in special cases it is worth making a special effort to recruit players. Some of these people can be salvaged. Others must be transferred to traditional work units, and still others discharged.

Managers at all levels must accept the role of follower in certain work, social, or recreational activities. Many otherwise capable leaders fail because they are inept or uncooperative followers. The manager with little finesse in followership may, like other team members, consistently argue with superiors or peers, become an obstructionist, try to dominate joint efforts, or reject solutions offered by others.

THE NEED FOR A FULL SPECTRUM OF COMPETENCIES

A well-balanced team possesses all the necessary professional and technical expertise. It is not enough that when all members of the team are present the team can offer a full range of services. This comprehensive service should be available as much of the time as possible. We have all experienced the annoyance of being told that we could not be accommodated because "Mary is off today," or "That procedure is not available on weekends." To accomplish this, team members must be able to staff several work stations. This means lots of cross-training and job rotation. At the same time, special technical or professional expertise is necessary. For these two reasons, team members should be both generalists and specialists.

We see good examples of this in sports. For example, on a basketball team, players have both general and special roles. First, there is role by position—forward, guard, and center. Each position involves the skills of running patterns, passing, dribbling, and shooting. Designated players must have special skills, such as three-point shooting, rebounding, shot blocking, and play selecting. Similarly, on most work teams, there are certain tasks that each team member carries out. The range of these tasks is increased by cross-training and work-station rotation. In a microbiology laboratory team, all of the professionals can perform most of the routine tasks, while one person specializes in microscopic parasitology and another in dermatologic mycology.

An alert leader knows when to provide apartness and togetherness or, to put it in another way, when to differentiate and when to integrate. Each team member should have a basic comprehension of all of the team activities and share responsibility for the team results.

The use of a skills inventory of your team is highly recommended. To assist in the formulation of such a document, it is helpful to have each team member prepare a personal skill inventory. Information on application forms and position descriptions is incomplete but can serve as a starting point. These inventories are updated as employees acquire new skills.

These records can be used to document accomplishments, spot need for additional training, assist in scheduling tasks, provide valuable data for

Table I
Personal Skill Inventory

Date
Name and title
Education and training

Primary competency (eg, "routine hematology")

Major skills and dates utilized (eg, "flow cytometry 1993–")

Describe briefly your experience in:

    Teaching

    Facilitating

    Quality improvement

    Special instruments/procedures

List names and dates of service on committees, task forces, etc.

What additional skills would you like to acquire?

Describe what you would like to be doing five years from now.

Signature and date

performance reviews, and justify salary increases or promotions. An example of such a skills inventory is illustrated in Table I.

Employees may be members of more than one team, just as they may serve on multiple committees or focus groups. Sometimes the same competency is needed on each team, eg, computer or financial expertise. In other instances, a person may utilize one capability on one team, another on a second team.

FOLLOWERSHIP STYLES

Leaders and team members must acknowledge that individual differences exist, that potential conflicts may arise from these differences, and that they, the stakeholders, must understand the differences. The Myers-Briggs Type Indicator,[3] which defines 16 different personality types, is widely acclaimed and taught to help individuals understand themselves and their associates.

THE TWO FOLLOWERSHIP ESSENTIALS

Commitment

Commitment must be reciprocal: what leaders expect of the employee and what the employee can expect of the leaders. Commitment kicks in during the employment process and is reinforced during the orientation and training phases. While worker loyalty to employers has declined in recent years as job security plummeted, employees are still expected to remain committed to their work as long as they remain on the payroll. More on loyalty in a minute.

Cooperation

Essential to teamwork, cooperation must be expected and rewarded. Use performance reviews and employee attitude surveys to get workers' feedback. At performance reviews ask questions such as "Who has been most supportive and most cooperative? least supportive and cooperative? Who has been obstructive?"[4] Questions of this nature not only identify the good team members but they also identify the people who need coaching.

NORMS FOR TEAM MEMBERS

As team players move from being controlled to being empowered, they will be required to do things that they never did before, such as select new employees, prepare schedules and budgets, and make important operational decisions. This demands that attention be given to team member norms.

Team member norms are documented and undocumented work and behavior standards. Formal ones are spelled out in position descriptions and employee handbooks, emphasized in orientation programs, and reinforced as part of the coaching process. Norms also reflect the values and ethos shared by team members. Team members apply pressures on deviant members who do not share these professional values, and such pressures are strong in effective work groups.

Teamwork places great demands on interpersonal skills. The most important of these are open, honest, direct communication; the ability to surface and resolve conflicts; and the ability to comprehend the feelings and apprehensions of others. Members must define what is acceptable behavior and what isn't. Inattention to the relationship functions in the team is a primary cause of problems later on.

Acceptable team behavior includes active listening; respecting others' needs, feelings, and rights; and sharing information, opinions, and expertise openly. Unacceptable team behavior includes unwillingness to set aside personal needs or agendas; displaying a negative attitude toward change, people, and team building; showing a strong preference to be the star rather than to be a part of the process; and judging others quickly.[5]

CHARACTERISTICS OF GREAT TEAM PLAYERS

1. Great team players find jobs that provide them with a sense of mission. They:
   > do not remain in boring jobs.
   > seek new knowledge, situations, and challenge in their work.

2. Great team players exhibit togetherness. They:
   > understand the roles of their teammates and how the work of the team fits into the "big picture."
   > share a common goal.
   > identify with the team. They talk in terms of "we," not "they" or "I."
   > learn to trust the other members of their team.
   > are friendly and relish team interactions.
   > defend their group against external criticism.
   > avoid competing with teammates for attention and influence.[6]
   > willingly share knowledge, resources, recognition, and opinions.
   > rely on each other for certain responsibilities.
   > endure frustration for the group.
   > tolerate fellow members who have idiosyncrasies.
   > help others, even when not asked to.

3. Great team players have faith in themselves. They:
   > overcome setbacks and temporary feelings of uncertainty.
   > strive to satisfy their need for self-actualization.

4. Great team players demonstrate a good work ethic. They:
   > think and act like business partners, not subordinates.
   > have good attendance records.
   > do what is expected without prodding.
   > are dependable and credible.
   > conform to group norms.
   > are cooperative, enthusiastic, unselfish, and caring.
   > do not shift blame or steal credit.
   > do not badmouth colleagues or management.
   > volunteer often, even for unpleasant tasks.
   > put in an honest day's work and more.
   > are respectful of other people's time.

5. Great team players are good communicators. They:
   > are available to each other for consultation and evaluations.[7]
   > share knowledge and are good listeners.
   > are teachable and have an open mind to new concepts.
   > participate actively and positively in meetings.
   > know what subjects and opinions turn other people on and off.
   > are sensitive to people's feelings and concerns.
   > keep others informed of their whereabouts, progress, and difficulties.

keep tuned into the formal and informal communication systems.

do not let distances between work stations interfere with the flow of information.

6. Great team players are skilled problem solvers. They:

confront problems openly.

ensure that problems are solved.

invoke techniques such as consensus and compromise.

try to prevent others, including their superiors, from making mistakes.

respect the opinion of others.

seek solutions, not scapegoats.

7. Great team players have a good sense of humor. They:

are generally optimistic.

have fun at work.

have the ability to laugh at themselves.

never poke fun at people or tell off-color jokes.

8. Great team players are innovative. They:

welcome change.

frequently offer suggestions or ideas.

listen carefully to suggestions of others.

keep abreast of technical and professional developments in their field.

PICKING TEAM MEMBERS WHO ARE POTENTIAL WINNERS

It's hard to teach a horse dog tricks.[4]
    M. Sanborn

Athletic coaches know that it is much easier to build a winning team when you start with talented and motivated players. Fortunate leaders have the luxury of "green field" sites where the team can be built from scratch and people can be hired to suit. They can hire for attitude and train for skill.

Do not always pick the most talented candidates. You want people who are flexible and eager to learn. It is much easier to improve people's competencies than to improve their attitudes. Candidates who are underqualified often work out better in the long run than do overqualified ones because once the former have been trained, they are more appreciative, less demanding, and more likely to remain on board.

Before selecting a specific player for your team, ask yourself what tasks this person will be doing, what strengths and weaknesses he or she brings to your group. Do not depend entirely on your human resources department for your recruiting effort. Tap your network of colleagues, friends, suppliers, and customers. Let them know exactly what you are looking for in the candidate.

Permit other team members to participate in the selection. The selection decision should reflect a consensus by the team. Avoid the flashy candidates

Table II
Items to Evaluate Teamwork Potential

Give me an example of how you handled unjust criticism.

How would you describe your followership style?

Give me an example of how you adjusted to a difficult change.

Tell me about any seminars or workshops you have attended recently.

Tell me about a time when your work group faltered. Why did it happen? What did you do about it?

Did you work alone much of the time? Do you prefer working in groups or being completely responsible for your own work?

What kinds of people do you get along with best? What kinds do you find difficult? How do you adjust to them?

How will your references describe your teamwork?

When have you had to convince people to do something differently?

Describe your participation in staff and committee meetings.

When was the last time you got angry at work? What did you do?

What do you do when a good suggestion you offer falls on deaf ears?

What were some of the stressful work situations you had to face?

What new competencies have you developed this year? What competency would your last supervisor say you need to improve?

What were your greatest frustrations on the job?

Give me an example of how your services could have been utilized better.

Describe your role in training others (substitute other responsibilities).

who lack substance. Check past performance carefully—it is the best predictor of future performance.

Personnel selection criteria should include descriptors that define the teamwork dimension. Experienced interviewers focus on key behaviors such as those already listed as indicators of good team membership. The questioning process should include problem solving and group discussion simulations.[8] Some appropriate questions for candidates are listed in Table II.

Tests of technical skill and cognitive ability are valuable, but employers must be able to prove test validity and reliability to avoid charges of discrimination. An ideal proving ground, if feasible, is the actual area in which the successful candidates will work. Candidates may be required to work (with pay) for a week or some other defined period of time before being hired. This form of testing is popular with Japanese car manufacturers.

MORALE AND THE IMPORTANCE OF EMPLOYEE SURVEYS

Employees should be regarded as customers. For the same reasons that health care institutions use patient and physician surveys, customer surveys for employees provide valuable feedback to leaders at all levels. They reveal strengths and weaknesses, information that is needed for development and training programs. Surveys can measure the quality of leadership, flow of communication, morale and loyalty, and more. Many software applications for surveys are available. A bare-bones example is presented in Table III.

Surveys must be followed by remedial actions. Failure to do so can be almost as devastating to employee morale as punishing employees for their comments. When the results of the survey have been analyzed, it is often useful to establish focus groups of employees to obtain more detailed information and to hold brainstorming sessions in which solutions to problems are addressed frankly and without fear of recriminations. Most experts recommend that surveys be repeated 12 to 18 months after the original one.

THE MATTER OF LOYALTY

According to some observers, corporate loyalty—that traditional bond between an organization and its employees—is rapidly becoming an obsolete concept.[9] For a significant number of workers, the concept of loyalty itself is dead.

What Loyalty Is

Loyalty is closely related to work ethic and duty, an unwritten contract that requires employees to be faithful to their duties, their organization, and their teammates. It is following orders and doing the best job one knows how to do. Put simply, the core of loyalty is genuine caring for the well being of the others involved in a work relationship.[10]

What Loyalty Is Not

The loyalty of employees has all too often been measured by how long they remain with a company.[10] According to today's behaviorists, however, staying put is seen less as an indication of loyalty than as a sign of lack of initiative or marketability.

Loyalty is not puppetry or blind compliance to all those in authority. True loyalty permits—even encourages—dissent and differences of opinion because values are in conflict. Only unresolved or malevolent conflict is harmful. It is not disloyal to express one's true feelings about a bad policy or practice and to relay that displeasure to those who can do something to change the situation.

What is needed is a new paradigm of loyalty. A team really comes into being only after each member begins to sense the loyalty of the leader to the group and to each other. The new vision of work and organizations fosters a more enlightened form of loyalty.[10] This begins with a consensus that employers cannot guarantee permanent employment, and that resigning from a job is not a sign of disloyalty.

Table III
Employee Attitude Survey

Do you feel that you have been accepted by your team? What makes you say that?

Are you satisfied with the orientation and training you received? If not, why not?

Describe your reaction to your last performance review.

How has your team leader helped you?

How could your team leader help you more?

Are your opinions and suggestions sought and appreciated?

In your own words, how would you describe the mission of this organization?

What changes would you like in your position description?

Circle any of the following that describe your leader's role:

    Facilitator
    Supporter
    Adviser
    Coach
    Mentor
    Expediter
    Counselor
    Critic
    Instructor
    Inspector
    Motivator
    Helper

What educational courses or workshops would you like to attend?

What additional training would you recommend for your team leader?

Are the salaries and benefits of this organization comparable with those of our competitors?

If you were the CEO of this organization, what changes would you make in your department? In other departments?

How would you describe the quality improvement program in this organization or in your unit?

How would you rate the morale of your team?

Does your department encourage open communication among employees and departments? Are you kept informed about what is going on?

How would you describe our recognition and reward system? How could it be improved?

Are you encouraged to be innovative? Give examples.

Are all safety standards enforced? If not, give examples.

Are you proud to be a member of this organization and team? Why or why not?

Do you feel that there are opportunities for advancement here? What additional ones should we make available?

How many suggestions for work improvement did you make in the past year? Name at least one that was acted on and one that was ignored.

Would you like to be a member of this organization five years from now? If so, in what capacity?

WHAT EMPLOYERS SHOULD BE ABLE TO EXPECT FROM THEIR WORKERS

If you work for a man, in heaven's name work for him! If he pays wages that supply your bread and butter, work for him—speak well of him, think well of him, stand by him, and stand by the institution he represents.[11]

Elbert Hubbard

Worker loyalty is refraining from bad-mouthing one's organization, colleagues, or boss in public. It is behaving in an ethical and moral manner. It is minimizing criticism and respecting confidences.

Loyalty is making superiors look good and doing everything one can do to help them meet departmental goals and deadlines. Communality is important. This is a sense of belonging to a work group and concerns issues of interdependence, mutual respect, and a sense of responsibility for other people. It is an imperative for successful team efforts.[9]

The decline of worker loyalty as expressed by longevity of service and acceptance of shabby treatment by employers has accelerated since few employers can offer permanent employment. Today's loyalty consists of employers treating employees as partners (participative leadership) and employees responding like partners should.

WHAT WORKERS SHOULD BE ABLE TO EXPECT FROM THEIR EMPLOYERS

Opportunities should exist for outstanding performance by individuals, as well as by teams, and the recognition that accompanies it. Some employees will advance out of the work cluster and into management ranks. To achieve this, employers must still have well-functioning performance appraisal systems.[12] For more on this topic, see Chapters 9, 10, and 15.

Employees should be able to expect that their assignments will be based largely on their areas of expertise and interests. Leaders can improve these assignments by asking the following questions before they assign specific tasks or responsibilities to individual members:

What do you like doing best?

What would you like to do that you have not been doing?

What are you currently doing that you would like to do more of?

What are you currently doing that you would like to stop doing or spend less time doing?

Where do you want this job to lead you professionally? By what date?

What concerns do you have about the tasks, authority, and performance standards described in your position description?

What additional training would you like at this time? Later?

Do you have any preferences as to the priorities of the various segments of this training and how it is provided?

REFERENCES

1. Black K. Staffing to win: an interview with Lou Holtz. *LAMA Rev.* 1990;3:6-10.

2. Hughes B. 25 stepping stones for self-directed teams. *Training.* 1991;28:44-46.

3. Myers IB, McCaulley MH. *A Guide to the Development and Use of the Myers-Briggs Type Indicator.* Palo Alto, Calif: Consulting Psychologists Press Inc; 1985.

4. Sanborn M. *Team Building.* Boulder, Colo: CareerTrack; 1990 (audiocassette).

5. Harrington-Mackin D. *The Team Building Tool Kit.* New York, NY: AMACOM; 1994.

6. Mossop MW. Total teamwork: how to be a leader, how to be a member. *Manage Solutions.* 1988;35:3-9.

7. Prince G. Recognizing genuine teamwork. *Supervis Manage.* 1989; 14:25-31.

8. Wellins RS, Byham WC, Wilson JM. *Empowered Teams: Creating Self-Directed Work Groups That Improve Quality, Productivity, and Participation.* San Francisco, Calif: Jossey-Bass Publishers; 1991.

9. Giallourakis M. Reforming corporate loyalty. *SAM Adv Manage J.* 1988;1:18.

10. Shea GF. *Company Loyalty: Earning it, Keeping it.* New York, NY: AMACOM; 1987.

11. Day RA. *How to Write and Publish a Scientific Paper.* Philadelphia, Pa: ISI Press; 1979.

12. Mills DQ. *Rebirth of the Corporation.* New York, NY: John Wiley & Sons; 1991.

12. Principles of Coping With Difficult People

W HILE EACH OF us may occasionally thwart or annoy or confuse one or the other of our fellow creatures, a Difficult Person's troublesome behavior is habitual and affects most of the people with whom he comes in contact.[1]

Robert M. Bramson

CHAPTER OBJECTIVES

- To categorize the three major kinds of people problems
- To elaborate on the importance of attitude
- To point out that the situation may be one of personal differences rather than difficult people.
- To analyze three groups of workers who require special handling: the high-tech professional, the nonconformist, and employees who have difficulty serving on teams
- To list group factors that can cause problems
- To state the three critical mistakes that team leaders may make when confronted with personnel problems
- To review the principles of behavior modification
- To present the four strategies for dealing with personnel problems and detail a seven-step practical approach
- To advise on what to do when nothing seems to work

Leaders must know precisely what they want, not just what they do not want. Then they must make their expectations and priorities known to their employees, and provide them with the knowledge, training, resources, systems or processes, time, and support to get the job done. Finally, they must monitor performance to ensure that they, the leaders, have been successful in these preparations.

The three major kinds of people problems:

1. Performance that does not meet expectations
2. Behavior that violates rules, policies, or ethics
3. Inability of people to get along with each other

THE MATTER OF ATTITUDE

Another way of classifying difficult people is to divide them into those who just can't do what they are supposed to do and those who can but won't do what is expected. We will explore these two groups in the next chapter when the subject of underperformance is discussed. For the moment, let's talk about the importance of attitude; or, more precisely, bad attitude.

Supervisors are often overheard talking about employees who have a poor work ethic, lack professionalism, or are disloyal—all really a matter of attitude.

Attitude may be defined as a way of thinking or responding to everyday situations. A "bad" attitude is one that affects performance or interpersonal relationships. We can control our own attitudes, but not those of other people. However, if we have the authority or personal power to do so, we can control their behavior, and behavioral modification can influence the attitudes. The Marine Corps accepts candidates with all sorts of unusual outlooks and dispositions and changes those attitudes by altering the recruits' behavior.

Attitude is exhibited through behavior, and dealing effectively with employee attitude problems depends on our own attitude. Since we cannot get inside people's heads, we cannot judge their attitudes. We can, however, evaluate what they say and do, and any complaints we have about performance should be expressed in behavioral terms. The same holds true for other subjective terms like *bad work ethic* or *lack of professionalism*. Instead of saying "Louise, you've got to do something about your attitude toward me," say exactly what you want Louise to do differently, eg, "Louise, when I am talking to you, please put down your book and look at me."

Signs of bad attitude are exhibited by all sorts of behavior from absenteeism to sabotage. Specific kinds are addressed in the next two chapters.

The three principal causes of poor attitudes:

1. Unfulfilled emotional needs. We all have our individual emotional

needs. These include need for recognition, affiliation, money, power or control, affection, advancement, or just an occasional hug.

2. Job mismatch. Employees may be over- or underqualified. They may be placed on a team in which they feel uncomfortable or when they prefer to work alone.

3. Personal problems. These include domestic discord, financial worry, poor health, or substance abuse. These will be discussed in the next chapter.

Solutions:

- Before taking any action, determine if there really is a problem. Does the behavior affect the department's work, the team, or you? If it does not, and you think you can learn to live with it, your best move may be no move.

- Always concentrate on behavior, not attitude. Failure to provide specific behavioral examples will elicit defensiveness or anger, confuse the person, or fail to get the desired behavioral change.

- If benchside suggestions and directions do not bring about the desired change, move on to counseling. Discuss the problem with the person very candidly. Explain how the behavior is affecting you, others, and the department. Give specific examples of what you have observed; for example: "Three people in your section have asked to be transferred. They cite the lack of willingness on your part to help with the blood collections when we are short-handed."

- Discharge or transfer may be the best solution when remedial measures fail. Do this before team morale has deteriorated. Be certain that you have sufficient grounds and documentation to avoid legal consequences.

DIFFICULT? OR JUST DIFFERENT?

No two people are exactly alike. The greater the differences in age, race, nationality, language, culture, religion, political affiliation, ethos, and personality, the greater the potential for interpersonal incompatibilities.

THREE GROUPS OF PEOPLE WHO CAN BE PROBLEMS IF NOT HANDLED INTELLIGENTLY

The High-Tech Professional (HTP)

We use the term "high-tech" to differentiate this group of people from other professionals such as administrators. The HTPs include physicians, laboratory scientists, researchers, and technical experts such as computer specialists.

The past decade has seen an influx into health care institutions of managers who have had no medical or hospital backgrounds. Most are graduates of business schools or are transplants from commercial enterprises. Often they are bewildered by HTPs and have difficulty coping with them. HTPs often ignore bureaucratic procedures, shun set schedules, and resist attempts to make them more efficient. Because of these characteristics, Geber refers to HTPs as "wild ducks."[2]

One major difference between hospitals and other businesses is the presence in hospitals of a second, and sometimes adversarial, organization: the medical staff. The medical staff has its own officers, its own rules and regulations (by laws), its own disciplinary measures. On top of all that, the attending physicians are major customers, and expect to be treated as such.

Why Are HTPs Different?

There are several reasons. In the first place, individuals whose interests are in, for example, medicine, microbiology, chemistry, or pharmacy have received different training from individuals whose education focuses on, say, accounting, business principles, marketing, and economics.

There is also a difference in the nature of the tasks performed by these two groups. The laboratorian, for example, may be more interested in scientific tasks and perfection, while the businessperson may be more interested in customer satisfaction and return on investment.

Fortunately, many health care professionals now receive training in both the healing arts and business administration. In the laboratory MT-MBA degrees are becoming more commonplace than MT-PhD degrees. This cross-education helps to eliminate attitudinal incompatibilities.

Characteristics of HTPs

HTPs are often impatient, especially with any organizational requirement that interferes with their work. This impatience is sometimes interpreted as lack of cooperation. They may be curt with people who lack their knowledge or education, and they tend not to mix with nontechnical people, often being conspicuous by their absence at staff social affairs.[3]

Some HTPs have big egos, and a few are difficult to control because they develop a "prima donna complex." Confident of their job skills or knowledge, they feel secure and irreplaceable. They may become abrasive to others, even to customers. Such attitudes and behavior can have a devastating effect on customer service and departmental morale.[4]

On the other hand, some HTPs suffer from low self-esteem and complain bitterly about lack of recognition or appreciation. When they are promoted to leadership roles, many are unhappy in those roles and wish they could go back to doing "professional" work.

Some members of this group have problems integrating into the formal and informal structure of organizations. They eschew conformity and repeatedly proclaim their independence. They want and expect technical freedom and dislike routine work and schedules. They may be unconventional in habits and appearance, often violating or bending rules. While they may come in late or leave early, they usually spend long hours on the job, and are frequently found in their work areas on weekends and holidays. They are seldom clock watchers.

How to Prevent Problems With HTPs

Job Applicants. Try to identify prima donnas and other potential problem people during the selection process. Ask their references how the applicants got along with others.[4]

Orientation. During orientation, be very explicit as to the responsibilities involved and the degrees of autonomy permitted. Emphasize the importance of customer service and budget restrictions. If the new employees dislike the restrictions imposed on them or they yearn for the academic atmosphere they left behind, it's better for all parties for them to discover this during their probationary period.

Communication. Learn the fundamentals and terminology of the HTP's specialty. Provide opportunities for HTPs to share their professional knowledge; eg, attend professional meetings, give lectures or workshops. Publicize congratulatory news such as results of special projects, research developments, and individual achievements.[5]

Educational and Training Opportunities. Encourage HTPs to continue their education, but don't force them into supervisory training against their wishes. Provide opportunities for them to use the skills they learn on the job or at meetings. Make reference books and periodicals available to them.

If HTPs have compatibility problems, encourage them to attend remedial seminars on interpersonal relationships. Be diplomatic, but persistent when you suggest these.

Insist on Acceptable Performance, and Don't Reward Poor Behavior. Counsel HTPs on the necessity for them to pitch in and help when necessary. Use peer pressure to reinforce group norms. Don't bend the rules too far for them.[4]

Prevent the "Prima Donna Complex." Use cross-training so that other employees can substitute for the "superstar," should that be necessary. A good time to initiate this is before the prima donna takes his or her next vacation.

The Nonconformist

The nonconformist requires special handling, which is not always easy. This is complicated when the person possesses expertise that is scarce and essential. You know this, and so does the nonconformist. If your assessment indicates that the employee's idiosyncrasies are not really detrimental to performance or team effort, it is probably best to adjust to the situation. Once you do that, you may find that there was not such a big problem after all.[6]

Let nonconformists know that you regard them as valuable members of the work unit. Tolerate their impatience and complaints. Do not accuse them of being stubborn or unreasonable. Bend the rules a bit.[7] Make them accountable for results, but release them from rigid schedules.

Employees Who Have Difficulty Serving on Teams

You may find employees have difficulty working on teams for a number of reasons. These may include people who

- prefer to work as individuals. If they are valuable workers, a spot should be found for them in which teamwork is not needed.
- demand higher pay or privileges for taking on a greater range of tasks or for performing a few administrative or supervisory responsibilities.
- possess higher status, greater knowledge, or more aggressiveness, and use these to dominate others.
- obstruct change because they perceive team building as a union-busting effort.[8]
- want to maintain the status quo. They are unwilling to make the needed effort, are reluctant to assume risk or to accept challenge. See Chapter 3 for advice on handling these folks. This group is likely to say, "That's not my job." When an employee objects to serving on a team, explain why the work must be done, why he or she was selected, and how long he or she will have to make the extra effort. Then accentuate any positive aspect of the task and possible relief from other assignments during the period when the person does the additional work. Finally, after the task has been completed, acknowledge the extra effort and reward the employee with praise and fun assignments or some time off.[9]

POTENTIAL GROUP PROBLEMS

- Destructive rivalry between teams.
- Active or passive resistance from unions.
- Cliques with private agendas that disregard ground rules. The hidden agenda of such a work group may be to control not only its members but also its leader. In the worst scenario, the members conspire to restrict the efforts of the team or even to sabotage its operations.
- Unhealthy rivalry between individuals for promotions, merit raises, bonuses, turf, resources, recognition, and access to superiors.

THREE CRITICAL MISTAKES BY TEAM LEADERS WHEN CONFRONTED WITH PERSONNEL PROBLEMS

1. They do nothing or wait too long before they act. Most managers are reluctant to tell an employee what they don't like.
2. They incorrectly ascribe the deviant behavior to "bad attitude" or "poor work ethic."
3 They "gunnysack." Gunnysacking is saving up all the problems and then exploding at a later date, often in response to some trivial transgression.

PRINCIPLES OF BEHAVIORAL MODIFICATION

- Decrease the reward and increase the risk of the unwanted behavior, eg, ignore temper tantrums (less reward) and warn person that the outbursts will affect performance rating (greater risk).
- Reinforce improved behavior, eg, give more recognition and praise.
- Ignore or object to unwanted behavior, eg, do not laugh at sexist or racial jokes or do reprimand the person telling the jokes.
- Check systems, processes, and policies that may make it difficult for the employee to meet expectations. For example, a blood bank marketing representative was accused of being lazy and ineffective when the real problem was lack of parking for blood donors. A lab tech was accused of being sullen and uncooperative until it was discovered that her supervisor refused to permit her to phone her "latch-key" youngster to ensure that he had reached home from school safely.
- Review your tactics and methods. You may be using the best strategy but not the best tactics. How do you go about praising good behavior and redirecting what you do not want? Could there be a mismatch between your words and your facial expressions or body language? An insincere or hurried praising may be perceived as a put-down or sarcasm.

FOUR STRATEGIES FOR DEALING WITH PEOPLE PROBLEMS

1. Avoid the problem. The problem may not be important enough to merit your attention. It may be a transient or self-correcting situation, or not be in your sphere of responsibility. Example: A team member is in the middle of divorce proceedings.
2. Apply temporary symptomatic measures. The resolution of the basic problem is postponed or may not require subsequent additional

action. Example: A team member is crying in the locker room over something a physician said to her. You send her home and tell her to see you tomorrow.

3. Change policy, procedure, or assignment so that what the person did or did not do is no longer a violation or a deficiency. Example: Liberalize a dress code.

4. Undertake a comprehensive investigation and resolution. This obviously requires much more time, know-how, and savoir faire. See the following seven-step strategy.

A SEVEN-STEP PRACTICAL COPING APPROACH

First, let's define "coping." According to *Webster's*, to cope is (1) to contend successfully or on equal terms, (2) to deal with problems, troubles, etc. Coping provides an alternative to acceptance (of behavior) or efforts to change personalities.[1]

1. *Analyze the problem.* When you find that you have a problem employee, before you lay the blame on that employee, try to figure out how you got yourself in that mess. Should this person have been hired? Did he or she receive adequate orientation and training? Were your expectations and priorities clear and specific? Did you provide adequate feedback? Have you shown favoritism? Have you been a good coach, facilitator, supporter, and counselor? Use this information to do a better job of problem prevention in the future.

2. *Define the problem in concrete terms, then determine if it is important enough to do something about.* Is it temporary or permanent? How does it affect work performance, other team members, and you? Document these effects. You may need these later to support a decision to discipline or to counter a grievance or other legal action.

3. *Review the remedial measures that have been tried and how effective they were.* If they did not work, why not? Try to determine what perceived or subconscious benefits of the behavior may be factors, eg, team member avoids unpleasant tasks by throwing temper tantrums when given certain assignments.

4. *Decide exactly what specific behavioral change you want to bring about,* eg, you want an employee to stop griping in front of customers.

5. *Brainstorm as many alternative solutions as possible.* Ideally, the solution comes from the difficult person with your approval. Solicit input from your boss, your human resource department, or a professional adviser.

6. *Design and implement your plan of action.* Ask yourself the what (what behavioral change is agreed on or mandated?), the when (when the new behavior is to start and when must it meet your expectation

or group norms?), the where (where is the new behavior to be demonstrated—at team meetings? at the work bench? in front of customers?), and the how (how will the change be monitored—by you? by team members? by customers?).

7. *Monitor progress, provide positive reinforcement, and modify plan if needed.* Note behavioral changes or get reports from other observers. Praise desired behavior and provide negative feedback when appropriate. Hold additional counseling sessions. Jointly modify goals and/or time schedule when indicated.

WHAT IF NOTHING WORKS?

Do not give up without giving each approach a stout try. You must be as determined to achieve a change as the person is to wear you down and to revert to former behavioral patterns.[10]

When all attempts to modify the behavior and attitude fail, you must decide whether to accept and tolerate the behavior or get rid of the person. The threat of firing sometimes has the desired effect.

REFERENCES

1. Bramson RM. *Coping With Difficult People*. New York, NY: Dell Publishing; 1991.
2. Geber B. How to manage wild ducks. *Training*. 1990;27:29-36.
3. Broadwell MM, House RS. *Supervising Technical and Professional People*. New York, NY: John Wiley & Sons; 1986.
4. Osborne JE. Supervising superstars: the talent and temperament conflict. *Supervis Manage*. 1991;36:4-5.
5. Lea D, Brostrom R. Managing the high-tech professional. *Personnel*. 1988;6:12-22.
6. Weiss WH. *The Supervisor's Problem Solver*. New York, NY: AMACOM; 1982.
7. Glassman E. Understanding and supervising low conformers. *Supervis Manage*. 1990;35:10.
8. Fisher BA. *Small Group Decision Making*. 2nd ed. New York, NY: McGraw-Hill; 1980.
9. *Practical Supervision*. March 15, 1993.
10. Tucker RK. *Fighting It Out With Difficult People*. Dubuque, Iowa: Kendall-Hunt Publishers; 1987.

13. The Underperformers

PRODUCTIVITY IS NOT the only thing that suffers when one or more employees do not carry their share of the workload.[1]
William Umiker

CHAPTER OBJECTIVES

- To differentiate between the "Can'ts" and the "Won'ts"
- To solve the problem of the "No-Shows"
- To cope with the "Goof-Offs"
- To increase the productivity of slow workers, perfectionists, time wasters, and older employees
- To provide a quick look at troubled employees
- To deal compassionately with substance abuse problems
- To handle the intoxicated team member and the chronic alcoholic

Not only does productivity suffer, but teamwork also suffers because the other employees resent having to carry the underperformers.

THE "CAN'TS" AND THE "WON'TS"

Permanent "Can'ts" are underperformers who simply could not do any better if their life depended on it; they have also proved to be not trainable. They should never have been hired in the first place; they must be transferred or terminated.

Temporary Can'ts are those who have not had adequate orientation, training, coaching, or incentives. The remedies for these people are obvious: provide the necessary training, coaching, or incentives.

The remaining underperformers fall into the general category of attitudinal problems. These are the "Won'ts." The Won'ts could perform adequately and could get along with their associates if they really wanted to. Some of these people are underperformers, but many carry out their assignments adequately; some are superior performers but can't get along with other people or are very unpleasant to be around (see next chapter).

EMPLOYEES WHO FAIL TO SHOW UP FOR WORK

Lateness and absenteeism cause more personnel problems than any other ones, perhaps more than all the others combined. Attitudes toward work and associates and personal factors influence an employee's decision to stay home or to arrive late consistently. Industrial behaviorists agree that satisfying work, sound group relationships, people-oriented leadership styles, and a positive work ethic affect employee attendance.[2]

It is important to take remedial steps expeditiously, because both tardiness and absenteeism can be contagious and have a direct impact on worker efficiency and productivity. Some leaders feel that they are too busy to monitor attendance or that the monitoring requires more time and effort than is justified. This inattention encourages absenteeism and tardiness, and lowers group morale.

Solutions for absenteeism:

- Good leadership skills are essential. These skills include the ability to screen out job candidates whose past history portends attendance problems and to place employees in jobs that suit their personal interests and work styles.
- Interpret, promulgate, and enforce policies. Articulate the policies periodically at staff meetings. Supplement these discussions with facts and figures on the costs of absenteeism and how those individuals who have good attendance records feel about the no-shows.
- Keep attendance records. These should show the number of days absent; the excuses given; and the relationships to holidays, vacations, hunting seasons, and paydays.
- Insist that people who call in sick talk directly to you. Question them in a supportive manner about their illness. Ask if you can help, how long they think they will be out, and say that they will be missed.
- Welcome them back and say that they were missed.
- Counsel and discipline chronic offenders.

Solutions for tardiness:

- Apply on-time rules to everyone, including supervisors and middle managers.
- Be on board when most employees arrive.
- Start the day with a brief meeting and count noses.
- Make monitoring part of a morning round of friendly greetings.
- When feasible, permit employees to select their tasks so the early birds get first choice, eg, phlebotomists picking which units they want to service.
- Other rewards may be putting out coffee and doughnuts at the start of the workday. First workers get first choice.
- Keep attendance records.
- Counsel and discipline chronic offenders.

THE GOOF-OFFS

Some underperformers are regarded as goof-offs by their peers. These individuals are frequently absent from their work stations. They seem to have a general dislike of work, but manage to look busy. They are great talkers and excuse-makers who have special talent for avoiding additional assignments. Their attendance records are seldom good and they slip in late and leave early when they can get away with it. At performance reviews they spend most of the time arguing over their ratings.

Frustration and anger cause their leaders to distance themselves from these people, but this only aggravates the situation.

Solutions:

- Make a special effort to keep these people busy. Give them very specific instructions and deadlines. Unfortunately, they require much more attention than their teammates.
- If coaching alone does not get the desired change, move on to counseling. Explain how the behavior affects you, the department, or others. It is even more important to show these persons that their behavior is self-destructive and detrimental to performance ratings, acceptance by the rest of the team, future assignments, or even their career. Be specific about what you expect henceforth.
- Detailed record keeping should begin when the results of coaching and counseling are not effective. Firing these employees may be the best solution, but you will need concrete proof of how the bad attitude affected performance or other employees.

SLOW WORKERS

These people just poke along at a slow work pace. If you mention their low productivity, they will usually brush that off with a comment about how their work is done more carefully and that "haste makes waste."

Solutions:

- Do not criticize them until you have done everything you can to show them how to work more efficiently.
- Let them know that there is a problem and what your productivity standards are.
- Set deadlines and priorities.
- Send them to seminars on time management.

PERFECTIONISTS

Perfectionists feel that they must do every task, no matter how small, exactly right. They insist on eliminating error by repeating or double-checking everything. They often become bottlenecks in the flow of work. If you insist that they work faster, they will make an error sooner or later and then trap you into the psychological game of "See what you made me do." Perfectionists may have difficulty getting along with their peers because they are critical of their associates, whom they regard as sloppy workers.

You cannot change their basic makeup, but you can modify some of their behavior, even when that perfectionist is your boss. Handling these people takes a lot of patience.

Solutions:

- Find work slots for them where their delays do not clog major work-flow channels.
- Assign them tasks that require a high degree of precision.
- Hold them to specific deadlines.
- When the perfectionist is your boss, find out what end results are expected of you. Determine the constraints within which you must work, what authority you have, and what resources are available. If you find some of these expectations to be unrealistic, tell him or her what you can handle, and negotiate the others. Give objective reasons why you cannot meet all of the expectations.

TIME WASTERS

The most common forms of time wasting are tardiness, early departures from work, excessive socializing, personal phone calls, and abuses of sick leave.

Solutions:

- Emphasize good work habits during orientation.
- Set a good example.
- Develop flexible work schedules.
- Avoid overstaffing or understaffing.
- Teach employees how to keep busy when waiting for further instructions.
- Provide backup assignments to fill spare time.
- Counsel and/or discipline chronic offenders.

OLDER WORKERS

Many older workers outperform their younger coworkers, display greater loyalty, and post more impressive attendance records. However, older workers do tend to slow down. This can be a matter of health or energy, inability to adjust to changes in assignments or staffing, loss of interest, or frustration over one's decreasing importance when their assignments become less demanding or their authority is curtailed.

Solutions:

- To prevent problems due to physical and mental changes, eliminate safety hazards that might cause a less agile employee to trip or fall. Confirm oral instructions in writing to prevent errors due to memory lapses.
- Retraining may be necessary as jobs and technology change. Send them to workshops or seminars. Even grumpy old-timers may return from these meetings with renewed enthusiasm.
- You may be able to rekindle their interest by making them preceptors or trainers.
- Be very hesitant about discharging older workers. To avoid running afoul of the Age Discrimination in Employment Act (ADEA) you must be able to prove that the person cannot do the job for which he or she was hired.

TROUBLED EMPLOYEES

For our purposes, troubled employees are those who have any personal problem due to family stress, substance abuse, emotional disorders, or legal or financial difficulties that limit their ability to perform their jobs. Health care employees are particularly vulnerable to substance abuse because they have stressful jobs and readily available controlled substances.[3]

Transient Problems

Many employees go through brief trying periods because of health, family, financial, or other crises.

Solution: Over the short haul, only compassion and understanding are needed in these situations. If the condition persists, urge them to get professional help. Recommend your Employee Assistance Program (EAP) if one is available.

Moodiness

Transient moodiness, such as that during a grieving period, usually does not require any reaction, but a persistent or markedly depressed state calls for professional help. Suicides are usually preceded by chronic moodiness.

Solutions:

- Ignore mild transient mood swings. If they persist, acknowledge them without agreeing with them.
- Ask questions and listen with empathy. Do not flood these folks with sympathy. It may result in the persistence of the moods, possibly leading to the martyr syndrome in which people feel sorry for themselves to an unrealistic extent.
- If the situation becomes chronic, suggest professional counseling.

Long-Term or Terminal Illness

What should you do, if anything, when one of your employees tells you that he or she has AIDS (acquired immunodeficiency syndrome) or ARC (AIDS-related complex)? There have been many opinions, ranging from moralistic to practical, on how to handle such long-term or terminal illnesses in the workplace.[4]

Solution: Federal law requires that employees with AIDS be treated as medically disadvantaged persons. Like any other minority group, they are protected against discrimination. With rare exception, coworkers must continue to work with infected employees or risk dismissal.

To answer the above question, when one of your employees tells you that he or she has AIDS or ARC, treat that person like any other employee. Try to verify that the condition was not work induced (eg, from unsafe handling procedures in the laboratory).

Substance Abuse

These troubled people bring grief to their colleagues, subordinates, management, family members, and themselves. When under the influence of these addictive substances, they may become abusive, irritable, or exercise poor judgment. Other members of their team may cover for them, which can cause the problem to persist longer.

Drug and alcohol abuse should be viewed as illnesses and treated as such. The US Federal Rehabilitation Act of 1973 protects workers who use alcohol and legal drugs as long as their usage does not interfere with job performance or cause a lowering of safety standards.[5]

Policies

Employee rights are those of privacy, confidentiality, and due process regarding disciplinary actions, availability of treatment, and any work accommodation during recovery phases. Employee responsibilities are to report for work in a sober, drug-free state and to refrain from imbibing alcoholic spirits or taking drugs that affect performance during working hours and on site.

Typical Reactions of Leaders

Most leaders are not professional counselors or law enforcement officers. They are, however, responsible for their team members' performance and safety. All too often they apply enabling behaviors that actually "help" addicted employees to continue their downward slide. To tolerate the abuse of controlled substances is unfair to the abuser as well as to the organization. A nurse in charge of an operating suite may fail to report a surgeon who reeks of alcohol; or the nurse may report the surgeon, but administration fails to take action because the surgeon brings many patients into the hospital.

Solutions: Termination is the quickest solution, but is seldom the best. It is more expensive to replace employees than it is to retain them by providing the help they need. Termination is appropriate only when attempts at treatment have failed.

Guiding employees to professional treatment is the best course. Because of possible negative ramifications, both personal and legal, team leaders should not attempt remedial counseling.

Here are Quick's common-sense recommendations for dealing with members of the work group who have abuse problems[6]:

- Learn their drinking or drug abuse patterns, and take damage control measures. For example, if the boss has long martini lunches, hold up any reports that he must approve until the next morning.
- Don't join the drinkers. They often like company.
- Don't get emotionally involved.
- Don't pretend that there isn't any problem.
- Learn how much authority you have when he or she is absent, which may be often.

Intoxication

Acute intoxication on the job calls for immediate action. The safety of the intoxicated person, the people around him or her, and the service activities are all at stake.

Solutions: If the employee is disorderly, security officers must be summoned. When employees cannot perform their duties, they should be seen by a physician, if there is one on board. If they are sent home, safe transportation must be provided. Disciplinary actions vary from employer to employer, but in all instances the episode should be documented.

Chronic Alcoholism

Solutions:

- Document all instances of declining job performance. Be specific. Record dates, times, places, nature of incidents, and any other important information.
- Confront the employee, but focus on performance, in basically the same way you would any employee whose performance is not up to standards. The tone of the interview should be one of support coupled with firmness. Describe how work is unsatisfactory, not what you suspect to be the cause. Do not voice suspicion of any drug, alcohol, or psychiatric problem.
- Be prepared for resistance. Don't argue or make idle threats. Be very reluctant to accept excuses (these individuals are masters at fabricating excuses).
- Be very specific as to what must be improved and how much improvement is needed. Warn as to what will happen if performance does not rebound. Specify a follow-up date to review the situation. Express confidence in the employee's ability to improve. After the meeting, document what was discussed and what agreement was reached. Give the employee a copy.
- If performance fails to improve, move from counseling to disciplinary interviews. Lay it on the line. State that the person's job is in jeopardy. One thing that people with alcohol or drug problems fear is loss of their jobs. Loss of job means loss of the wherewithal to support their habits.
- If the employee cooperates and gets treatment, continue your support and observation. Expect occasional backsliding. Give positive strokes for good work, while resisting the temptation to lighten the workload too much. Treat the person as you would other employees. Remember that a reasonable transition period may be required before performance reaches the desired level.

REFERENCES

1. Umiker W. *Coping With Difficult People in the Health Care Setting.* Chicago, Ill: ASCP Press; 1994.

2. Steers RM, Rhodes SR. Major influences on attendance: a process model. *J Appl Psychol.* 1978;63:391-407.

3. Bensinger PB, Fitzpatrick SB. Facing up to substance abuse. *Health Maint Q.* 1987;9:9-11.

4. Ross JK III, Middlebrock BJ. AIDS policy in the work place: will you be ready? *SAM Adv Manage J.* 1990;55:37-41.

5. Pace L, Smits SJ. Workplace substance abuse: a proactive approach. *Pers J.* 1989;68:84-88.

6. Quick TL. *Managing People at Work.* New York, NY: Executive Enterprises Publishing; 1987.

14. Unpleasant Colleagues and Superiors

THESE PEOPLE HAVE an effect on you like swallowing steel marbles. By the end of the day you feel weighted down and tired. You may regurgitate the pellets, pelting the culprit or some innocent bystander.[1]
Roger Mellott

CHAPTER OBJECTIVES

To describe the following unpleasant people and recommend practical strategies for coping with them:

- Critic
- Someone with bad appearance and language
- Pessimist
- Someone who goes over your head
- Cynic
- Gossip
- Chronic complainer
- Liar
- Someone who is supersensitive
- Incessant talker and socializer
- Know-it-all
- Someone with explosive temper
- Fake know-it-all
- Sniper
- Concealer
- Manipulator
- Someone who is uncooperative
- Someone who is unethical

CRITICS

In most instances, occasional mouthing off by one or two employees is not serious—it may be regarded as normal. There are two instances, however, in which you must take vigorous action before serious harm is produced. The first is when these people run down their organization in front of patients, visitors, clinicians, or other customers. The second is when they start affecting the morale or performance of others.

Solutions:

- If the person is not a member of your team, insulate yourself from him or her.
- If you share accountability for the person, and either of the above two situations occurs, you must take action—counseling or disciplinary—based on charges of disloyalty.
- Check your organization's policy manual or consult with your human resources department.

PESSIMISTS

Pessimists may be hard workers who are competent, productive, and loyal, but they have a bleak outlook toward most things and most people. They are always ready to question your judgment and decisions. In meetings, when any new idea is proposed, the pessimist can be counted on to come up with "the trouble with that idea is...." Their resistive persuasion is not only depressing and self-defeating, it can become pervasive.

Solutions:

- Remain cheerful and matter of fact. Avoid acceptance of the contrary outlooks expressed by these individuals.
- Project realistic optimism. Give examples of past successes of any action now being proposed.
- Concede that every action carries some element of risk.
- Using a worst-case scenario, show that the possible consequences are not threatening, and the chances for success are great.
- Do not argue: you won't convince them. Your goal is not so much to convert them as it is to get them to be more cooperative and less vocal. Avoid arguments by simply stating that the pessimist may be right, but that you want to go on, or that you agree with the others on the best course of action.
- Have an open mind. Once in a while they may be right. Use their negativism when you get to discussing pitfalls and contingency planning. They can tell you everything that can go wrong.
- If the pessimist is a colleague and the work situation does not demand that you work together, avoid him or her if you value your optimism.

CYNICS

Cynics are consistently critical of people's motives, ideas, proposals, or directives. They often exhibit a condescending or sarcastic attitude that may be lacking in the pessimist.

Solutions:

- Leaders must show integrity and model the behavior expressed in the organization's mission statement and value system. An egalitarian culture is helpful because it makes these people feel out of step with their colleagues.

- Cynicism is reduced when leaders earn the respect of their teammates and display the leadership skills we have emphasized throughout this book. Listening skill, delegative style, and employee empowerment are essential, and may mandate a significant paradigm shift by management.

- Coaching and counseling of individual cynics involves paying more attention to them, inviting their opinions, providing more recognition, and maximizing the use of their individual skills.

- Consensus seeking at problem-solving meetings is helpful.

CHRONIC COMPLAINERS

Chronic complainers are more interested in registering feelings than in getting problems resolved. They complain the most to people who cannot do anything about their complaints. They are seldom willing to participate in finding or implementing solutions. Chronic complainers constantly use certain words like "never" or "always," eg, "They never consider us" or "We always get the dirty end of the stick."

The typical chronic complainer is idealistic, conscientious, competent, and easily frustrated. Some are perfectionists (see Chapter 13). They display little flexibility and are loath to take risks.

Whiners are chronic complainers who add a plaintive vocal register to their complaining repertoire. They sound like youngsters in the supermarket whose mothers keep saying "stop your whining!"

Chronic complainers often expect others to measure up to their own unattained standards and feel that factors over which they have no control make them powerless to correct what they perceive as problems.

Solutions:

- You must listen to them because sometimes all they need is someone who pays attention to them. If you fail to pay attention to their complaints, you risk diverting their complaining to upper management, customers, or competitors.

- Listen without passing judgment to validate their right to opinions. Ask for details, sometimes in writing. This shows interest on your part and eliminates the more frivolous gripes. It often helps to ask them to put their complaints in writing. If the gripes are minor, you may not hear any more about it.

- State what you will do, if anything, and what you will not do. Do not go into long explanations.

- Challenge them to develop with you a mutually agreeable way of handling the situation.

- Sometimes you simply run out of patience with a persistent complainer and must end his tirade with something like "Bob, there are only two people standing here who care about your complaint, and one of them is rapidly losing interest."

SUPERSENSITIVE TYPES

These individuals take offense at whatever they perceive to be a put-down. They are extremely sensitive to criticism, often bursting into tears, shouting, or dashing off to the restroom.

Solutions:

- Handle with care, but avoid being manipulated by these reactions. Never withhold negative feedback because of previous overreactions. Do not apologize for what you said or did, eg, "Gosh, I'm sorry that I hurt your feelings."

- If the person loses his or her temper and starts shouting, wait a minute or so. If the person does not calm down, get up and leave your office.

- In the case of the weepers, try to establish better rapport. They probably need more moral support than your other employees do.

KNOW-IT-ALLS

These egotists are knowledgeable, but they sound as though they know everything about everything. No matter what subject is brought up, they have opinions or advice. Their condescending, domineering manner makes them all the more annoying. The constant intimidation and belittling makes their associates feel incompetent and humiliated.

According to Geneen,[2] egotists are impaired as much by their narcissism as alcoholics are by their booze. Subordinates and associates resent the arrogance of these people and are very reluctant to divulge any bad news. These people attack any messenger of bad news or anyone who disagrees with them. Team members stifle their own innovative ideas in order to get along with know-it-alls. They offer only the mildest debate on any issue, and learn how to cater to the know it alls' whims, agree with them, and praise them.[2]

Solutions:

- Avoid these insufferable people when possible.
- When you must disagree, be certain that you know what you are talking about. Present your ideas tentatively, using phrases like "what would happen if...."
- Instead of challenging, ask probing or extensional questions such as a series of "and then what would you do?" This forces them to take a second look at their concept.[3]
- If the person is an insufferable boss, learn what you can from him or her and then find another job!

FAKE KNOW-IT-ALLS

These phonies simulate the previous group, but their knowledge is very superficial. They are easily tripped up by people who know what the score is. They differ from liars in that they really believe what they say.

Solutions:

- To test their knowledge on a topic, ask for specifics.
- Let them down gently by presenting your data as an alternative set of facts. Even better, congratulate them on what they said and then merge your ideas into theirs.
- In some cases it is best to say nothing but to get them aside later and clue them in on the real facts.

CONCEALERS

Concealers like the powerful feeling of withholding information that other employees need. Their colleagues may react by doing the same. The result is that work and morale suffer.

Solutions:

- Try to find the motivation behind the lack of communication. Confront the person when you know that important information is being withheld, and praise them when they are more open.
- Sometimes they respond favorably when they are given training or leadership roles, but be careful when you try the latter, for unless these individuals show evidence of becoming more open in their communication, they will likely perform very poorly in any leadership

role. Increased authority plus their unwillingness to share information can pose a threatening situation for the work team.

Uncooperative Types

You learn that these people are not silent because they have nothing to say or because they are listening intently. These silent ones reflect fear or suppressed rage by their silence. Their muteness may be preceded by a perfectly congenial conversation until you suddenly touch a sensitive area. You are most likely to encounter this glum silence during a counseling or disciplinary session. All parents have experienced this at one time or another.

Solutions:

If you are faced with this situation during an interview, whether it be an employment, counseling, or disciplinary interview, try the following approach:

- When it is the person's turn to speak but he or she remains silent, lean forward and counter with your own silence, accompanied by eye contact and raised eyebrows. Maintain this silent expectant stare for at least 10 seconds. That 10 seconds will seem much longer, and you will feel the urge to renew the conversation sooner. Resist that urge. If the person still does not speak, say "You haven't answered my questions, Louise. Have I said something to upset you?" If the only response is a shrug of the shoulders, say "Louise, I'm still waiting."
- If the speechlessness persists, follow with "Louise, you may have a good reason for not talking, but this is not accomplishing anything." If no response, end the interview with "Since we still must resolve this problem, I want to see you here tomorrow at the same time."

Bad Appearance and Foul Language

Determine if the person's appearance offends customers or violates any policy or rule or is a safety hazard, eg, women's shoes with high heels are dangerous on slippery or uneven floors. The use of four-letter words and other foul language should never be tolerated in front of customers or visitors.

Solutions:

- During orientation of new employees, emphasize the importance of appearance, especially if they have direct contact with customers. Discuss the dress code and what your personal expectations are. Forewarning is always better than later criticism.

- If gentle reminders do not work and counseling is necessary, be certain of your authority and the validity of your stance.
- Sexist remarks and profanity must never go unchallenged. Do not buy their "freedom of speech" protestations.

EMPLOYEES WHO GO OVER YOUR HEAD

Ideally, your boss will send these people right back to you when he or she realizes that the employee has not given you an opportunity to respond. Unfortunately, some managers are all too willing to lend an ear to employees who bypass their leaders.

Solutions:
- When you become aware of this situation, confront your superior. Relate exactly what you have observed or have been told. Correct inaccuracies and pinpoint outright lies. Encourage your boss to send for you on these occasions so that you can respond in the presence of the person. Describe how this affects your department...and you.
- Let the employee know that you know what has been going on and how you feel about it. Illustrate how such activities are counter-productive and ultimately backfire.

GOSSIPS

Gossips thrive on creating and spreading rumors, usually about other people. The gossip may be very charming, and what they peddle may or may not be true and may or may not be meant to harm. When character is attacked or misinformation affects work or morale, something must be done.

Solutions:
- Tell the gossip that you appreciate sharing information but you do not feel comfortable talking about others. Often you must defend the gossiper's target.
- Spike misinformation by insisting on validation or by correcting false comments. One practical way of aborting these conversations is to tell the person you are very busy, but would be free after working hours. They rarely will show up.
- Explain how gossip has an adverse effect on the work team, and that people are withholding information because they fear that what they say will be repeated in distorted forms.
- Do not encourage gossips by reacting positively to their messages. Instead, supply the attention they seek by engaging in healthy and helpful dialogues.

LIARS

You soon get to know the people who stretch the truth beyond acceptable limits. Lie detection is based on an individual's track record, your own information, the implausibility of statements, evasive body language, and your gut reactions.

Solutions:

- Confrontation is usually required.
- Be tentative if there is some doubt about the truth. After saying that you apologize if you are wrong, state your reasons for challenging them. Relate the negative consequences of their untruths, and state that you appreciate the bare bones truth even though it is unpleasant.
- Point out that misinformation can shake your trust in the person and can adversely affect teamwork.

THE INCESSANT TALKERS AND SOCIALIZERS

These folks suffer from verbal diarrhea. You must act when these time-wasters become bottlenecks.

Solutions:

- Give the verbose ones extra assignments. When they learn that too much talk and too little work results in extra assignments, they will modify their abuse of time.
- If possible, isolate them from willing ears. Encourage them to do their socializing during breaks.

EXPLOSIVE TEMPER

Some people have an explosive temper on a short fuse, and they become angry at the slightest provocation. These individuals often are job hoppers. They stay on a job only until they blow up, "tell the boss off," and quit or get fired.

Solutions:

- Thorough employment screening usually weeds out these people. If you are stuck with one, keep him or her away from customers. They can do a lot of damage.
- Do not take personally what they say in fits of temper. Reply with "I'm sorry you said that. I'd think that over if I were you. You've nothing to gain by offending me."

- If the session continues to degenerate, end it. Simply say that the session is no longer productive, and you will meet again later. Get up and move slowly from around your desk and toward your door. If they do not react to this move, ask them to leave.

- Professional counseling is not often helpful in chronic cases, but is worth recommending. More often these employees are terminated via the disciplinary route. If they resign during one of their rages, do not let them change their minds.

SNIPERS

Snipers have discovered that masked, sharp, stinging remarks lets them get away with attacking you without assuming any responsibility. They do most of their dirty work in front of other people who provide their cover.[4] Snipers utilize innuendoes, sotto voce remarks, not-too-subtle digs, and nonplayful kidding. Their remarks usually drip with sarcasm.

Their assaults are not always carried out in your presence. They often talk behind your back, knowing that what they say will reach you. When you respond angrily, they retort "Can't you take a joke?" or "I was only kidding."

Solutions:

- When you hear one of their little zingers do not laugh, even if it is a little funny, or other people giggle, etc. But don't ignore it either. Stop what you are doing or saying, turn towards the sniper, and repeat exactly what you heard—these "jokes" lose their punch when repeated.[5] Then say "Larry, are you making fun of what I just said?" As soon as you have called the sniper on this, you have blown his or her cover. Now he must either confirm what he said, or try to weasel out of it with something like "Where's your sense of humor?" Respond with a sour smile, "Well, it did not sound funny to me."[5]

- After a meeting during which a sniper did his or her thing, take the sniper aside and make a direct accusation. Snipers do not function well in one-on-one situations. Do not buy their "Oh, you're just too sensitive." Reply that you enjoy a good joke like everyone else, but that what you are hearing are not good jokes.

MANIPULATORS

The chief characteristic of manipulators is that they use people for their own selfish purposes. This often involves taking unearned credit and blaming others. They may exhibit a winsome demeanor and are skilled at extracting confidential information from people. Just as children can get what they want by pitting one parent against another, these devious folks have developed that skill to perfection.

Employees who bypass their leader to get the approval of someone higher up in the organization are manipulators. Those who drop names to achieve personal agendas are manipulators. Leaders who promise much but deliver little are manipulators.

Solutions:

- Learn to recognize manipulative behavior and resist it. Develop the ability to refuse to divulge the information they seek or to get involved in activities that can be detrimental to your career or interpersonal relationships.

- Do not trust these devious people. Think carefully before you make commitments. Try to ferret out what they really are after. Often it is best to seek a new leader.

UNETHICAL TYPES

Ethics represents what we should do, not necessarily what we must do. Unfortunately, everyone does not agree as to what is ethical and what is unethical.

Staff members may demonstrate unethical behavior that represents disloyalty to superiors or employers. Unethical staffers may purposely create crises or promote disharmony. Technical specialists sometimes make unreasonable demands, knowing that they are indispensable.

The pilfering of supplies comes under the rubric of theft and is therefore subject to severe penalties. More controversial, and within the realm of ethics, is the "borrowing" of equipment for personal use.

Professionals can create dilemmas for their associates who witness their unethical behavior, for example, if a nurse witnesses a physician physically abusing an obstreperous child.

Solutions:

- Usually it is best to confront a colleague and tell him or her that you are aware of what is going on and will have to report it if these transgressions continue. In the case of severe violations, the report should be made without an antecedent warning. Judgment is required in many ethical dilemmas.

- If you are a supervisor or team leader, discuss the situation with your superior or a member of the human resources department.

- Read your policy manual concerning unethical behavior.

- If you are a member of a professional organization, consult with a representative of that organization.

REFERENCES

1. Mellott R. *Stress Management for Professionals*. Boulder, Colo: CareerTrack Publishing; 1987 (audiocassette).

2. Geneen H. *Managing*. New York, NY: Avon Books; 1984.

3. Bramson RM. *Coping With Difficult People*. New York, NY: Dell Publishing; 1981.

4. Solomon M. *Working With Difficult People*. Englewood Cliffs, NJ: Prentice-Hall; 1990.

5. Brinkman R, Kirschner R. *How to Deal With Difficult People*. Boulder, Colo: CareerTrack Publishing; 1988 (videocassettes).

PART III
Systems and Culture

15. Recognition and Reward Systems

THE GREATEST MANAGEMENT principle in the world: 'You get more of the behavior you reward.[1]
Michael LeBoeuf

CHAPTER OBJECTIVES

- To emphasize the importance of making recognition and reward systems congruent with team building
- To provide an overview of practical recognition strategies
- To help readers design plans for better team recognition
- To review the major contemporary systems for monetary rewards
- To describe some powerful nonmonetary strategies for improving morale
- To offer suggestions for negotiating rewards for your team
- To recommend a technique for discussing salary changes with team members

TEAM BUILDING REQUIRES CHANGES IN RECOGNITION AND REWARD SYSTEMS

Some extremely important and potentially highly disruptive effects on teams lie in company reward and compensation systems that continue to focus on individual effort, not on team performance.[2]
Charles R. McConnell

Table I
Individual Performance That Merits Special Recognition

Team effort

Work that is "above and beyond the call of duty"

Reliable, steady work that may not be spectacular but is usually dependable

Work shows improvement, even though it is still not up to expectations

Creative ideas or suggestions for improvements

Reducing cost or increasing productivity

Reducing customer complaints or increasing customer commendations

Offering solutions for problems

Compliance with policies, rules, and procedures

Handling a difficult situation or a difficult person

The ways that performance is evaluated and rewarded are the primary factors that affect employees' values and beliefs. Employers who build successful teams emphasize their new expectations by switching to new performance objectives, work standards, and reward systems that emphasize teamwork and team results. Their new reimbursement models feature a combination of individual skill-based incentives and team outcomes.

Since team building is a modality for increased productivity, cost containment, quality improvement, or customer satisfaction initiatives, these outcome factors enter into modifications of traditional recognition and reward systems. Teams, like individual employees, can receive bonuses and other forms of monetary rewards, but appreciation for their efforts is more often expressed in various forms of recognition. Individual performance that merits special recognition is shown in Table I. Note that team effort is at the top of the list.

A feature of self-directed teams is that the team members establish performance standards and participate in the evaluation of the work of their colleagues. (Performance appraisal was discussed in Chapter 8.) Management must not only commit time, money, and personal involvement to work evaluation, recognition, and reward systems, it must ensure that managers at all levels are trained in the appropriate application of these systems.

RECOGNITION SYSTEMS

The philosophical core of recognition is developing self-esteem.[3]
    Roger Hale

Hale and Maehling[3] define recognition as a broad, all-encompassing process that boosts employee self-esteem and builds an environment of trust, respect, and independence. Recognition can be formal, informal, or one-on-one.

The Importance of Goals

Before a company can implement an effective recognition program, it must articulate goals and a system of measurement. This begins with a baseline measurement that provides a framework for measuring improvement, goal achievement, and recognition based on results. Some goals, such as laboratory costs and turnaround times, are readily delineated by hard data. Others, such as employee morale and leadership qualities, are more difficult to quantify.

The Benefits of Effective Recognition Systems

- Recognition gives employees a better understanding of how and why their work is valued.
- Recognition reinforces performance and encourages workers to continue to do their best.
- Recognition is empowering and enhances stress resistance.
- Recognition reduces chronic complaining and grievances. People complain when they fail to receive sufficient attention.
- Recognition enhances employee self-esteem and personal satisfaction.
- Recognition helps to limit absenteeism, turnover, and motivational problems.

To achieve an effective recognition system, people at all levels of the organization must participate. In addition to management commitment, there must be employee involvement, special training, loads of cooperation, and the willingness on the part of many people to provide time, energy, and persistence.

Individuals Differ in the Kinds of Recognition They Seek

The same type of recognition does not work for everyone, so employing a variety of recognition and reward techniques is preferable to a cookie-cutter approach. Team recognition is great, but most employees still need some individual recognition. Experienced leaders individualize rewards based on what they know about their people, and sometimes it pays to ask those people what they want. Some employees have dollar signs for eyeballs. Money is all they talk about. However, most employees are motivated more by nonmonetary factors. They may switch to jobs that pay less but are more satisfying. When employees regard the awards as valueless, the reward program is in trouble.

Formal Recognition Systems

A formal recognition system is a structured and defined process that is consistent, infrequent, relatively expensive, involves few interpersonal skills, and provides delayed feedback for specific behavior. It consists largely of public displays and tangible awards.[3]

Table II
Nonmonetary Rewards for Good Performance

Less work they dislike, more they like
Change of work partners or team
More or less responsibility
More or less repetitive work (stressed workers will appreciate some relief)
Change in work schedules (flextime, part-time, job sharing) or additional
    time off
Title change
Personal library, work space, or access to special facilities
Verbal or written thank you from you and your superiors
Management learns about team progress
Write-up in organizational newsletters or local newspaper
Display of picture of team receiving an award
Team seated at special table during award ceremony
Special parking area for a week
Skill acquisition and more educational support
Suggestion that person serve as a mentor for a new employee
Opportunity for research and development
Assignment to special committees, task forces, or other special groups
Opportunity to specialize

Awards are usually based on customer service, quality improvement, cost cutting, safety, and attendance. They may consist of rings, pins, plaques, or trophies. Celebrations may consist of banquets, company picnics, midnight cruises, or dances. Notices usually appear in the organization's newsletters or local press.

Informal Recognition Systems

Informal recognition is unstructured, less defined, and used to single out groups as well as individuals. Such recognition usually celebrates attaining a particular goal or achievement, and it usually comes from a superior.

A celebration or a small gift such as a coffee mug can be a symbolically significant kind of informal recognition. The gift itself is not as important as the way it is given—personal congratulations from the manager, a note or letter from a supervisor, or a phone call from top management.

A caveat: Some departments celebrate with pizza parties, lunches, or dinners. The more elaborate the departmental or unit celebrations, the greater the risk of interdepartmental jealousy. Therefore, it is important to establish an informal recognition policy throughout the organization and to permit the use of discretionary funds for these activities. The ground rules spell out the basics: what kind of recognition is appropriate for what sorts of

Table III
Suggestions for Providing Team Recognition

Teams presentations of their accomplishments to senior managers, customers, other teams, or community groups

Team displays at professional meetings or to other groups

Photographs or videotapes taken of teams in action

Articles printed in bulletins and newspapers

Display of charts, posters, photographs, and commendations

Circulation of commendations and thank you notes from customers, senior officials, and inspecting agencies

Prizes, certificates, award pins, arm patches, and other symbols of recognition

Field trips to customers or suppliers

Celebrations of all kinds

Rituals like brief birthday celebrations

Delegation of more responsibility and authority to team

Better work area and facilities

Departmental "brag" sessions at which team members extol their team's accomplishments and praise the individual performance of fellow team members

efforts, what the recognition is trying to accomplish, who is responsible for implementing it, and where the funding comes from to pay for it.

Recognition is based on the amount of effort the group put into the project beyond the members' regular job responsibility, the amount of time expended to accomplish the task, and the importance of the accomplishment. Determining what to recognize and the type of recognition to give a group is the responsibility of managers in traditional organizations. Under participative management, these decisions are made by the teams themselves. Among the more popular choices of informal recognition are parties, luncheons, special coffee breaks, picnics, tours of other organizations, visits to customers or suppliers, or trips to reference laboratories. Gifts or gift certificates are often valued more than cash bonuses. Verbal and written expressions of appreciation or commendations are prized highly. A list of nonmonetary rewards is presented in Table II.

It is essential to monitor employee reactions to the informal recognition programs. The most common forms of recognition are often the least valued by employees. Identify what works and what does not. A list of methods for providing team recognition is given in Table III.

One-on-One Recognition

One-on-one recognition is a highly personalized system that costs little in cash but requires advanced interpersonal skills on the part of the giver. A high percentage of employees should be recipients, and the offerings are much more frequent than the formal and informal systems. This recognition comes from peers as well as from superiors.[3]

People need day-to-day recognition to perform at consistently high levels. This positive feedback consists of verbal or written recognition that can be as simple as a "thank you" or writing a short note. Even a smile and a "good morning" is a form of recognition. The type of reward most preferred by employees is personalized, spur-of-the-moment recognition. A 1992 survey by Professional Secretaries International revealed that many secretaries prefer a simple letter of appreciation to receiving flowers from their bosses.[3]

The high value of one-on-one recognition is enhanced by its immediacy. The one-minute praising of Blanchard and Johnson[4] is highly recommended. This consists of providing specific and immediate feedback, explaining how good performance benefits the organization or team, how good it makes the praising person feel, encouraging more of the same, and shaking hands. These praisings are made even more effective when accompanied by smiles, eye contact, and use of the person's first name.

Some people have trouble giving and receiving positive feedback. A supervisor may say "I never get any recognition, why should they?" or "That's what they're paid to do." Some recipients are embarrassed by public praise, but appreciate it when it is delivered in private. To be effective, this praise must be earned and sincere, otherwise it becomes flattery or manipulation. Trained team facilitators encourage team members to give more positive feedback to each other.

MONETARY REWARD SYSTEMS

As organizations strip away layers of management, broadbanding—the merging of large numbers of pay grades into a few pay bands—is becoming more popular. At the same time, other employers may increase the number of pay grades to encourage team members to accept cross-training and to acquire multiple skills. In some organizations focus groups are used to help formulate new compensation strategies and policies.

Money can be effectively used to recognize employees. One of its best uses is to reward cost-saving suggestions. Despite all the reports that money does not motivate, listen to family conversations when the subject turns to job satisfaction. Salary is a major determinant of which job offers people take or which jobs they abandon. A 1993 survey revealed that 90% of 2,400 managers polled at an outplacement center ranked salary as their number one consideration.[5]

Most behaviorists agree that money has limited motivational power, with two exceptions: (1) when a person does not receive sufficient pay to live decently and (2) when money is perceived as a reward for performance. In the latter instance, the amount of the reward must be substantial and tied closely to performance—a 3% to 5% raise won't get you much motivation.

Kohn[6] is critical of most monetary incentive plans. He believes that rewards only secure temporary compliance and are ineffective in producing lasting change in attitudes and behavior. He presents anecdotal evidence and the support of pundits like W. Edwards Deming that higher pay does not produce better performance. Hale and Maehling[3] claim that a salary raise only improves job satisfaction for three to 10 days. Since first-line supervisors have limited powers of dispensing financial rewards, we will only outline some of the popular monetary reward systems.

Kinds of Monetary Reward Systems

Base pay increasingly reflects a shift from internal equity to the economics of the marketplace. This shift has some impact on the paradigm of compensation strategies.

- *Raises based solely on length of employment (longevity raises).* While these are condemned by most, they still persist.

- *Annual bonus.* When everyone gets an annual cash award that is not based on performance or profit, employees regard this as an entitlement and get angry if it is skipped. Even when the annual bonus is based on performance, it is relatively ineffective because of the delay between the accomplishments and the reward and the lack of correlation between specific performance and the reward.

- *Pay-for-performance (merit pay).* The fact that in some organizations over 90% of workers get the "merit" raises suggests that a merit increase is an oxymoron in that organization. The design of most merit pay programs rarely provides an adequate pay differential for increasing levels of performance. Fairness in awarding merit pay is also a problem. Merit pay systems place a strong emphasis on individual performance, creating a competitive situation among employees that is destructive to team-building efforts. Merit pay increases to marginal performers is counterproductive. Many of these people probably should be fired. Meritorious team awards are usually superior to individual awards. The latter can actually erode team spirit because of envy or charges of favoritism.

- *Pay-for-skills or pay-for-knowledge.* Linking pay increases to skill-based competencies will become the norm of future evaluations as the fiscal crunch increases. These systems reward employees for what they know or can do. Skill-based pay may be based on knowing much about one area (depth); learning multiple tasks of the team (breadth); or organizational necessities such as safety, quality improvement, training, or meeting skills (height).[7] Under these plans, an employee's salary increases each time a new task or skill is mastered. This encourages team building, cross-training, and multiskilled goals.

  Zakian[8] asserts that skill-based pay allows employees the flexibility to perform a wide range of tasks. Workers must perceive that this type of compensation is fair compared with what colleagues within and outside the organization receive. Each team member must also be given sufficient opportunity for training to implement skill-based pay. Many, if not most, employees believe that little or no link exists between their performance and their pay.

- *Gainsharing.* Gainsharing is a bonus system that rewards increased productivity, reduced costs, enhanced quality, or overall increased performance. It is not to be confused with profit sharing, which is based solely on bottom-line gains. If a work unit surpasses a predetermined goal, all members of that unit share in a bonus. The goals do not have to be based on finance. They can deal with quality, customer satisfaction, safety, or some other desired outcome. Gainsharing avoids the weakness of annual bonuses and promotes team building. Base salaries remain relatively flat, and only cost-of-living salary increases are given. According to the Doyles,[9] gainshares are not limited to monetary rewards but may include employment security, personal growth, or promotions. In one hospital, nursing personnel participated in a gainsharing plan that rewarded excellence based on a competitive team model. Quality of care improved, costs were reduced, and sick time dropped.[10]

NONMONETARY STRATEGIES FOR IMPROVING EMPLOYEE MORALE

In the business world, everyone is paid in two coins: cash and experience. Take the experience first; the cash will come later.[11]
    Harold Geneen

- Start by hiring individuals who are self-motivators and who are more likely to respond to your recognition and reward system. This requires careful screening of candidates, including the use of appropriate batteries of questions to determine motivation, maturity, initiation, teamwork, self-discipline, conscientiousness, and work ethic.

- Take a second look at your orientation and training programs. Are new hires as enthusiastic at the end of these programs as they were when they were first hired? Do you encourage innovativeness or conformity? Do your initial assignments take advantage of individual strengths? Are people encouraged to take charge of their own continuing education and career development? Do you explain your organization's compensation system?

- Improve your leadership skills. Treat everyone as a winner or a potential winner. When constructive feedback is needed, focus on the behavior, not on the person. Practice situational leadership that takes into consideration differences in motivational needs, maturity, and self-efficacy. Become a praise master without manipulating or flattering. Delegate effectively (see Chapter 4).

- Encourage your associates to develop personal networks and to acquire an active mentor (see Chapter 26).

- As much as possible, assign individuals to tasks they like or want to learn. Ask them what they want to do more of and what they would like eliminated or reduced. Instead of segmenting tasks, assign them start to finish so that workers can see the fruits of their labors and take pride in them.

- Manage-by-walking-around (MBWA). I like to call this "stop and listen" management. Are you perceived as a facilitator and supporter who helps associates get their work done, or are you seen as a critic and fault-finder? Use MBWA to show you know what your associates are doing, and take advantage of that knowledge to compliment them and to express your appreciation. Catch them doing something right. When senior managers appear on the scene, point out some of the accomplishments of your team and individuals.

- Take advantage of the motivational aspects of team building (see Chapter 8).

- Satisfy associates' communication needs, especially the need to be listened to. Seek out their advice. Make sure that you do not ignore anyone. The most demotivating leadership behavior is to ignore people until they make a mistake and then to take them to task—the "ignore-zap" approach.

- Reward teamwork and cooperation as highly as you reward individual achievement. People who can subordinate personal goals to group goals merit extra consideration in raises and promotions. The ability to work as part of a team is now often included on individual employee appraisal forms. Consider some of the rewards listed in Table II.

How to Negotiate Pay Raises for Your Team

Pleading and threatening are usually ineffective in winning significant pay raises for your team. A more effective technique is to do your homework and present a convincing case to the people who control the purse strings. Best[12] won significant pay raises for her laboratory staff using this approach. She and her team presented their superiors with the following information:

- The results of a survey of staff morale based on a series of exit interviews and a special questionnaire.

- The record of turnover, which featured an estimate of the cost of turnovers for a period of time (employers are influenced most by bottom-line figures).

- Findings of a regional salary survey.

- Results of an in-house salary survey that compared laboratory salaries with those of other hospital professionals.
- Laboratory productivity records documented using nationally standardized analyses.
- Revised laboratory position descriptions that emphasized expertise, responsibility, risk taking, and impact on other personnel.
- The cost of projected salary changes.

How to Discuss Salary With a Team Member

Too often, salary discussions take place during performance reviews. Unfortunately, as soon as pay enters the conversation, nothing else seems to matter and the dialogue often becomes adversarial. It is much better to hold separate meetings for the salary discussion. If wages are frozen or if financial conditions mandate restraint, employees should know about this as soon as possible.

You must be able to explain to top performers why their increases are not commensurate with their performance ratings, eg, "That's the most we can pay given the size of our merit pay pool this year," or simply, "I wish we could be more generous."

When You Must Reject Requests for More Money

Every experienced team leader has had to look someone straight in the eye and say that a raise is not possible at that particular time. Fuller[13] offers the following practical suggestions for dealing with people who complain about pay raises.

Do not overrate performance or make unrealistic promises.
Find out what competitors are paying.
Be familiar with how salary changes are determined.
Be prepared to counter arguments.
Let the employee blow off steam.
Do not get drawn into salary comparisons.
Refuse to discuss the salaries of other employees.

At the confrontation, the best strategy is to let employees make their pitch and then say something like "You certainly make some interesting points, but I can't approve it because...." If possible, inform them what they can do to make a future pay raise more possible.

Never accept pleading that employees just must have more pay to take care of their families or any other reason. If you start basing salaries on financial need, you will constantly have an office full of sobbing people telling you how much they need help. This does not mean one must be hard-hearted about the matter. Be willing to listen to employees' financial woes and offer advice on how they can get expert help in managing fiscal matters.

REFERENCES

1. LeBoeuf M. *The Greatest Management Principle in the World.* New York, NY: Berkley Books; 1985.

2. McConnell CR. Getting maximum value from employee teams and keeping them legal. *Health Care Supervis.* 1994;13:66-73.

3. Hale RL, Maehling RF. *Recognition Redefined: Building Self-Esteem at Work.* Exeter, NH: Monochrome Press; 1993.

4. Blanchard K, Johnson S. *The One Minute Manager.* New York, NY: Berkley Books; 1983.

5. *HR Focus.* 1994;71:14.

6. Kohn A. Why incentive plans cannot work. *Harvard Bus Rev.* 1993; 71:25-35.

7. *Implementing Self-Directed Work Teams.* Boulder, Colo: CareerTrack Publications; 1994:23.

8. Zakian AL. Toward a new pay strategy. *MLO.* 1994;26:25-27.

9. Doyle RJ, Doyle PI. *Gain Management: A Process for Building Teamwork, Productivity, & Profitability Throughout Your Organization.* New York, NY: AMACOM; 1992.

10. Markowich MM. Does money motivate? *HR Focus.* 1993;70:1,6.

11. Geneen H. *Managing.* New York, NY: Avon Books; 1984.

12. Best M. Laboratory administrator's role in retaining professionals. *MLO.* 1990;22:46-50.

13. Fuller G. *Supervisor's Portable Answer Book.* Englewood Cliffs, NJ: Prentice-Hall; 1990.

16. Organizational Culture and Cultural Diversity

 UT SIMPLY, A CULTURE is the way we think and do things here.

> Unknown author

CHAPTER OBJECTIVES

- To define corporate cultural change
- To describe corporate cultural values and norms
- To discuss the importance of cultural diversity in health care institutions
- To review common biases, prejudices, and stereotypes
- To alert ourselves to the dangers of neglecting cultural diversity
- To delineate the multicultural impact on medical care
- To recommend a cultural diversity administrative program
- To detail a practical diversity awareness training program
- To advise on helping potential victims of harassment
- To provide tips for supervisors and team leaders when dealing with a multicultural workforce

ORGANIZATIONAL CULTURE

What Is Organizational Culture?

Organizational culture is nebulous. Few stakeholders consciously recognize what their organization's culture is because it is a difficult concept to understand. Anyone who has worked for more than one employer knows that each organization has its own cultural idiosyncrasies or personalities. For example, the navy has "tight ships" and "happy ships." While the former reflect an authoritarian leadership style and the latter represent a more delegative or even a laissez-faire style, the values and operations throughout the ships reflect that "top dog" approach.

Likewise, some hospitals, especially the ones affiliated with medical schools, tend to be "high-tech," while small community hospitals feature the "high-touch" culture. Because of this, many patients prefer their local institutions over the regional training centers when a high degree of specialization is not required.

Ketchum[1] offers Hofstede's definition of culture as "the collective mental programming of the people in an environment." Culture is composed principally of the beliefs and values that guide an organization in its daily activities. It is the sum total of all the standard ways people are expected to act. It is what employees do, not what executives say.

In addition to beliefs and values, an organizational culture also includes the norms, unwritten rules of conduct, management style, priorities, organizational philosophy, communication protocol, operational systems, rituals, taboos, and interpersonal behaviors. Each organization is unique. Formal culture is expressed by organizational charts, mission statements, policy manuals, and other formal structures.

Corporate Cultural Change Does Not Come Easily

Cultural change is often painful. It is one of the most difficult changes to which employees and managers must adjust. The transition from an authoritarian leadership to participative management or semiautonomous teams provides a good example.

Sullivan and Guntzelman[2] describe the grieving process that people go through when they must let go of the comfortable past. Such loss is proportional to the investment made in the job before the changes. Understanding the reasons for the change and participating in decisions about its implementation can make the transition less painful.

Who Is Responsible for Organizational Culture?

Culture trickles down from the top. The most important determinant of culture is the behavior of the chief executive. The CEO is the designer and articulator of the culture, the head cheerleader who draws on the strengths of employees and listens carefully at all levels.[3] This CEO attends the orientation programs and talks enthusiastically about the mission, philosophy, values, and goals of the organization.

People watch closely how senior managers adhere to the stated values, especially during a crisis. They note whether or not employees are provided with benefits that make it possible to fulfill their family obligations. They bolster the morale of older plateaued employees by providing lateral transfers. They institute training programs for employees who have language difficulties.

Employers who seek an egalitarian workforce strive to integrate (to bring different groups into free and equal association) rather than to assimilate (to make like or alike).

Corporate culture cannot be completely imposed from above by executives. It is also created and maintained by every member of the organization, chiefly by front-line employees who represent the vast majority of customer contacts.

Values and Norms

The culture of progressive organizations features partnership management, psychology of worker ownership and self-management, search for excellence, and integrity. Rindler's[4] five corporate values are honesty and integrity, pride and quality, hard work, communication, and customer service. And let's not forget respect for the individual. If team-building initiatives do not enhance—or if they threaten—respect for these values, the efforts will be counterproductive.

Establishing a new culture means setting an example regarding work ethic where it is manifested by conducting business rather than socializing at business meetings, working long hours, not tolerating poor performance, and insisting that everyone look professional. The lines of responsibility for customer satisfaction and high-quality performance are stated clearly and rewarded frequently.

If you can answer the questions in Table I about your organization, you have a good handle on what its culture is like.

CULTURAL DIVERSITY

The Importance of Cultural Diversity in Health Care Institutions

Cultural diversity is the watchword of the 1990s. Each of us is influenced to some degree by our racial, religious, ethnic, and cultural heritage and by variables such as age, gender, socioeconomic background, geographic location, education, and intergenerational solidarity. These differences must be recognized and respected by health care providers, especially since health care institutions treat so many women, senior citizens, minorities, and foreign-born individuals.

Table I
Questions That Reflect Corporate Culture

How is money spent? What gets rewarded?

Is the dress code acceptable? How do people dress?

What is talked about in meetings?

For what do people get fired?

How well do the leaders conform to the organization's mission statement, philosophy, and values?

Do you constantly hear the word "customer"?

What is the main thrust of memos?

Are leaders consistent in enforcing quality and safety standards or are these sacrificed when workloads soar?

Are the opinions of patients, physicians, and service providers sought frequently?

Who are the heroes and what did they do?

Are openness, fairness, trust, mutual respect, and a commitment to safety and health supported?

Are opportunities available for growth and security? Do employees know risk taking will be rewarded, not punished?

Is individuality respected and teamwork encouraged?

Are people inspired to be creative?

Are lines of communication open and is everyone tapped in?

Are workers given adequate time, equipment, supplies, and space?

Biases, Prejudices, and Stereotypes

We all have biases, prejudices, and stereotypes. One experience with a member of a minority group—or a story from someone else—may lead people to generalize about the entire group. Too many employees believe that Asians lack leadership traits, that blacks are not competent, and that older workers are inflexible. Gender stereotypes also persist, eg, "Women don't understand mechanical things" or "Real men don't cry." To facilitate coordination, leaders must recognize the presence of these impediments and take measures to overcome them. For example, racial or sexual jokes should not be tolerated.

The Benefits and Dangers of Cultural Diversity

In most instances, appreciation of cultural differences can lead to increases in potential customers and job applicants. However, failure to adjust to the cultural beliefs and practices of patients and other recipients of our service leads to loss of customers. Failure to make those adjustments when dealing with employees leads to resentment, low morale, increased turnover, poor performance, less successful recruitment, and possible lawsuits.

Multicultural Impact on Medical Care

Alternative healing beliefs and practices among some cultural groups may involve practices such as voodoo medicine or the use of herbs, rituals, and ceremonies. Any of these may have a powerful psychological impact on a patient's well-being.[5] These cultural variations influence acceptance and success of treatment. They also explain why some patients refuse therapy or do not show up for their medical visits.

Religious beliefs often overlap the cultural beliefs about illness. Patients should be encouraged to use these support systems and their symbols and ceremonies.

Cultural nutritional variables must be faced. For example, ingestion of pork is prohibited by some groups for religious reasons.[5] Food differences include style of preparation, kind of food, time of eating, and whether or not alcohol is accepted. Native Americans may be afraid to drink water with ice. Some bring warm drinking water when they come to the hospital. Normal values for biochemical and hematologic tests show some variations according to age, sex, and race.[5]

Administrative Programs for Cultural Diversity

The key to becoming an intercultural ambassador is to realize that majority and minority cultures do not always share beliefs and behaviors. Managers responsible for training should include programs that will help supervisors and employees be more aware of cultural differences.

Formulate a Strategy

A strategy for cultural change starts with a review of current practices. This can be elucidated through focus groups or culture surveys. The basic strategy is simple: change what is not working, but leave other areas alone. Develop separate policies on equal opportunity, affirmative action, and cultural diversity.[6] Be sure that you abide by all Equal Employment Opportunity Commission (EEOC) requirements.

Rethink Your Orientation Program

Prepare your staff for the arrival of an employee who is may be unlike the rest of the team. Review any dos or don'ts you feel may be necessary.

Diversity Awareness Training

Diversity awareness training needs are best adapted to the culture of the organization—it can go all the way from a one-time session to a series of interventions.[6] If people have had limited contact with these cultural differences in the past, they feel uncomfortable when faced with them. It is up to each employee to appreciate and value these differences, and not to expect that minority customers and employees want to "blend in" with the mainstream culture. It is more likely that they prefer to maintain their cultural identity.[1]

Course Content

Do not think in terms of broad categories. For example, the word "Hispanic" is often applied to people from Puerto Rico, the Philippines, Mexico, and other countries, but they do not share a common culture. You must be alert to the differences.[1]

Communication

Language and dialect are cultural variables. A Filipino patient is likely to view a caregiver as an authority figure and thus be quiet and subdued in a clinical situation.[5] Asians and others will not admit to not understanding your instructions because they regard that as an insult to your teaching ability.[7] Therefore, you must ask them questions to ensure that they comprehend what you have said.

Care providers should make a greater effort to learn the verbal and nonverbal languages of their customers. Body language is important. For example, eye contact when speaking is not accepted by Native Americans and some Eastern cultures. In the United States when you hold up your hand with thumb and forefinger together, this means "OK," but in France it means that you are a zero, in Japan it is a request for some change, and in some countries it is an obscene gesture. The "V" gesture in the U.S. means victory, but in Australia it is the "one-finger salute."[7]

Customs

An American might think that a brass clock would be an appropriate gift to someone. A Chinese person, however, might interpret this differently because clocks are associated with death in traditional Chinese culture. To make a slurping sound while eating soup or pasta is considered bad manners at a typical American dinner table; however, in Japanese culture, making such a sound is appropriate and expected.[1] This knowledge can be important when considering awards for service or when joining associates in the dining room.

Multicultural Values

Another variable is a person's value orientation. Values provide the basis for attitudes and behaviors. For example, different cultures place different values on privacy, courtesy, respect for elders, and the work ethic.

In the Philippines and Arab countries, unequal power distribution in institutions is highly valued. Status symbols are regarded as deserved and expected. In Austria and Sweden, power disparities are anathemas.[8]

In many corporations in the U.S. and Canada, policies limit the hiring of one's relatives, labeling it favoritism. In contrast, the cultures of Korea, Pakistan, and Taiwan view the hiring of a relative as desirable, even obligatory.

Japan, Austria, and Italy emphasize assertiveness, competitiveness, and the acquisition of money and material things as desirable. In the

Netherlands and Sweden, the opposite holds true—nurturing and quality of life are valued more.

The Greeks and Japanese like to minimize the discomfort of risk by adhering to strict laws and rituals, while Jamaicans and Swedes have little aversion to risk.[8]

HELPING THE POTENTIAL VICTIMS OF HARASSMENT

Help new arrivals feel more comfortable by discussing the unwritten rules and practices. These may include appearance, acceptable language, how to disagree or complain, and how to ask for help from others. Discuss the importance of cultural diversity at orientation sessions and at staff meetings. Don't tell people that they shouldn't feel the way they do when they feel mistreated. They will defend that feeling as much as their assertiveness will permit. Do make it safe for them to have and to express those feelings no matter what they are.[9]

Karp[9] warns against reinforcing the role of victim of prejudice or discrimination. This focuses on pain and weakness. When this occurs during a training program, "suffering contests" may emerge among subgroups to determine who has suffered the most. People leave such meetings feeling more vulnerable, victimized, and weaker than when they came in. Instead, it is better to develop a program that reinforces the role of survivor of discrimination. This strengthens the individual. Ask them how it felt and what they did to overcome it. This reinforces people's responsibility for and ability to take care of themselves.[9]

TIPS FOR SUPERVISORS AND TEAM LEADERS

- Challenge all stereotypes and assumptions about minority groups. Avoid terms like "yuppie" (young, upwardly mobile professional), "DINK" (dual income no kids), "old," "white male," "subordinate," "honey," and "girl."[7]

- Show interest in people's differences without prying into their personal lives. Seek information regarding various special ethnic observances and events, such as Chinese New Year (February), Black History Month, Martin Luther King Jr's birthday, Asian Pacific Heritage Week, National Hispanic Heritage Week, and Yom Kippur.

- Find out about the religious, family, and food customs of coworkers. Tactfully ask someone from that national culture after establishing appropriate rapport.

- Involve representatives of all minority groups in the decision-making process. If permitted, introduce policies for more flexible dress codes.

- Use humor carefully and avoid ethnic, sexist, or stereotypic jokes.
- Be familiar with your organization's policy on sexual harassment and follow it to the letter.

REFERENCES

1. Ketchum SM. Managing the multicultural laboratory, part I: tools for understanding cultural differences. *Clin Lab Manage Rev.* 1992;6:287-307.
2. Sullivan MF, Guntzelman J. The grieving process in cultural change. *Health Care Supervis.* 1991;10:28-33.
3. O'Donnell KP. Shared values, corporate culture, foster good hiring. *Mod Healthcare.* 1989;44:44.
4. Rindler ME. *Managing a Hospital Turnaround.* Chicago, Ill: Pluribus Press; 1987.
5. Bloch B. *Cultural Assessment Health & Sciences Network and The American Journal of Nursing Company CNE 7633.* Carrollton, Tex: Westcott Communications, Inc; 1993.
6. Jensen J. Diversity: how to walk the talk. *BNAC Communicator.* 1994; 14:3.
7. Blackstone SG. *Managing a Multicultural Workforce.* Clinical Laboratory Management Association Meeting. Palm Desert, Calif: Convention Cassettes Unlimited; 1992 (audiotape).
8. Hofstede G. *Culture's Consequences: International Differences in Work-related Value.* Beverly Hills, Calif: Sage Publications; 1984.
9. Karp BB. Choices in diversity training. *Training.* 1994;31:73-74.

17. Principles of Project Management and Process Reengineering

PROJECTS ARE SAID to be similar to the mating of two elephants. They start at a very high level with lots of noise and activity, but it takes forever for anything to materialize![1]

  Knutson and Bitz

CHAPTER OBJECTIVES

- To define and delineate work projects and describe some project systems and tools

- To review the use of quality circles as a project tool

- To depict a procedure for preparing a project proposal

- To define management reengineering and process reengineering

- To contrast traditional management with the reengineering approach

- To encourage managers to focus on flawed systems instead of blaming workers for poor customer service

- To outline the principles of process reengineering

- To describe applications and results of process reengineering

- To discuss barriers to process reengineering

181

PROJECTS AND PROJECT MANAGEMENT

A project is a special—usually formal—initiative to change something. The change may be a topographic, structural, or operational alteration; a staffing change; a new diagnostic or therapeutic technology; an innovative communication system; or a research study. The objectives of projects may be to increase productivity, customer service, quality, or profit; to introduce new products or services; to improve morale or communication; or to lower costs. Some projects concern staffing, job redefinition, performance competencies, or work standards. In other words, projects can address almost any aspect of management. Projects may or may not utilize process reengineering. Projects are finite and must be completed within the parameters of time, cost, human resources, and material assets.

A project is not part of a work group's regular responsibilities unless the group is in a research and development department. Projects may be transferred to temporary or "break-out" teams, committees, quality circles, task forces, brainstorming groups, or focus groups. The members of projects may be from one or more permanent work teams.

PROJECT TOOLS

- Mission statements, goals, objectives, schedules, and action plans
- Data collection and analyses
- Progress meetings and terminal debriefings
- Computer programs
- Budget spreadsheets
- Charts and storyboards
- Project systems

Computer Applications

Computer software can be used to store data, to investigate "what if" simulations, to prepare spreadsheets, and to generate "to do" lists. Project management software is no longer simply an option for experts. Advantages are ease of updating, quality of graphics output, option to track numerous tasks, and the ability to avoid inadvertent overallocation of resources.

Charts

Charts are essential to most projects. They help participants make decisions and illustrate results. These will be discussed at greater length in the next chapter.

Storyboards

A storyboard is an information-sharing vehicle for "talking" the story of a project team—what the team has been doing—and to brag about its achievements. Storyboards usually include before and after flowcharts.

Project Systems

Project systems include quality circles, customer service teams, quality improvement systems, focus groups, or special committees.

THE QUALITY CIRCLE: A PROJECT PROTOTYPE

The idea that evolved from quality circles is now embedded in total quality management in the form of self-directed work groups.[2]
    George R. Gray

A quality circle consists of a small group of employees doing similar work who meet voluntarily on a regular basis to identify, analyze, and solve work problems relating directly or indirectly to quality, productivity, or cost.

Anticipated Results of Quality Circle Activities

Anticipated results are both tangible and intangible. The tangible ones can be measured by hard data such as costs, output, audits, and documented customer comments. Intangible results such as improved communication, a sense of ownership, and improved morale are more difficult to measure. Employee attitude surveys, turnover rates, and attendance records may be used, but these are less susceptible to statistical analysis.

History

Quality circles became popular in the United States because they had succeeded in Japan, promised immediate improvements in productivity and quality, and utilized the bottom-up participative philosophy espoused by behavioral psychologists. One study estimated that 90% of Fortune 500 companies had introduced quality circles into their organizations in the early 1980s.[3] The health care industry followed suit. Hospital-wide circles were mandated, and laboratorians reported favorable results in a broad spectrum of applications.[4,5]

Like many management paradigms, quality circles have lost some of their glitter. Many quality circles have resurfaced with new titles like "customer service task forces" or "self-directed teams."

Appropriate Topics

Originally the subjects dealt with by quality circles were limited to quality, productivity, or cost cutting. Topics now may include safety, job structure, control mechanisms, and even aesthetics of the work environment. The quality circle concept can be integrated into current quality improvement initiatives.

For example, a laboratory quality circle or customer service committee may seek to reduce the amount of blood taken from patients, especially from children and newborns. The group would check into the frequency of unnecessary tests, the practice of drawing excessive amounts of blood (in anticipation of possible additional tests being ordered), and the problem of duplicate ordering.

Advantages and Disadvantages

Quality circles can increase productivity, reduce costs, encourage problem solving by workers, improve morale, and serve as a mechanism of change. Disadvantages include time required, initial costs, and resistance to change. If the recommendations of quality circles go unheeded, morale suffers and frustration sets in.

PROJECT PROPOSALS

A proposal is actually a sales presentation. As in all sales pitches, the more effective the presentation, the greater the chance for approval. The amount of justification required generally increases in proportion to the cost of the project. Contact the funding agency or convening authority for information and guidelines on a particular proposal, and then follow these guidelines meticulously. Write the proposal in clear, concise, and understandable language, devoid of technical jargon.

The Components of a Typical Proposal

- Overview
- Statement of problem or need
- Benefits of proposal
- Experience of others
- Past initiatives and available resources relating to what is being recommended
- Plan

  Scope

  Technical factors

  Facilities and resources needed

  Budget

  Financing/equipment/installation/training/supplies/schedule
- Biographical sketches of participants
- Summary

Tips on Selling Your Proposal

- Select the best time to make a verbal request.
- Define the situation as precisely and specifically as possible. Do not make the current situation appear worse than it really is.
- Show how the end result will be an improvement.
- Provide all the information needed, but keep it concise.
- Have the facts and figures ready and in writing.
- Do not downplay potential barriers.
- Use carefully selected graphic illustrations.
- Avoid jargon and keep acronyms to a minimum.
- Present procedures in step-by-step fashion.
- Use highlighting techniques in documents to clarify key points.

Politics and marketing strategies are as important as the technical details. For example, one project director used positive responses from the clinicians of a hospital as a wedge to sell a new service to reluctant executives.[6]

Complete and Report Project Results

When the work has been done or the report submitted, wrap up the administrative details, evaluate the experience, and celebrate! Hold debriefings with your team and with management to critique the process, review successes and problems that occurred, identify lessons learned, and make recommendations for the future.

Evaluate your project management experiential skill by answering the following questions. Did you:

make sure the project met your customers' needs?
get management approval and support?
establish doable goals?
plan each step of the process?
anticipate problems?
give each team member a project timeline?
stay in touch with the customer?
get frank feedback from team members?
provide frequent status updates to stakeholders?
analyze how to do better next time?

CORPORATE AND PROCESS REENGINEERING

Corporate reengineering refers to the restructuring of an organization and its workforce. Most often this translates into reducing personnel costs, usually by downsizing, outsourcing, or transferring administrative responsibilities from managers to workers by means of self-directed teams, empowerment, and participative management. Corporate reengineering also concerns strategic alliances, decentralization, structural changes, reorganizing, and mergers. It includes abandoning obsolete systems, forming cross-functional or self-directed teams, merging jobs, introducing new technologies, and instituting fresh principles of task organization.

Corporate reengineering in the clinical laboratory may involve consolidating sections, eg, hematology and chemistry or microbiology and histopathology. It may be establishing outreach programs, off-site phlebotomy centers, or immediate response laboratories.

Services often are more efficient if they have multiple operational channels. For example, a large emergency department may be more efficient if one unit cares for major trauma cases, another handles minor injuries, and a third treats nonsurgical patients. A large chemistry laboratory may restructure along decentralized lines to provide more efficient service.

Process reengineering is the redesign (restructuring, reconfiguring) not only of processes and systems, but also of the policies and structures that support them, in order to optimize work flows and productivity.[7] An example of an operational process is the sequence that begins when a physician orders a test and ends when the physician receives the results of that test.

Process reengineering is a tool for creative problem solving, quality improvement, better customer focus, and increased productivity, operational efficiency, and cost containment. Process reengineering improves work flows by modifying or eliminating dysfunctional processes. It is not merely improving existing procedures or modifying departmental flowcharts. It often cuts across departmental and functional boundaries and across traditional organizational boundaries between the work unit and its customers and suppliers. Process reengineering does not necessarily involve clusters of employees holding series of formal meetings. For example, Check[6] solved a knotty hospital problem simply by holding a series of one-on-one encounters plus a few informal small group meetings.

TRADITIONAL VS REENGINEERED PROCESSES

Most organizations still organize around functions and departments instead of around customers and key strategic objectives. Hospital processes are often fragmented. Seldom is one person, one work group, or one department responsible for a major customer service process. For example, the handling of a severely traumatized patient requires the cooperation and coordination of several teams of professionals and their support services. This loosely controlled situation often leads to confusion and squabbles.

Departments are highly differentiated, and their managers may track only what goes on within their own walls. For example, marketing tracks market share and finance monitors costs. Laboratory managers have traditionally monitored only the work performed within the laboratory—essentially the analytical phase of the work.

Reengineering demands a shared governance of the activities that take place within a given service.[8] In the laboratory, this includes the pre- and postanalytical phases of patient testing. Preanalytical activities include patient preparation; specimen collection, transport, and storage; instrument preparation; and transcriptions. Postanalytical activities are those that take place between the time of test completion and the time a physician acts on a test report.

FLAWED SYSTEMS: THE REAL CULPRIT

In the past, bad employee attitude, work ethic, and behavior were blamed for inefficiencies and poor customer service. Enlightened observers have concluded that the underlying villains are not the people doing the work, but the work systems, processes, procedures, and policies that control their activities.

This is true of hospital activities as well. For example, an audit of hospital inpatients revealed that the most common complaints were noise; quality of food; room temperature or appearance; and waiting for admission, discharge, or radiology procedures. Almost all of these problems were attributed by the observers to faulty processes.[9] Along this same line, an extensive study of phlebotomy services revealed that greater quality gains could be achieved by focusing on administrative inefficiencies rather than on phlebotomist skills.[10]

Thus, a paradigm shift is needed. When we get complaints from customers, we must stop looking first for someone to blame and look at the processes or systems. That is not easy to do, especially when we are the ones accountable for those processes.

PRINCIPLES OF PROCESS REENGINEERING

An engineering methodology must focus on two strategic guidelines: empowering people and enabling technology.[7]

■ Successful reengineering requires a shared governance that features participative management, delegation, employee empowerment, and cross-functional or self-directed teams.

■ Reengineering sometimes requires a radical redesign of systems, procedures, and networks for maximum effectiveness.

■ Reengineering is organized around outcomes, not tasks, functions, or departments. It begins by looking at the desired outcome, then identifying what stands in the way of achieving it.[11] It often involves an overhaul of organizational structures, job descriptions, and management systems.

■ Health care work processes are complex, nonlinear, and often cannot be simplified into a string of quick, sequential tasks. The desired end result often requires a high degree of collaboration among individuals and functions.[12]

■ As few people as possible should be involved in the performance of a process. Combining several jobs into one provides a single point of contact for customers. It eliminates time-wasting handoffs and enables a team to provide complete service when some of its members are absent.

■ Each team member must have at least a basic familiarity with all parts of a process.

■ Computers and automation play a vital role in making reengineering in the laboratory a reality.

APPLICATIONS OF PROCESS REENGINEERING

Process reengineering is often facilitated by team building and has increasing significance in health care settings for a number of reasons, most of which boil down to demands for better and faster service, lower charges, and delivery by competent, respectful employees. These incentives encourage medical facilities to take new looks at the way they provide services. Process reengineering provides the means for addressing most of these demands.

Lathrop,[13] commenting on the findings of a three-year hospital study, pointed to many hospital processes that require improving. Some of these deficiencies have been around so long that hospital employees do not perceive them as problems, such as the line of gurneys waiting in the corridors of radiology departments and the inch-thick medical records for three-day stays. He observed that a five-minute EKG often requires an hour's worth of scheduling, documentation, and transportation, and that it took a half-day for a patient to get the ubiquitous triad of chest x-ray, EKG, and phlebotomy. Lathrop complained bitterly that out of every dollar of hospital employee wages, only 16 cents goes for real medical care. According to Stoddard,[14] process reengineering can reduce such operating costs by 10% to 30%.

Here are some laboratory processes waiting for remedial action:

■ Long waits in phlebotomy collection stations

■ Lengthy turnaround time for some laboratory reports

■ Too many signatures required for purchase approvals

■ Excessive inventory and outdating of reagents

■ Crisis contingency plans, such as what to do if an armed intruder holds a receptionist hostage

Two important considerations are how seriously customer service, employee morale, and service costs are affected and how feasible any changes would be. Sources of data include focus groups, consultants and specialists, committees, incident reports, and complaints.

Some Health Care Results of Process Reengineering

"Process-focused, multifunctional teams can dramatically improve the way their companies deliver products and services to customers."[8]

The real benefit of reengineering is the streamlining of patient care delivery processes and systems. Unnecessary tasks are eliminated, some processes are automated, and new processes are designed. Reengineering eliminates much of the monitoring, checking, waiting, tracking, and other unproductive work, leaving more time for doing real work.[15]

Patient-Focused Care

Hospitals throughout the country are designing and implementing patient-focused care (PFC) initiatives. The concept of PFC involves redesigning entire functional units into self-contained units. Nursing service goals are to improve inpatient care, decentralize nursing stations, reduce the need for graduate nurses, and make better use of ancillary personnel. This change can affect the clinical laboratory in at least two ways. Blood drawing is transferred from the laboratory to the PFC units, and more and different kinds of service providers will be communicating with the lab.

The average patient who stays in a hospital for two or three days will have contact with dozens of hospital employees more than 50 per patient have been counted by some observers. PFC can reduce this number by as much as two thirds. In addition, the members of the new cluster groups have greater interest in the welfare of their patients than do the hordes of folks from ancillary departments. An example of such an endeavor is outlined in Tables I and II.

Point-of-Care Testing

Point-of-care systems bring testing to the bedside. The major systems include satellite labs, labs on wheels, and testing by primary care providers at the bedside.

One laboratory developed two types of remote, automated testing stations, one with robotics and one without. Both networked to the central laboratory computer for results, review, and quality control.[16]

In another facility, a mobile laboratory unit operated by a technologist and capable of performing all the most frequently ordered tests reduced turnaround time and decreased costs.[17]

Reduced Turnaround Time

Turnaround time (TAT) can be reduced by altering the pre- and post-analytical phases of testing as well as the analytical phase. Pre- and post-

Table I
Saint Joseph Hospital's* Pods: An Example of Process Reengineering and Team Building

Goal:	To improve patient care and reduce costs
Objectives:	Direct patient care provided by RNs to increase from present 40% to 60%. Expenses to decrease by 15%. Fewer RNs utilized.
Structural Change:	Nursing floor with 32 patient rooms was divided into four pods. Each unit contains supplies, patient's charts, computer terminal, telephone, and fax machine. Each RN has cellular phone.
Team Members:	Care Manager, RN, Clinical Associate II (LPN), Clinical Associate I (Patient Care Technician [PCT]), Patient Service Associate (Support Generalist), Unit Secretary (share with other pods)

* Saint Joseph's Hospital, Lancaster, Pa.

analytical variables include laboratory information systems (LIS) that support remote order entry, bar-coded specimen collection labels, consolidated report printing, remote printing or autofaxing capabilities, and client account billing.[18] Any process that facilitates specimen transport—such as pneumatic specimen tube delivery—can shorten TAT. Palmtop computers that enable the mobile clinician to access test results and order tests on the run also reduce TATs.[19]

Analytical variables that can shorten TAT include instruments that use whole blood instead of plasma or serum (no need for centrifugation), test systems with self-contained cartridges or strips, (no reagent preparation), devices with internal checks for quality control, operator/patient identification and test dating (reducing transcription errors), robotic specimen handlers integrated with highly automated instruments and interfaced to LISs, and analyzers that have more rapid flow-through capabilities.[20]

Cross-Functional Teams

A cross-functional team cut hospital admission waiting time by 17%, while another team at that facility reduced the paperwork process of hiring from an average of 9.5 days to 4.5 days.[21] Other cross-functional teams reduced laboratory stat volumes and turnaround times.[22] In one institution, patient care was improved by engaging patients and their families as partners in the care-giving process.[23]

Table II
Qualifications and Typical Responsibilities of Pod Members

Care Manager (Registered Nurse)
Coordination and expedition of care with other disciplines and
physicians, resource for staff, staff education, manage resources,
analyze cost, patient problem solving, rounds with physicians,
assist pod RN if needed

RN (Registered Nurse)
Patient assessment and instruction, discharge planning, interpret
glucose checks, wound assessment and care, care of infusion pumps
and IVs, clinical pathways, orders from MDs, QA activities, plus
many other complex nursing tasks

Clinical Associate II (Licensed Practical Nurse [LPN])
Many of the same duties performed by RN including medications,
wound care, patient teaching, intravenous fluids, respiratory care,
and documentation

Clinical Associate I (formerly nurses aides, phlebotomists, or
respiratory technicians)
Vital signs, urine and blood glucose, I & O, spirometry, phlebotomy,
EKGs, patient personal care, patient teaching

Patient Service Associate (Formerly housekeepers or dietary aides)
Feed and bathe patients, fill water pitchers, answer call light, change
linens, make beds, clean room, empty trash, run errands for
patients, escort patients

Unit Secretary* (No change in qualifications)
Transcribe orders, operate tube and fax systems, retrieve and
return charts, contact dietary, order supplies

* Share with other pods on floor.
Reference: Personal correspondence with Elizabeth McIntyre, RN, Director of Support
Services, Saint Joseph's Hospital, Lancaster, PA.

Barriers to Successful Process Reengineering

The paradigm shift to process reengineering is hampered because although
most work processes are horizontal, the table of organization is vertical, and
traditionally communication moves in that up-and-down direction.
According to Champy[24] management turned out to be a major obstacle to
reengineering success. Specific barriers include:

- Facilities are too functionally focused. Their departments represent
  silos of independent activity separated by fields of service gaps.
- Neglect of the human factor

Table III
Problems That Can Result in Project Failure

Turnover, especially of leaders or other key players
Communication problems: lapses, misconceptions, faulty perceptions, and erroneous assumptions
Powerful opponents
Supplier problems
Lack of necessary resources
Failure to consider contingency factors
Budget slippage
Leader or team lacks authority or resources
Leader or team members lack professional or technical expertise or interpersonal skills
Failure to follow required steps
Steps not carried out effectively
Goals, objectives, or timetables are unrealistic
Lack of opportunity of members to participate
Too much interference

- Cost, time, and effort
- Possible adverse effects on customers, employees, or suppliers
- Problems of team function or personnel turnover
- Interference by outsiders or in-house executives
- New challenges or management initiatives that divert attention from the reengineering efforts
- Loss of interest and support of top management
- Employees who are not convinced of the need for change and who do not cooperate or even obstruct progress
- Union opposition

See Table III for a list of problems that can result in project failure.

In the next chapter we will concentrate on the practical aspects of setting up a process reengineering project.

REFERENCES

1. Knutson J, Bitz I. *Project Management: How to Plan and Manage Successful Projects*. New York, NY: AMACOM; 1991.

2. Gray GR. Quality circles: an update. *SAM Adv Manage J*. 1993;58;41-47.

3. Lawler EE, Mohrman SA. Quality circles after the fad. *Harvard Bus Rev*. 1985;63:64-71.

4. Tilley KL. Putting quality circles to work in chemistry. *MLO*. 1987; 19:41-49.

5. Jimenez J, Turley CF, Quiggins CS. A quality circle improves pediatric phlebotomy. *MLO*. 1988;20:85-87.

6. Check WA. Teamwork at its best. *CAP Today*. 1991;5:36.

7. Smith B. Business process reengineering: more than a buzzword. *HR Focus*. 1994;7:117-118.

8. Meyer C. How the right measures help teams excel. *Harvard Bus Rev*. 1994;72:95-103.

9. Rollins RJ. Patient satisfaction in VA medical centers and private sector hospitals. *Health Care Supervis*. 1994;12:44-50.

10. Howanitz PJ, Schifman RB. Inpatient phlebotomy practices. *Arch Pathol Lab Med*. 1994;118:601.

11. McManis GL. Reinventing the system. *Hospitals & Health Networks*. 1993:30;7-8.

12. Montebello AR. Teamwork in health care: opportunities for gains in quality, productivity, and competitive advantage. *Clin Lab Manage Rev*. 1994;8:91-105.

13. Lathrop JP. The patient-focused hospital. *Healthcare Forum J*. 1991; 34:17-20.

14. Stoddard WG. Process reengineering: the key to successful restructuring. *Boardroom Rep*. 1994;23:3.

15. Hammer M, Champy J. *Reengineering the Corporation*. New York, NY: Harper Business; 1993.

16. Skjei E. Reengineering the lab. *CAP Today*. 1994;8:1.

17. Travers EM, et al. Changing the way lab medicine is practiced at the point of care. *MLO*. 1994;26:33-40.

18. James K. Relax: you may be reengineering the right way. *CAP Today*. 1994;8:38-39.

19. Friedman BA. The laboratory information float, time-based competition, and point-of-care testing. *Clin Lab Manage Rev*. 1994;8:509-513.

20. Phillips DL. "Hook-Up": a laboratory/industry exchange. *CAP Today*. 1995;9:70.

21. McKenzie L. Cross-functional teams in health care organizations. *Health Care Supervis*. 1994;12:1-10.

22. Ramirez O, Lawton J. Quality improvement team uses FOCUS-PDCA method to reduce laboratory STAT volume and turnaround time. *Clin Lab Manage J*. 1994;8:130-145.

23. Austin N, Orr R, Fritz R. The patient-driven hospital. Audiovisual presentation by Hospital Satellite Network CE MGR 6608. 1986:1.

24. Lancaster H. Barrier to reengineering. *Wall Street Journal*. January 17, 1995: B1.

18. Practical Aspects of Process Reengineering

To REENGINEER A COMPANY is to take a journey from the familiar into the unknown.[1]
Michael Hammer

CHAPTER OBJECTIVES

- To suggest how to detect situations that can and should be improved
- To provide some tips for effective benchmarking
- To list the advantages of thorough planning
- To codify plans
- To propose an eight-step strategy for developing a process reengineering initiative
- To outline and illustrate practical charting techniques

DETECTION OF SITUATIONS THAT SHOULD BE IMPROVED

Every organization has a process or system that could and should be improved. Every institutional or service change that comes down the pike creates a need for some process reengineering. Quality improvement programs are never ending, and process reengineering is a major instrument for improving quality.

- Start with your customer service. Learn more about what your customers want and what would delight them. If possible, watch them go about their daily routines.

Examples:

Make rounds with physicians and listen to what they say when they order laboratory tests and receive the results.

Watch how blood donors, outpatients, or employees hunt for parking space.

Talk to patients about your admitting or billing process.

Visit a physician's office and talk to the office manager about the problem of scheduling several hospital services for a single patient on the same day.

Ask family members and visitors to your special care units how they can be serviced better at all hours of the day and night.

Form a focus group of customers and front-line service providers who have personal or telephone contacts with your clients. Your front-line service providers can tell you more than any consultant or in-service specialist.

Ask outpatients if the hours of your phlebotomy service are suitable.

■ Do not neglect your internal customers. External customers such as physicians, patients, and blood donors cannot be served well when internal customer relationships are strained or antagonistic.

Internal customers are the departments or individuals you serve or who work with your unit in a joint service operation. Every personal interface in a work process involves a provider and a recipient. That interface may be between a supplier and yourself, between a nurse and a laboratory technologist, or between your blood bank and the surgical suite.

Process reengineering of any magnitude crosses departmental lines. This requires lots of collaboration and cooperation, often including the formation of task forces or cross-functional teams.

■ Consider innovative approaches. Identify and attack assumptions or time-honored practices such as paying suppliers only after they have delivered the goods. Consider eliminating a large inventory storage space by instituting a just-in-time inventory system. Recommend outsourcing of complicated procedures that cause your laboratory quality control problems or that the laboratory cannot perform as economically as an outside one.

■ Try benchmarking. Visit facilities that are on the cutting edge of process reengineering and note what they have or do that is superior to yours and how they provide that exemplary service.

Two cautions are frequently overlooked when benchmarking is discussed. The first is that benchmarking only helps you to catch up with others, not to get out in front of them. The second is that no two organizations are exactly alike. What works well at one facility may fall flat on its face at another. Therefore, use benchmarking more as a creative practice in which new possibilities are recognized, then adapt those ideas to your own unique circumstances.

PLANNING

Planning is the most fundamental management function, and it logically precedes all other functions. Planning is the projection of actions to reach specific goals. In other words, a plan is a blueprint for the future.

Planning starts with the questions of what and why. It then focuses on the how, when, who, and where. In the opening of this chapter we discussed the detection and selection of processes or systems that need improving. This is the "what" of planning initiatives.

The Benefits of Planning

Planning ensures that we work effectively and efficiently. It reduces procrastination, ensures continuity, and helps us use resources more intelligently.

Planning helps to do things right the first time, resulting in that great feeling of having everything under control and knowing what to do next.

Planning is proactive. It decreases the need to manage by crisis. It is a prerequisite for practically all important managerial activities—teaching, committee and staff meetings, performance appraisals, employment interviews, and budget preparations.

Planning is essential for coping with crises such as fires, natural disasters, strikes, bomb threats, or hostage situations.

Classification of Plans

Strategic plans are plans for achieving long-range goals and living up to the expectations expressed in statements of mission and values. Without strategic planning, few visions are realized.

Organizational plans start with a table of organization and include position descriptions, staffing, and channels of communication.

Physical plans concern topography—the site of a building, the layout of an office, or the location of diagnostic and therapeutic equipment.

Functional plans are directed toward major types of activities such as clinical laboratory, human resources, finance, and clinical services (internal customers).

Operational plans deal with systems, work processes, procedures, quality control, safety, and other supportive activities.

Financial plans address the inflow and outflow of currency, profit and loss, budgets, cost and profit centers, charges, and salaries.

Career plans, time management, and daily work plans are also vital forms of planning.

STEPS IN THE DEVELOPMENT OF A REENGINEERING PROJECT

Step 1: Determine a Need for Change

Answer the following questions:

Why is there a need for change? What is wrong with the present service or product?

What are the strengths and weaknesses of your unit and those of your competitors?

What are the potential gains, losses, or risks of process reengineering?

Who will be affected?

What will it cost?

What is likely to happen if this project is not carried out?

Conduct an Analysis

For example, studies of how patient procedures are scheduled and coordinated in most hospitals reveal that much time is wasted.[2]

Bachert[3] reported that SWOT analyses were helpful in studying their problems in a regional blood bank. One of her SWOT analyses pointed to the following significant factors:

S = Strengths ("a strong community donor base")
W = Weaknesses ("lack of a bloodmobile")
O = Opportunities ("untapped donor potential")
T = Threats ("four large competing units")

Collect Data

Select a method of collecting information and build a data bank. Be thorough when you collect information. Become familiar with statistical analysis and the use of charts, electronic data interchange (EDI), electronic mail, and work flow automation.

Step 2: Focus on Visions, Goals, and Objectives

Winning teams hold brainstorming sessions in which members bring up many "whys" and "what ifs." Leaders share their visions and involve their associates in setting goals and objectives. "A vision is an image without great detail. It acts as a flag around which the troops will rally."[1]

Goals describe long-range benefits or general statements of purpose. Objectives are the steps needed to achieve goals. They should be realistic, understandable, measurable, behavioral, achievable, and specific (RUMBAS). An objective such as "to reduce inventory costs" is not sufficiently specific. A better objective would be "to reduce inventory costs by 10% within 12 months." Objectives should be assigned priorities.

In addition, an element of challenge should be present and a target date set. While challenges should be included—employees are motivated to achieve difficult but not impossible tasks—objectives must be reasonably attainable. If a plan has little chance of success, it will frustrate rather than motivate. Written objectives are much more likely to get attention and to be updated on a regular basis. They also provide a permanent record.

Examples of Objectives

■ Within 12 months, a repeat morale survey of employees will indicate an average employee satisfaction rating increase from the current level three to at least level two.

■ By the end of the next quarter, we will provide bedside laboratory testing to all patients in the north wing.

■ Before the next round of performance appraisals, all of our patient and physician contact providers will demonstrate the ability and have the authority to make most daily decisions without requiring assistance or approval of management.

Step 3: Prepare a Detailed Plan

Develop a plan, contemplate alternative actions, and select the most appropriate one. In some instances, this step follows rather than precedes step 4. When plans are very complex or involve much expenditure of time and resources, or when the likelihood of approval is not great, prepare an abbreviated proposal and test the waters first. The approving authority can always ask for more detailed information.

Action plans should answer the questions of:

What is to be done?

Why must it be done?

When should it be started and completed?

Who is to do it?

Where is the action to take place?

How should it be done?

The plans include:

Identifying resources (people, supplies, equipment, facilities, time, and funds)

Preparing and prioritizing checklists of important tasks to be performed

Assigning tasks, authority, and responsibilities

Preparing work schedules

Providing necessary training

The plans may require new policies, systems, and procedures. Policies are usually needed to help accomplish a series of plans.

Executive Summaries

Complex plans should include an executive summary that touches on key issues such as how the proposal will affect the mission statement of the institution, how it will affect quality of services and operational costs, and how clients and employees are likely to react to the changes.

The six essentials of a plan:

1. It must be doable.
2. It must be understandable.
3. It must be comprehensive.
4. It must be cost-effective.
5. It must be approved.
6. It must be reviewed periodically.

Task Identification

This work breakdown structure is nothing more than a comprehensive "to do" list. You may wish to organize your list into various categories or project phases.

Task Sequencing and Time Allocations

Use Gantt and flowcharts or other logic diagrams to document tasks and to analyze the times required for the work processes.

Schedule Preparation

On a chart, list the tasks chronologically down one side and appropriate calendar periods horizontally.

Budget Preparation

Estimate all costs associated with each task. Build in some slack for inflation or other unanticipated costs. Prepare a cost spreadsheet with tasks listed vertically and cost factors such as labor and supplies listed horizontally and totaled at the right of each line.

Contingency Planning

Because of the risk factors involved, a contingency design is part of the overall endeavor. Risk factors are those that may affect schedules, resources (including funding), changes in product or service requirements, competition, and failure of acceptable results or costs.

Review of Plan

Your plan should now answer the following questions:

How long will it take? When is the deadline?

Can it be completed in phases over time?

Will the dates affect (or be affected by) other project dates? (Note: When estimating time give special consideration to those tasks that could be affected by factors beyond your control.)

What work will be done in-house and what will use outside contractors?

Are you certain that the in-house people will be available when needed?

Have you prepared an inventory of the skills needed and matched with the skills available on the team?

Have you done an attitude check? The attitude and degree of enthusiasm of each member are important considerations, especially if work on the project must be in addition to routine duties. How do the team members' temperaments match the project needs?[4]

Are all resources available and when are they needed? Negotiate with other departments for resources and cooperation. See Chapter 24 on negotiating skills.

Has the complete funding been approved? Are there contingencies for cost overruns? Can anything be deleted if cost cuts become necessary?

Establish Priorities

Priorities are a vital part of any plan. They indicate what you think is important and what can be postponed or implemented only if time permits. To avoid frustration, be prepared to modify your priority list. Unexpected interruptions are the rule rather than the exception—an instrument breaks down, your leader has an urgent request, or a key employee calls in sick.

When appropriate, let your teammates know what your priorities are. Individual and team priorities are not always the same. Give priority to an item that is emotionally upsetting to you or your team.

Communication Strategy

Communication strategy is critical and should be planned by the members, not dictated by the leader. Will there be formal, regularly scheduled meetings of the entire group? If so, how often will they be held and where? Will information be disseminated informally, one-on-one, or via voice mail as needed? Will written messages (reports, memos) be used?[5]

Step 4: Assign Tasks and Responsibilities

Use a human resource matrix to know who is doing what. This matrix lists tasks or responsibilities, the team members, and allocated times. See Table I.

Table I
Example of Human Resource Matrix Chart

Project: To make recommendations to comply with regulations of the Americans with Disabilities Act (ADA).

Task	Team Member	Time
Review ADA guidelines and list current deficiencies	Sue	5 days
Make recommendations for physical change	Alice & Tom	2 days
Make recommendations for procedural/policy changes	Sue & Corinne	2 days
Draft final report	Sue	2 days
Get chief's input and make modifications	Sue & Tom	2 days

Step 5: Monitor, Control, and Record the Activities

Formal control is planned and consists of data gathering and analysis. These data are used to produce status reports that indicate whether or not performance is meeting time and quality standards. The planning techniques and computer data management systems are essential. The reports generated serve as the basis for remedial measures.

Informal control consists of the day-by-day observations and one-on-one meetings of individuals of the team and their leaders. Supporting or correcting actions are taken promptly. Alert colleagues spot potential problems before they result in any damage or when they are easier to alleviate. Thus, informal controls can be much more proactive than formal ones. Status reports are issued at meetings with the team, superiors, and others in your information loop. Leaders must avoid micromanaging—constantly looking over the shoulders of the workers or repeatedly making minor changes. In other words, they should be perceived as supporters, advisors, and facilitators, not as obstructionists or nitpickers.

Step 6: Solve Problems and Make Modifications or Adjustments

Progress monitoring often leads to tying up loose ends. These may involve changes in plans, reassignment of tasks, removal of barriers, or seeking additional resources. The earlier a problem is identified, the easier it is to correct. When step 6 is followed conscientiously and data collection and analysis are thorough, trends can be spotted early and corrective action taken.

Note: Keep a master file of the problems you encounter and your solutions (whether they worked or not). If you encounter a problem once, you will likely encounter it again, and next time you will know what worked or what did not.

REFERENCES

1. Hammer M, Champy J. *Reengineering the Corporation.* New York, NY: Harper Business; 1993.
2. Brider P. The move to patient-focused care. *Am J Nursing.* 1992;92: 27-33.
3. Bachert LB. Strategic management in blood banking. *MLO.* 1986;18: 48-52.
4. Douglass ME, Douglass DN. *Time Management for Teams.* New York, NY: AMACOM; 1992.
5. Knutson J, Bitz I. *Project Management: How to Plan and Manage Successful Projects.* New York, NY: AMACOM; 1991.

19. Union-Management Partnership in Team Building

FREQUENTLY NOBODY AT the top of the organization has any solid idea of what is really troubling the ranks of nonmanagerial employees. If management does not listen to the employees, the union organizers will.[1]
Charles R. McConnell

CHAPTER OBJECTIVES

- To explain why employees join unions
- To describe a typical union organizing drive
- To elucidate the role of the union representative (steward)
- To discuss the changes in group relationships after unionization
- To make recommendations concerning the relationship between the supervisor and union representative
- To review the steps in handling complaints and grievances
- To advise managers on how to avoid charges by the National Labor Relations Board that teams or committees are functioning as illegal unions

Readers may wonder why the subject of unions is brought up in this book. The reason is that while it is possible to introduce delegative management, participative leadership, and self-directed teams into a unionized organization, such efforts are more difficult when the constraints of a union contract must be overcome. Therefore, it behooves supervisors and other managers to make strenuous efforts to keep their organization union free. Additionally, recent interpretations of the National Labor Relations Board (NLRB) pose threats to organizations that have introduced self-directed teams or other forms of employee empowerment and participation. The first-line supervisor and team leaders play key roles both in preventing union intrusions and, when operating within the context of a unionized institution, in working as harmoniously as possible with union representatives. Many companies find that a union that formally opposes the use of teams often will not object to its members being part of a team if it is working on a specific problem.[2]

WHY EMPLOYEES JOIN UNIONS

Organized labor thrives on management apathy. Unions exist because they fulfill employee needs that have been neglected by management. If management would do for labor before it is organized what it is forced to do after it is organized, it is not likely that it would be organized in the first place.[3]

John A. Patton

If CEOs would insist on better exit interviews and more frequent employee morale surveys, they would have a better handle on the status of their employee morale. It would also help if they interrupted some of their daily shuttles between executive suites and corporate meeting rooms long enough to get out to where the customer action is taking place.

Most employees are convinced that they work hard but are underpaid and underappreciated. They believe they often get shabby treatment and unfair criticism. They think unions may remedy some of these inequities, and the unions tell them just that.

Unions capitalize on a growing feeling of discontentment. They promise professional and technical employees greater roles in decisions that affect their work and in securing more control over their work. Unions breed in discontent.

Inadequate pay or benefits is often given as the major reason people join unions, but more often than not, the real cause can be traced to non-economic factors such as poor interpersonal relations with their immediate superiors. In many instances the behavior of one tyrannical manager provokes an avalanche of union activity or a strike if a union is already in place.

Low morale, increased turnover, high absenteeism rates, and increased worker's compensation claims usually attract union organizers. Conversely, organizations in which participative management is pervasive are resistant to unionization. Those employers who have succeeded in getting employees to buy into the employee ownership concept have watched unions being voted out of their organizations.

Job insecurity can be a potent factor, especially in times of economic turmoil when unemployment, downsizing, mergers, and restructuring are rampant. The first-line supervisor is often regarded by employees as

Table I
Reasons Why Employees Join Unions

Inadequate pay or benefits
Job insecurity
Lack of communication—not knowing what is happening
Unfair, inconsistent, or tactless discipline
Inappropriate rules, policies, procedures, or practices
Management indifference to complaints
Management ignoring employee needs
Autocratic or bureaucratic leadership
Low quality of work life
Lack of management appreciation of work or skills
Management perceived as uncaring
Major changes without employee input

"management." Unless an organization's leadership style is to some degree participative, its employees see the playing field as tilted against them. They perceive themselves as powerless victims under the thumbs of uncaring managers.

Employee gripes expressed as monetary ones and directed against top management—the "they"—may really be based on dissatisfaction with their immediate boss. Supervisors often fail to realize that because employees rarely can bring themselves to confront their supervisor and say that the problem is the supervisor. A list of reasons why employees join unions is given in Table I.

The Union Organizing Drive

In the event of a union drive, team leaders selected by the teams—unlike supervisors who are appointed by management—would be regarded by the union as another employee of the work group, not as an exempt supervisor. If there is no formal team supervisor, the role of that person would probably be the manager to whom the team reports. That person is also referred to in this chapter as the supervisor. Supervisors are the bridge between employees and their employers, and they are often targeted for assault by labor unions during a union drive.

The Union Contract

Shortly after a union has been certified, an initial contract is negotiated. The contract covers union recognition, management rights, compensation and benefits, seniority and employee rights, job-related factors such as security and safety, duration of the agreement, and grievance procedures.

At best, the union contract can set forth only the broad outline of labor-management relationships. The supervisor through daily decisions and actions gives the contract real meaning. Therefore, the supervisor must be familiar with the contract and do things that are consistent with it. All supervisors and team leaders should receive intensive training in labor agreements.

It takes time for the ill feelings created during the organizing campaign to disappear. The introduction of a union into a health care facility may be a traumatic experience for supervisors. Gradually, however, the union and the administration learn to accommodate each other.[4] The unit may break into cliques, one supportive of and the other antagonistic toward the steward and the union.

Union-Management Relationships

Management must be careful not to authorize teams or committees to represent other employees (as sham unions once did) or to obstruct union representation. Teams, committees, or quality circles cannot get involved in areas that are mandatorily bargainable under the law, such as wages, hours, working conditions, or benefits. Management should make every effort to work with the union to break down barriers and to include the union in revising mission statements, planning strategies, and clarifying expectations. Any attempt to withhold information or to circumvent union participation in change will be perceived as being anti-union and will erode union-management cooperation.

THE UNION REPRESENTATIVE

The labor steward supplements what the supervisor should have been doing in the first place.[3]
John A. Patton

The union representative is the first-line official of the union and is called a steward, a departmental committee member, or some other term. These people normally remain employees of the health care facility. Stewards are elected by the employees they represent. They may or may not be the informal leaders of the groups and often get the job because they are the only ones who want it. The steward may not be popular and is often someone who has been a highly vocal critic.

This obviously is a difficult position since the steward has to serve two masters. As employees, they have to follow the supervisor's orders and directives; as union officials, they have responsibilities to fellow coworkers. Supervisors must appreciate the political agenda under which the steward functions.

Certain privileges of the steward may be specified in the union contract, such as how much time on the job the steward can devote to union business and whether collection of dues may be carried on during working hours.

Stewards often want to be perceived as partners with the supervisors in running the unit. They must be able to convince the employees that they are reliable and that the union will protect its members. They are usually well informed as to the content of the contract, management's obligations, and employees' rights. The most important responsibility of the steward is in relation to complaints and grievances of employees. In grievance matters, the steward challenges management decisions or actions, while the supervisor must justify what was done.[4]

The steward may antagonize the supervisor. It is all too easy to perceive the steward as a hindrance to getting employees to respond or as a competitor for their loyalty. Supervisors may find their authority constantly being challenged by a steward who is always second-guessing what they plan to do and questioning the intent of their actions.

THE CHANGE IN GROUP RELATIONSHIPS

The immediate supervisor or team leader has the greatest responsibility for seeing that the clauses of the union agreement are carried out. The manner in which the day-to-day problems are handled within the framework of the union contract will make the difference between positive labor-management relations and a situation filled with tensions and bad feelings.

The supervisor or team leader must now perform the managerial duties within the framework of the union agreement. The union agreement limits some managerial activities, especially assignments and disciplinary actions.[4] Relationships with employees may become more formal. Contract clauses may affect cooperation and teamwork. Rigid rules may regulate relationships. To some workers a "fair day's work" has come to mean doing the least amount of work that is acceptable.

Reward systems may be affected. Unions attempt to equalize everyone and to have personnel decisions based on seniority rather than performance. Cross-training and job rotation may be inhibited because unions often insist on rigid position descriptions that lead to employees refusing to carry out certain tasks.

When supervisors are intensely disliked by their associates, the latter can team up with their union representatives to get rid of them. They simply overwhelm the supervisors with grievances, many of which are bogus. Then they refuse to accept the supervisors' adjudication, thus moving the grievance up the chain of command. When that continues, upper management grows tired of supporting the supervisors and either transfers or fires them.

GETTING ALONG WITH THE UNION REPRESENTATIVE

Establish good rapport with the union representative. Some managers and group leaders are intimidated and others become emotional when their decisions or actions are challenged, feeling that their wisdom or fairness is in question.

Communication between the supervisor and the steward should be free and open. Notify your steward when anything extraordinary occurs so the steward can trust you. Be available and listen patiently.[4] Some supervisors use stewards as sounding boards, which is not a bad idea. However, frequent social contacts outside work or friendships on the job may undermine the steward's credibility with the workers. Seasoned supervisors take great care not to give the impression that they are undermining the steward's authority or relationship with the union members. Remember that the steward is under pressure from the employees who want to get their money's worth for their dues.

Whenever site visits are scheduled, union representatives should be included. Union input should be solicited at team planning and problem solving meetings. When teams have hiring and firing authority, union input must be obtained to ensure that contracts will not be violated.

AREAS OF SUPERVISORY DIFFICULTY IMPOSED BY UNION CONTRACTS

These include disciplinary action, assignment of work, and distribution of overtime, as well as questions of promotion, transfer, and downgrading. Another area of difficulty involves problems in which a member of the management team is called on to interpret a clause of the contract. In such instances, supervisors and team leaders should consult higher authorities because such a decision may set a precedent. Also, if a grievance goes to arbitration, the arbitrator will attach great importance to precedents set by supervisors.

COMPLAINTS AND GRIEVANCES

The proper adjustment of grievances is one of the important responsibilities of team leaders and supervisors. A grievance is a formal, typically written charge based on real or imagined feelings of injustice. It often results from a misunderstanding, misinterpretation, or violation of a provision of the labor agreement.

Steps in Handling Grievances

Step 1. An employee registers a complaint—with or without the assistance of the union representative—with the supervisor.

Step 2. If the problem is not resolved by the supervisor, the employee and/or the union representative present the grievance to the next higher level, usually the department head.

Step 3. The grievance, with the support of the union's chief steward, business agent or union president, or grievance committee, is presented to senior management.

Step 4. If the dispute cannot be settled by the first three steps, the issue may be submitted to an outside arbitrator who hears testimony and renders a final and binding decision.

The Role of the Supervisor or Team Leader

The supervisor must be readily available to the steward and to the aggrieved employee. Availability does not mean just being physically present but also requires that one be approachable and ready to listen with an open mind. The supervisor must learn to define the problem, get the facts, and review the appropriate clauses of the contract. The supervisor must be well qualified in handling complaints and settling grievances. The supervisor gets all the facts as quickly as possible because the grievance procedure usually sets a time limit within which the grievance must be answered. It is also wise to settle grievances early, before they grow larger, become contagious, or fester internally.

If it is impossible for the supervisor to obtain the necessary facts at once, the aggrieved parties must be informed, instead of leaving them under the impression that they are getting the runaround. If a delay cannot be avoided, the grievance should be reduced to writing and signed by the steward and the employee so they do not forget what is involved.

Provisions in the contract are reviewed when any reference to a violation of it is made. Most organizations require that supervisors check and consult with a labor relations specialist in the personnel department when handling formal grievances. Major facts can be gleaned by asking pertinent questions of the complaining employee and others. The supervisor seeks answers to the questions of who, what, when, where, and why.

Empathetic listening by the supervisor is likely to minimize hostilities and tensions during the settlement of the case. The supervisor must give the steward and the employees a chance to say whatever they have on their minds and take great caution not to get angry. The supervisor must clearly summarize what has been presented and must know how deeply to delve to get at the root of the situation and to summarize its disposition. The supervisor should not come up with a decision that is not consistent with previous decisions because this exception is likely to become a precedent. Table II lists some practical tips when responding to grievances.

Records

Unless required, a written reply to the grievance should not be rendered. If such a reply is required by the labor agreement, then it is appropriate for the supervisor to discuss all the implications with higher management or with the personnel department so that a properly worded reply is available.

Table II
Practical Tips for Responding to Grievances

Seek win/win solutions (see Chapter 23 on conflict).

Be willing to compromise.

Try to determine what the real or most important issue is and if there is a hidden agenda.

Try to narrow differences by establishing as much agreement as possible.

Overcome stalemates by settling easy things first.

Demonstrate that you can hold your own without using trickery or pressure.

Never threaten or embarrass the union representative.

Know when to break off a discussion that is starting to heat up—do not lose your cool.

Do not give the impression that you can only say no or must always check with your superiors. The union representative and the employees will feel that they are wasting their time with you.

Keep records whenever a formal grievance decision has been made. If the employee's request is satisfied, this decision will probably become a precedent. If the complaint cannot be settled in the first step, it is risky for the supervisor to defend the action by depending on memory. Indeed, good records are an absolute necessity because the burden of proof is usually on the supervisor. Management has the right to decide, but the union has the right to grieve.[4]

KEEPING EMPLOYEE TEAMS LEGAL

Some risk exists of employee teams being ruled illegal labor organizations. The basis for such challenges may be the following:

- The team or committee is employer-dominated.

- The group deals with wages, hours, benefits, grievances, or other conditions of employment.

- Meetings appear to involve negotiations between employees and management.

- Participation is mandatory.

- The employer picks the members or controls the method of their selection.[5]

How to Stay Out of Legal Trouble

Stay out of legal trouble by observing a few simple guidelines:

- Avoid the conditions listed above.
- Make service voluntary.
- Teams concentrate on projects and issues that are mutually beneficial to both management and workers.
- Avoid topics that could be construed as negotiations over terms and conditions of employment.
- Do not establish such committees or teams in the wake of a union organizing drive.
- Do not let meetings degenerate into gripe sessions that focus on conditions of employment.

REFERENCES

1. McConnell CR. *The Effective Health Care Supervisor.* 2nd ed. Gaithersburg, Md: Aspen Publishers; 1988.
2. Harrington-Mackin D. *The Team Building Tool Kit.* New York, NY: AMACOM; 1994.
3. Patton JA. Managers and productivity. *Manage Rev.* 1982;71:13.
4. Haimann T. *Supervisory Management for Health Care Organizations.* 3rd ed. St. Louis, Mo: Catholic Health Association of the US; 1994.
5. McConnell CR. Getting maximum value from employee teams—and keeping them legal. *Health Care Supervis.* 1994;13:66-73.

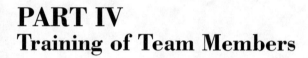

PART IV
Training of Team Members

20. Training Team Members

LACK OF EFFECTIVE training is the number one barrier to successful team implementation.[1]
Richard S. Wellins

CHAPTER OBJECTIVES

- To equate team training with workstation education
- To describe the benefits of team training
- To elucidate the role of management in training programs
- To explain how to perform a job analysis
- To emphasize the importance of the timing of training
- To list training sources, tools, and topics
- To provide guidelines for trainers
- To present a six-step approach for apprentice-type training
- To counsel coaches on cross-training and leadership training
- To characterize an effective orientation program for new employees

Team building requires intense and continuing education and training. The greater the responsibility, authority, and independence assumed by teams, the greater their training needs. A good example of this is the bedside testing or point-of-care service, where teams of employees perform multiple dissimilar functions of patient care.

BACK TO APPRENTICESHIPS

The old-fashioned apprenticeship that aimed to create a well-rounded craftsperson was replaced long ago by competency-based training that focused on identifying and training workers for only the skills that were directly related to a particular job. Training for self-directed teams turns the clock back to those apprenticeship days. Now our basic premise is that each team member learns all of the jobs in the team and sometimes other job skills beyond their own team—back to the well-rounded craftsperson.[2]

Job-specific technical and professional training is provided to ensure that jobs can be rotated among team members. In addition to learning how to do other team members' jobs, participating employees may have to learn some or all of the supervisory and administrative functions previously performed by first-line managers. In other words, members of successful self-directed teams now receive more training than did their old supervisors before they took over unit leadership.

Because team building often is concomitant with other major changes, such as new technologies, quality improvement, cultural diversity, accommodations for mentally or physically challenged new employees, downsizing, mergers, and acquisitions, the need for continuing education burgeons. For self-directed work teams, training is an ongoing and unending process. In some organizations, team members spend 15% to 20% of their time in training.[1]

BENEFITS OF TRAINING

Training not only enhances job and team performance, it is also fundamental to empowerment. A comprehensive training program sends the message that management is really serious about empowerment and team building. Management's commitment of time and resources to training makes a far bigger impression on team members than mere speeches.[1]

Another advantage of a good training program is that entry-level workers can be hired and trained for more challenging jobs. Underqualified candidates are more numerous than qualified ones, and when they develop competency they have higher morale and retention rates. Personnel costs are lower and turnover is reduced. Some laboratories hire high school graduates as testing personnel. Under CLIA '88, a high school graduate with appropriate training may perform tests of moderate complexity.[3]

Organizations use simulations because experience is a powerful teacher. Team simulation games, either outdoor experiential exercises, such as wilderness survival, or indoor exercises that mimic practical work situations, help to develop trust and cohesion within teams as well as to build specific skills, such as how to give feedback and deal with conflict resolution.[4] Simulations can also be used as assessments of existing teams.

MANAGEMENT'S ROLE

The team concept will work if management supports not only a training program but also the implementation of what team members learn. Organizational structure, policies, and practices often inadvertently undermine the behaviors management seeks. For example, when participants of training seminars return to their work stations they often find that they lack the time or managerial support to apply what they have learned.

Management must provide direction (goals, standards, strategy), knowledge (skills, information, feedback), resources (facilities, supplies, time), and support (coaching, encouragement, protection). Team coaches must know not only the skills and competencies of each team member, but also what additional training each individual needs to reach his or her full capability. This necessitates the use of a skills inventory chart of some type, preferably maintained on a computer.

WHO DETERMINES SPECIFIC TRAINING NEEDS?

The input of the person to whom the employee reports should have great weight in determining training needs. This person initially is the supervisor-in-transition and later the team leader in consultation with other team members, customers, and anyone else who affects the person's job (eg, systems experts, suppliers, higher management, and the organization).[5]

JOB ANALYSIS

The most logical starting place for a training effort is a job analysis that identifies the job dimensions for team members. These dimensions serve as content or curriculum areas around which to develop training. A job analysis generates a list of the behaviors, technical knowledge, skills, and motivational areas that differentiate between successful and unsuccessful performers. A good analysis establishes a clearly defined set of job requirements. If these requirements are used for the evaluation of job applicants, they are dimensions against which candidates can be compared. A dimension is a description under which specific behavior, knowledge, or motivation elements that are associated with job success can be classified reliably.[1]

IN-HOUSE RÉSUMÉS

You may want to supplement each team member's employment résumé with one that provides information that is useful in determining what additional training is needed or desired by the incumbent. An in-house résumé briefly describes the person's education, training, and special skills. It answers questions that determine how the person feels about working in groups, helping in orienting or teaching others, task rotation, supervisory or administrative responsibilities, and committee or brainstorming assignments. It lists their current and long-range goals.

TIMING OF TEAM TRAINING

Team training usually starts with the executives and cascades down the ladder.[6] Skills and competencies are not all learned at once but can be taught over a period of months or years. Ideally, the just-in-time approach is used, where the training is provided as close in time as possible to the actual use of the new skill. Much training is rendered useless because the participants do not have an opportunity to put the new skill to work right after it has been learned. Spaced training works better than massed training, ie, training four hours a week for ten weeks is more effective than a solid week of intensive training.

TEACHING SOURCES AND TOOLS

Many team-building or quality-improvement initiatives start with benchmarking—when managers and workers visit sites of successful self-directed work teams. Such visits are also helpful after programs have been started. These visits not only provide a wealth of practical information, they also inject enthusiasm into the visiting team, something that is invaluable when spirits sag.

Formal programs make use of consultants, commercial teaching programs, seminars, and printed handouts. It is not enough to send people to outside training courses or to bring in temporary trainers. The role of trainer must exist as a full-time and permanent component of the team-building endeavor.[7]

Instruments such as the Myers-Briggs Type Indicator for self-awareness training and personal growth are often useful.[8] "Excel," "Outward Bound," and other outside adventure offerings help to build team spirit and interdependence. A department training center that consists of appropriate books, handbooks, journals, videotapes or audiotapes, catalogs, procedure manuals, and other educational materials is highly recommended.

Associates, staff people, and superiors are invaluable sources of informal learning. Organizations can create opportunities for new employees to talk with and observe others by encouraging mentoring programs that match rookies with veterans, holding substantive meetings, and establishing multifaceted educational programs.

TRAINING TOPICS

Skills vs Competencies

Skills and competencies are different, and both should be addressed in training programs. Skills are how-to-do procedures and techniques, such as how to draw a blood specimen. Competencies integrate knowledge, attitude, and skill, such as the ability to make decisions regarding ethical behavior or to cope with emotionally disturbed patients. Skills are specific to certain situations, whereas competencies have generic, broad applicability.[9]

The training need must be perceived by the recipients as important, and they should have a major say in what they receive and perhaps in who should provide the training. Training for teams consists of three major categories: (1) professional competencies and technical skills, (2) team and interactive skills, and (3) administrative/supervisory competencies.

If employees at lower levels are to make decisions, they need not only job skills but also teamwork skills and decision-making skills, as well as skill in managing their time and the company's resources.[10]
    David E. Bowen

Professional competencies and technical skills are those capabilities that relate to task performance and consist largely of what other members do. Cross-training, teaching, and coaching are used in the training process. One goal of most self-directed work teams is that each team member will learn all of the routine technical or professional tasks that the team performs. This may include using and repairing special equipment, quality control measures, and troubleshooting. In the case of special projects, team members may perform tasks usually handled by other departments. For example, in point-of-care hospital services, nurses may assume the additional roles of phlebotomists and radiology assistants.

Team and interactive competencies include one-on-one communication, handling conflict, influencing others, and understanding the dynamics of team building and function. See Table I for a list of these competencies.

All too often, organizations spend considerable training dollars developing the task skills (how to set up and run meetings) and pay little attention to the relationship competencies that fundamentally make or break a team.[11]

Administrative/supervisory competencies are all the managerial activities that self-directed work teams inherit from their supervisors. The administrative component concentrates on forms, procedures, record keeping, purchasing, payroll matters, and other paperwork. The supervisory element consists of activities involving directing or controlling the activities of other people. See Table II for a list of these competencies.

Table I
Team Maintenance and Membership Competencies

Differences in temperaments and personalities
Meeting and negotiating skills
Communication skills
Giving and receiving positive and negative feedback
Assertiveness and self-awareness
Stress and time management
Cultural diversity
How to operate and repair equipment
Handling conflict and confrontation
Presentation skills
Influencing others without using authority
Computer literacy
Coping with difficult people

Table II
Administrative/Supervisory Competencies

Decision making
Problem identification and solving
Project planning and implementation
Quality improvement tools and techniques
Process analysis and work flow improvement
Selecting candidates and equipment
Project initiation and proposal writing
Presentation skills
Identifying customer expectations
Working with customers, suppliers, and others
Negotiating skills
Budgeting and cost control
Customer satisfaction
Just-in-time principles of inventory control
Evaluating team and individual performances
Selecting and training new team members
Safety measures
Meeting skills
Conflict management
Managing and sustaining the change dynamic

Table III
How to Evaluate Your Current Training Program

Examine current practices and systems
Determine why real behavior is not ideal
Study performance reviews
Test skills
Define desired level of performance
Define performance gap
Establish specific abilities employees are expected to gain
Determine whether or not training is needed
Ensure that the trainers understand the needs
Discuss the training needs with the trainers
Make certain that the employees know why they are being trained

TRAINING GUIDELINES

Tell me and I'll forget. Show me and I'll understand. Involve me and I'll remember.

> Old Chinese Proverb

Evaluate the Present State of Affairs

Before you know where to go, you must know where you are. The first step is to review and appraise your current programs. Table III lists specific things to research.

Choose the Right Trainers

Trainers are selected carefully. They should be individuals who are respected by the trainees, have the necessary skill, enjoy sharing their expertise, are provided with sufficient time and support, and have a positive attitude toward the team building or partnership initiative. As much as possible, the training is given by team leaders and members. Informal peer training is usually better than formal education because the recipients are more receptive and the material is on target.

Set Group Rules for the Formal Training Sessions

Formal group training is planned carefully with team leaders and members conferring with trainers about subject matter and schedules. The material is presented in an adult learning style with major input from the participants. Department heads get frequent progress reports. Educational meetings are given high priority, with attendance being given precedence over most other activities. Titles and beepers are left at the door!

SIX-STEP APPROACH FOR ONE-ON-ONE PEER TRAINING

The six-step approach for one-on-one peer training is based on an old practical learning sequence: find out what they know, tell them, show them, let them tell and show, and then make them practice until competent.

Step 1: Explain the purpose and importance of what you are teaching. Ensure that the trainee recognizes the need for the skill and wants help. Describe how the skill will make the work easier or more interesting. Show how it correlates with other areas of responsibility and relates to the team's efforts.

Step 2: Define a goal for the training process. After determining the trainee's present skill level and agreeing on what is needed, establish a training goal and estimate a time needed to reach that level of competency.

Step 3: Develop a plan. Decide on how the material is to be presented. If it is a complicated skill, break it down into segments.

Step 4: Explain the teaching process and tools to be used.

Step 5: Demonstrate how the task is done. Use a variety of methods to communicate the steps involved in doing the job right. Recognize the neurolinguistic preference of the learner. Auditory learners want to hear the instructions; visual learners prefer documented procedures or visual aids; kinesthetic learners want hands-on experience.

Step 6: Observe and coach. Establish two-way feedback. Encourage the trainee to ask questions. Be ready to repeat. Provide specific feedback on what you observe. Go light on the criticism. Negative feedback only confirms people's initial expectation that they are incapable of doing the task successfully.

Use mistakes as opportunities to clarify concepts and improve performance. Praise every sign of increased comprehension and skill. Give lots of positive feedback and minimal negative feedback. Never ridicule, reprimand, or use sarcasm. Be patient. Provide sufficient practice time. Encourage trainees to use their new skills.

THE FOLLOW-UP

The efficacy of a training program should be evaluated in terms of the application of skills on the job. Ratings by trainees immediately after a training session are often misleading. Participants should be surveyed a month or more afterward to see how the skills are being applied.[1] The best way to tell whether a training session has succeeded is to use the same measurements you defined earlier for performance expectations.

Trainees may get enthusiastic about a formal program but find it difficult or impossible to implement at work, either because they failed to discuss with colleagues what they learned and how it could be implemented or because of resistance from colleagues or superiors. This problem can be minimized if the managers receive the same training, participate actively in the planning process, and make a greater effort to support the necessary changes.

CROSS-TRAINING

In cross-training, employees learn to do each other's jobs. This works best when employees have the time, interest, and ability to share knowledge. It is a form of apprenticeship training.

Rotation of work stations provides employees with an opportunity not only to learn a variety of competencies but also to have a helicopter view of the unit's operations. Such rotations can be in the form of refresher courses for more senior employees. The increasing rate of technical obsolescence makes such endeavors even more important.

To facilitate cross-training, team members can take responsibility for their training program through the use of a skill inventory chart. New team members usually start in "doer" roles—performing routine and then special technical or professional tasks. The cross-training continues until the employee can perform a range of tasks. Post opportunities for cross-training in your department.

Advantages of Cross-Training

- When problems arise, cross-trained employees are better equipped to brainstorm and find solutions.
- With cross-trained teams, supervisors can spend less time solving problems and more time preventing them.
- Absenteeism is less disruptive because another worker is able to step in and do the job of the person who is absent.
- Since cross-training, almost by definition, creates teams, it gives management the option to make more extensive use of them.

LEADERSHIP TRAINING

An appropriate period of skill enhancement helps supervisors-in-transition appreciate the effort that will be required to make self-directed teams function effectively. It will also alleviate some of the pride and self-esteem issues that arise when supervisors and hourly staff are first blended as a team.[11]

Since supervisors will be switching from directive roles to those of coaching and facilitating, they require competencies in encouraging initiative, coaching for success, reinforcing effective performance, overcoming resistance to change, managing conflict, and developing collaborative relationships. Some of them must learn how to change from micromanaging to

Table IV
Orientation Topics for Team Leaders

Study of vision, mission, and value statements of organization and team

Meeting members of staff, leaders of other work teams, superiors, and other key personnel

Review of quality assurance, budgetary, and leadership programs

Review of policies, practices, and work processes

Discussion of operational and personnel problems

Duties and responsibilities not listed in the position description

Overview of educational programs

Establishing or updating a filing system

Listing all reports and due dates

Preparing an employee skill inventory chart

Developing an action plan

empowering and facilitating. Their skills in performance appraisal, feedback, discipline, and achieving commitment to goals must be updated. Leaders must learn to be change masters and master delegators. In addition, they are expected to deliver some of the team training. Thus, basic instructional techniques should be part of their repertoire.

In organizations that use a rotating team leader position or have no formal team leader, every team member may be expected to acquire some team leadership skills.

When a team member or someone from the outside is hired as the team leader, he or she should have the benefit of an orientation program that is more comprehensive than that provided other new employees. All too often, the new leader actually receives less. Table IV lists some of the special items that should be included in such an orientation program.

ORIENTATION OF NEW EMPLOYEES

Because we've always done it this way' isn't the right answer when a new employee asks questions.[3]
    Catherine A. Hargrove

Strike early! It is important to make new employees part of the team as soon as possible. This is the best opportunity to open lines of communication with new hires. They are free from the distortions of peer groups, they have not yet formed strong opinions about the job, and they are so eager to please. Yet the indoctrination process is often abbreviated because of the fact that new arrivals come on board when the department is short-staffed.

Even when new hires are experienced, they need to learn the policies, procedures, computer system, and specific types of instrumentation. Your goal is to help them see their jobs as contributions to the organization's total impact on the customer. Early on, the new arrivals should be shown how what they do is part of a chain reaction in the servicing of customers.

Create a welcoming environment for all new employees. Convince them that they are part of an elite team made up of winners and that they have been selected because they are considered to be winners too. Stress the accomplishments of the team. Ensure their early successes by assigning them tasks you know they can handle. Make them feel that they are contributing.

Who Does the Orienting?

The training of new team members is usually shared by the team members, although in some instances having the new member work one-on-one with a senior team member is preferable.

Give Them the Big Picture

Tell them the history of the organization, its mission, values, strategic and operational goals, strategies, and plans. Identify the various customers and discuss policies, rituals, and ethics.

One Step at a Time

Trying to teach new employees everything that each team member eventually can do is usually foolhardy. The employees are overwhelmed and forget much of what they learn because they do not have the opportunity to put all the new knowledge to use. It is much better to spread the training out over a longer period of time.

Take the time and effort to assess the knowledge and skill needs of each individual. Avoid the "cookie-cutter" approach. Checklists are highly recommended. After technical and professional responsibilities have been learned, new team members are introduced into team leadership roles.

Do Not Destroy Their Creativity in Favor of Conformity

During orientation programs, a tendency exists to emphasize conformity at the expense of creativity. Trainers must respond kindly to questions about why the procedures being taught are different from those they learned elsewhere. Put-downs such as, "You're not working at the Mayo Clinic now. Just do it our way and you'll get along fine," will discourage new employees from voicing opinions or challenging processes. It does not do much for their self-esteem either.

REFERENCES

1. Wellins RS, Byham WC, Wilson JM. *Empowered Teams: Creating Self-Directed Work Groups That Improve Quality, Productivity, and Participation.* San Francisco, Calif: Jossey-Bass Inc; 1991.

2. Hamilton C. Training is a vital link in the process. *HR Focus.* 1992;69:4-5.

3. Hargrove CA. Developing a more effective training program. *MLO.* 1993;25:50-56.

4. Geber B. Let the games begin. *Training.* 1994;31:10-15.

5. Byham WC. *Zapp! The Lightning of Empowerment.* New York, NY: Harmony Books; 1988.

6. Geber B. From manager into coach. *Training.* 1992;29:25-31.

7. Thompson PC. *Quality Circles: How to Make Them Work in America.* New York, NY: AMACOM; 1982.

8. Haddox CE. MBTI's value. *Training.* 1992;29:21.

9. Parry S. The missing 'M' in TQM. *Training.* 1993;30:29-41.

10. Bowen DE, Lawler EE III. Total quality-oriented human resources management. *Organizational Dynamics.* 1992;20:29-41.

11. Harrington-Mackin D. *The Team Building Tool Kit.* New York, NY: AMACOM; 1994.

21. Power Communication: The Foundation of Team

HE CORNERSTONE OF participative management is communication.[1]
    Frank Sonnenberg

CHAPTER OBJECTIVES

- To emphasize the importance of multifaceted and multidirectional communication
- To explore the important facets of communication
- To list the reasons why some verbal messages lack power
- To critique constructive feedback
- To articulate the three essentials of effective listening
- To point out the importance of nonverbal communication
- To list suggestions for better verbal skills
- To recommend when to write and when to talk; when to use a memo and when to write a letter
- To advise on how to answer complaints
- To provide practical tips for improving writing skill
- To summarize the current use of computers at the workplace

Vertical, horizontal, and diagonal communication are needed to implement any strategy for quality improvement, personnel empowerment, and process reengineering. Interdepartmental communication is increasingly important because greater coordination among services, departments, and units is necessary in providing comprehensive, time-saving, cost-saving, and even life-saving service. Improved customer service demands this.

The increasing complexity and scattered distribution of units of health care institutions strains our communication systems. Fortunately, this is balanced by the availability of new or improved communication tools. Voice mail, answering machines, electronic mail, beepers, cellular phones, audio and videotapes, television, and computer systems have affected how we provide service and education. Microcomputers and cellular telephone connections should be available to key personnel to establish an interconnected network.

COMMUNICATION BY LEADERS

The three purposes of downward communication in the workplace are to express what you want done, to persuade the people to carry out what you want done, and to keep people informed.

Directive (command) messages must be clear, concise, and easy to understand. They should express not only what actions are to be carried out but also where, when, and sometimes how.

Information messages are customized to meet specific needs. Newsletters or brief notes on bulletin boards are not enough. Employees are more interested in people news, especially when it concerns people they know. An announcement that their organization is building a satellite in another town elicits shoulder shrugs, but news that someone in their department has been promoted gets lots of comments.

Electronic bulletin boards and voice mail are effective communication channels. Desktop publishing provides another convenient modality for providing knowledge and personal information to employees. Modern databases allow information previously available only to management to be made widely accessible.

The two most important verbal communication skills for team leaders are the abilities to listen empathically and to ask high-gain questions.

Good communication is more than good enunciation, careful phraseology, and eye contact. It is listening for feelings as well as for content. It is letting teammates know that they have the right to express their opinions and feelings, that those opinions and feelings are expected and will be acknowledged.

Why Some Verbal Messages Lack Power

- The sender is perceived as lacking expertise or has a history of manipulation, waffling, or deceit.
- Too many links in the communication chain. It has been estimated that information loses 20% of its meaning with each transfer.[2]

- Poor choice of words or phrases. Here are some of the big offenders:

  Using questions to make requests, eg, "Would you like to help me with this?"

  Using fillers like "ya know," or "uh."

  Listener does not comprehend the words. The influx of employees who do not speak English has created problems for many employers.

- The senders are too passive or timid. They are guilty of:

  Inserting self-deprecating words, eg, "This is probably a stupid question, but...."

  Articulating weak verbs or qualifiers, eg, "I wonder if we should..." or "I sort of believe that...."

  Tolerating interruptions without objecting.

  Hesitant or tentative delivery, defensive posture, or lack of enthusiasm.

- The listener fails to listen or the sender does not listen to the responses of the listener.

The Essentials of Constructive Feedback (Criticism)

Managers often avoid giving negative feedback because they fear the possible conflict it may evoke. They wait for others to do it for them, or they hope the condition will self-correct. Feedback must be consistent. If you emphasize quality on Monday and demand faster turnaround time on Tuesday, you will induce frustration and stress.

The goal of criticism is to improve performance, not to humiliate or humble others. Criticism is rarely welcome, and calling it advice or suggestions does not alter that. Here are some practical tips:

- Before criticizing, consider your objective and take a realistic view of the likelihood that what you are to say will achieve that objective. If that likelihood is slim, it is probably not worth the effort unless this is the first step in a disciplinary series of actions. Picture a distraught mother yelling at a teenage son about his messy bedroom. How many times has she done this and how effective has it been?

- Criticize as soon as possible after the deed, but not while you or the other person is upset. Do not gunnysack. Gunnysacking is failing to articulate feelings about a person's behavior until one dark day when all these stored emotions erupt—often following a minor provocation.

- Be certain that the person understands why a change is needed, eg, "Callers feel that we don't think they're important when they're kept waiting on the phone."

- Make the discussion a dialogue between adults, not a parent/child kind of verbal transaction. Express empathy and when appropriate be tentative or flexible. Limit the session to one item.

- Make certain that the person knows what you want.

- Do not attempt to soften the impact by sandwiching criticism between slices of irrelevant or unearned praise. The recipient will either be confused or will feel manipulated. Do link positive and negative comments when there is relevance. For example, "Edna, I rely on you to help me with these emergency requests. You're so good at getting things organized and enlisting the help of others. I would appreciate it even more if it were not accompanied by grumbling or remarks about being taken advantage of."

- When dealing with a peer or someone who has a quick temper, it may be helpful to express your opinion in a nonjudgmental context. For example, "Louise, I'm not suggesting that you are doing anything wrong, but how do you think others perceive derogatory remarks about our CEO made in public?"

- Express your confidence in the ability of the person to perform up to your expectations: "Joe, the fact that I have brought up this matter shows that I know you can do something about it—not all people can."

- When necessary, provide the training needed by the person.

- Feedback fails when you do not make a special effort to observe the person's subsequent performance. Concentrate on achievement rather than failure. Support improvement with a smile and a pat on the back. Do not wait until the performance has reached the target level. Reinforce each small step with recognition and praise.

Avoid the following:

- Absolute terms such as never, always, or without fail, eg, "I can never rely on you," or "You are always late for our meetings."

- Asking why when you really mean you shouldn't have, eg, "Why do you keep interrupting me?"

- The word but. Instead of "Your reports are on time, but they often lack clarity," say "Your reports are on time, and I appreciate that. Now let's try to work on their clarity."

- "You" language. This focuses on the person instead of on the behavior. "We would appreciate more sharing of responsibility," is less likely to elicit defensive reactions than "You don't seem willing to share responsibility."

- Giving advice that is not requested or that is not within your area of expertise. For example, unless you are a professional counselor, refer people to your employee assistance program (EAP) or to other qualified persons.

- Criticizing when you or the other person is upset.

TEAM COMMUNICATION

Communication is the nervous system of teams. It is even more important for health care teams because these groups are often under extreme stress and operate in circumstances that have a confusing array of communication senders and receivers. Messages sent under these conditions often confuse, anger, or humiliate the recipients. One of the quickest ways to destroy morale is to withhold information from the workers.

Poor communication leads to conflict and unhappy relationships with clients. Patient surveys show that many patients are dissatisfied with the communication they have with health professionals. Interruptions, poor listening, use of professional jargon, and a lack of concern or respect are frequently cited.[3]

Any change that improves communication will have beneficial effects. A hospital venipuncture team improved its turnaround time and quality of service by implementing voice communication technology through the use of two-way headsets.[4]

Employees for whom English is a second language must be educated to the point where they can understand the information on signs and in newsletters, memos, and at meetings.

LISTENING SKILL

Poor listening is the most frequent cause of communication failures. Despite all the recent emphasis on the importance of active listening in interpersonal relationships, most of us are still atrocious listeners. We listen reasonably well to people who outrank us or whom we respect or fear. We tend not to listen to spouses, children, and people who lack equivalent education or prestige.

Empathetic listeners listen with their eyes as well as their ears, and they tune in on feelings as well as content. This requires that one listen to what is said, what is not said, and how the person is saying it.

The Three Essentials of Effective Listening

1. Look like you are listening. Avoid furniture between you and the other person. Face the speaker, lean forward without wiggling, or stand upright without shifting weight from one foot to the other. Look relaxed and interested. Establish and maintain eye-to-face contact without staring down the other person. Use facial expressions, frowns, smiles, raised eyebrows, head shakes and nods, and gestures as appropriate.

2. Sound attentive. Use phrases such as "Uh-huh," "Go on," "I see," or "Tell me more." Ask open-ended questions relating to both content and feelings.

3. Prove that you have received and understand the message. Interpret the message using your own words to indicate content and feelings, eg, "What I hear you saying is…and that you felt humiliated, is that right?" Summarize frequently if the message is lengthy or complicated.

The Power of Silence

Most people are embarrassed by silence. It is as if they do not want to give up their air time, so they insert a host of "ya knows" or "uhhhhs." Silent pauses have several advantages. They provide opportunities to prepare what you are going to say next, minimize slips of the tongue, and encourage the other person to speak up. Silence is a great way to get people to reveal what is on their minds when they are reluctant to speak up. This powerful tool is used by psychiatrists and experienced interviewers.

The Importance of Body Language

How you say something and the accompanying body language often determine whether or not you get the responses you seek. Parents provide good examples. "John, stop teasing your sister," expressed in a whining, exasperated tone gets little response, but the same message delivered in a loud stern voice is more likely to be effective.

Mehrabian[5] found that the words themselves account for less than 10% of the emotional impact of verbal messages. Voice quality (pitch, volume, rate, and enunciation) and nonverbal messages (facial expression, eye contact, gestures, and posture) account for over 90% of the impact.

Tips for Better Verbal Communication

- Control emotions—yours and theirs.
- Make certain that your voice, facial expressions, and body language are congruent with your words.
- Mirror the volume and rate of the other person's voice.
- When in doubt, check it out. Rephrase or repeat as needed.
- Personalize by using their names.
- Always be polite and respectful.
- Do say how you feel about it.
- Ask open-ended questions, eg, "How can I help?"
- Insist on feedback to ensure understanding.
- Establish facts with specific details.
- Try to anticipate the impact of your message.
- Avoid distractions and interruptions.

Practical Workplace Writing Skill

Written vs Oral Messages

Verbal communication is usually faster, provides more opportunity for dialogue, and transmits nonverbal as well as verbal messages. On the other hand, written messages can mute hostility or emotion, are more permanent, are less likely to contain errors, provide proof, and can be reviewed at will. They are prepared when it is convenient for the sender, and read at the convenience of the receiver. Important verbal messages should be substantiated by written reports.

Memo or Letter?

Memos are letters in shirtsleeves. They comprise the most common type of in-house written communication. A good general rule is that anything that requires a stamp should be a letter.

Memos, like meetings, are overutilized in many institutions. Many memos are poorly prepared and suffer from lack of clarity. In many instances the recipients do not know what, if anything, is expected of them. Is the purpose for information only or is some action on the recipients' part required? Do use memos to clarify verbal messages.

How to Answer Complaints

Supervisors and team leaders may have to respond to complaints from external or internal customers. Start with an apology to deflate anger, if an apology is indicated, but avoid culpability statements. For example, "I'm sorry that you had a problem with our service," is better than "I'm sorry that our receptionist was rude to you." If a danger exists of legal action against your organization or personnel, turn the complaint over to your risk manager or legal adviser.

If you or your unit is not at fault, express sympathy and offer advice, eg, "I can understand why you were upset when you had to wait for service last Saturday. Our emergency room gets very busy late on Saturday nights. Next time you have a cold, try to avoid a late night visit, especially on weekends."

If you are at fault, explain briefly what happened and what you are going to do about it. Even if you are not able to solve the problem to the complainer's satisfaction, do something about the situation and end on a positive note by thanking the person for bringing the situation to your attention. Express the hope that the person will continue to use your service, eg, "We appreciate your comments and value your support."

Reply as soon as you have the necessary information. Do not use a form letter, blame a specific individual, hide behind policy, or be condescending or patronizing.

Tips for Better Memo and Letter Writing

Getting Started

Ask yourself: Is this message really necessary? Should it be oral or written? Memo or letter? Typed or handwritten? Should you use voice mail (telephone) or electronic mail (computer)?

Consider the relative effectiveness, cost, convenience to receiver, degree of urgency, and availability of channels when selecting a medium.

Individuals who have limited education prefer oral messages, and employees for whom English is a second language can handle typed messages better than handwritten ones.

- "Freewrite" a rough draft.
- Imagine the reader sitting across from you.
- Write as fast as you can.
- Write like you talk.
- Don't worry about grammar or punctuation at this point.
- Start off with a "you" or the reader's name. If possible use a "thank you," a compliment, or good news, eg, "I'm pleased to share this information with you."
- The first paragraph gets most attention, so use an attention-grabbing "hook" to urge readers to read on. For example, in a letter to your current supplier, "We may have to select a new supplier."
- Rewrite.
- Check for message content.
- Check for brevity and clarity.
- Avoid jargon, acronyms, or abbreviations unless they are familiar to your readers.
- Avoid "bizlish" and "legalese," eg, "Pursuant to..., whereas..., duly noted..., aforementioned."
- Eliminate vague or abstract words or statements: "We must decrease our turnaround time" is not as good as "We must decrease turnaround time by 10%."
- Improve appearance and readability by using double spacing and wide margins.
- Edit carefully.
- Check the words: Will your reader understand them? Avoid an abundance of polysyllabic words.
- Eliminate unnecessary words or phrases, such as "The consensus of opinion" or "It has a gray color and a round shape."
- Replace roundabout phrases. See Table I.
- Emphasize by underlining or using bold or italic print.

Table I
Roundabout Phrases and Their Substitutes

Roundabout Phrase	Substitute
prior to	before
with regard to	about
in the event that	if
in view of the fact that	since or because
in the near future	soon
at the present time	now
due to the fact that	because
concerning the matter of	about
in order to	to
in the case of	if
in the majority of instances	usually
by means of	by
inasmuch as	since

- Highlight by capitalizing or using bullets.
- Check grammar, spelling, and punctuation. Use computer software when possible, but do not rely on it completely. A useful style and punctuation guide is that of Strunk and White.[6]

THE COMPUTER

It was just a few years ago that hospitals and other health care institutions either had no computer systems or their systems dealt only with demographics and finances. The mainframe computer has largely been replaced by myriads of small computers that enable anyone to tap into systems within and outside of the organization. The amount of information available to anyone who wants it is mind-boggling.

The opportunity in advanced information technology lies in mobilizing information about customers, in identifying costs, for process reengineering, and in connecting people throughout the organization who can work better together than separately.[7] The gains in productivity come from giving employees access to information. This information is transmitted person to person, person to computer, and via other electronic devices such as E-mail, fax, management information systems (MIS), and laboratory information systems (LIS).

These are supplemented by electronic performance support systems (EPS), an all-purpose reference that people can access while they're running other software to do their jobs.[8] This reduces the need to struggle through large manuals or seek advice from superiors or technical specialists, thus reducing the time wasted while perplexed people scratch their heads. Customer service representatives have quick access to answers in the field. There is also less need for classroom instruction and makes "just-in-time" learning feasible. This kind of teaching on the job is much more practical and meaningful. The communication system should include a complete database about the business and its activities, including both financial and nonfinancial elements.[7]

REFERENCES

1. Sonnenberg F. Internal communications: turning talk into action. *Supervis Manage.* 1992;37:8-9.

2. Doyle RJ, Doyle PI. *Gain Management: A Process for Building Teamwork, Productivity, and Profitability Throughout Your Organization.* New York, NY: AMACOM; 1992.

3. Gerrard BA, Boniface WJ, Love BH. *Interpersonal Skills for Health Professionals.* Reston, Va: Reston Publishing Co; 1980.

4. Field T, Whitehead R. How we improved turnaround time through voice technology. *Hosp Topics.* 1992;70:32-34.

5. Mehrabian R. *Nonverbal Communication.* New York, NY: Addline-Atherton; 1972.

6. Strunk W Jr, White EB. *The Elements of Style.* New York, NY: Macmillan Publishing Co; 1979.

7. Mills DQ. *Rebirth of the Corporation.* New York, NY: John Wiley & Sons; 1991.

8. Hequet M. Should every worker have a line in the information stream? *Training.* 1994;31:99-102.

22. Decision Making and Problem Solving

MOST LIKELY, A DECISION will be a compromise between what the manager wants and what actually can be done.[1]

Charles H. Kepner

CHAPTER OBJECTIVES

- To posit why decision making is of increasing importance
- To present the essential triad of effective decisions
- To describe the analytical approach to problem solving
- To mention the use of the computer in analytical problem solving
- To characterize the intuitive approach to problem solving
- To present an overview of group problem solving and consensus reaching
- To delineate creative group problem solving
- To discuss traps in the decision-making process
- To emphasize the importance of problem prevention

Upper management deals chiefly with decisions that relate to end results, bottom lines, or long-range strategies—the "what." First-line supervisors and self-directed teams deal principally with decisions about operational processes—the "how."

239

Decisions about people are by far the most important. The spirit of the organization is shaped by the decision it makes about its people. These decisions are highly visible and meaningful. Decisions about hiring, training, disciplining, promoting, and discharging employees are of such great consequence that they are among the last responsibilities to be signed off on by delegating managers.

Decision making is largely a matter of sound judgment, and sound judgment is based on innate ability, values, knowledge, intuition, and experience. Experienced supervisors and team leaders find it much easier to make the myriad of daily decisions they face than do novices who are disadvantaged by their lack of operational know-how or the experience from past successes, obstacles, and failures.

WHY DECISION MAKING IS MORE IMPORTANT NOW THAN EVER BEFORE

- The rate of organizational, technical, and operational changes increases constantly. Changes require decisions and often present problems.
- It is more difficult to reverse some decisions, eg, firing new employees.
- Our society grows more litigious; bad decisions mean more time in court.
- Critical shortages of certain specialists demand quick hiring decisions or competitors will snatch these people up.
- Financial pressures, especially those relating to capital expenditures or cost containment, are great. Poor decisions can be costly.
- Problems of employee and patient safety, satisfaction, and ethics have been increasing in number and complexity.

THE ESSENTIAL TRIAD FOR EFFECTIVE DECISIONS

1. Quality is a sine qua non.
2. Timeliness includes the time to make a decision plus the time to implement it. For example, an employment selection process may be too slow, or it takes the employment office too long to notify candidates. The Japanese use of teams to make decisions results in a longer time required to make decisions but less time to implement them.
3. Commitment. The decision must be reasonably acceptable to the people who must implement the decision. For example, a new instrument may look good on paper, but the technicians who use it do not like how it operates.

PROBLEM SOLVING IS MUCH MORE THAN DECISION MAKING

Decision making only concerns the evaluation of alternative actions. When our alarm clock goes off in the morning our daily decision-making process starts, and it continues until we decide when to go to bed. A problem is a deviation from some standard of expected performance, and it is identified by comparing what is actually happening with what should be happening. In most instances, a problem follows some kind of change.

Problems are inevitable when people work together. The hallmark of a well-managed team is not the absence of problems, but the effective resolution of problems at an early stage.

Problem solving starts with analysis of a performance variant and the search for a cause or causes.

THE ANALYTICAL APPROACH TO PROBLEM SOLVING

There are two cognitive approaches to problem solving: the analytical and the intuitive. Analytical or left brain function provides rational, logical, scientific thinking, while right brain function gives us our intuitive, creative, emotional thinking.

Left brain thinking is like a flowchart process. Analytical people rely predominantly on algorithmic processes such as plans, reports, computer printouts, and step-by-step procedures. The analytical thinker selects the most promising approach to a problem. Judgment is exercised at each step, and each step must be correct. Anything that is irrelevant is excluded. The search ends when what appears to be a good alternative is found.

Individuals who treat decision making as a science often fail to come up with creative ideas because they depend entirely on the rational approach. A logical father assembles his son's complex toy only after reading the instruction steps carefully. An intuitive dad dumps out all the parts, glances at the assembly diagram, and goes ahead.

THE RATIONAL STEPS IN SOLVING A PROBLEM

Step 1: Specify the problem.

Diagnosis is the most important—and often most neglected—part of problem solving. Novices look for solutions before they have delineated the problem and detected the cause. Jumping to solutions may be jumping from the pan into the fire.

The cluster pitfall is lumping deviations under broad rubrics like "attitudinal problem" or "communication problem." This lumping process leads to attempts to attribute all deviations to a single cause. The problem statement should be specific.

The skilled problem solver starts by comparing what actually happened or is happening with what should be happening. This may immediately suggest an etiologic agent. The facts used in specifying the problem and the analysis of those facts are the key to successful problem solving.

What the deviation or problem is must be clearly separated from what it is not.[1] For example, if an outbreak of diarrhea strikes a hospital staff it is important to know if all shifts were affected, if only the employees who ate in the main dining area had symptoms, and if only the people who ate the ham salad were affected.

A problem clearly stated is a problem partly solved. The more specific the problem statement, the less time is needed to find its cause.

Problem analysis often requires backtracking to determine what changes were made and when those changes went into effect. The identification of changes that may be causal factors is facilitated by maintaining a log of changes of methods, equipment, solutions, etc.[1] For example, in a tissue pathology laboratory the quality of microscopic slides suddenly deteriorated. A review of the log revealed that one of the reagents in the tissue processing machine had been replaced by an inferior substitute on the day before the onset of the problem.

Step 2: Obtain and interpret the facts or data.

We must know what information we do have about the problem, what information we do not have, and how we can get it. The search is aided by asking questions such as:

When was the problem first noted?
How serious is it?
Whom does it affect?
Is it getting better or worse?
Is it more complicated than first appeared? How?
What things changed about the same time the problem developed?
What is the cause? (The "sixty-four dollar" question.)

To find the cause, ask a spiral of why questions. For example, employees suddenly start to resign. The laboratory director asks the supervisor:

Why did she resign? Answer: "She was very upset."
Why? Answer: "She said she never felt like part of the team."
Why? Answer: "She was never invited to socialize with us."
Why not? Answer: "She always got into arguments with Kate."
Why? etc.

The use of diagrams, especially cause and effect (Ishikawa or fishbone) diagrams and Pareto charts, are useful in this step.

Step 3: Formulate objectives and criteria to evaluate the alternatives.

Setting objectives against which to choose solutions is a key activity. The objectives should match what is specified in the problem statement. They should be specific, relevant, measurable, achievable, and written. Often objectives are divided into musts or wants.[1] The criteria for acceptance for the wants will obviously be more demanding than those for the musts.

Absolute criteria are those that must be met by an acceptable solution, eg, "No increase in costs or personnel." Differential criteria are used to judge the various alternatives, eg, turnaround time, schedule convenience, availability of supplies, and the degree of expertise required. Setting objectives and articulating criteria lay the groundwork for a decision. You cannot choose the best way of getting somewhere until you have determined where you want to end up. That means you have to define your objectives and criteria in detail.

Step 4: Generate as many alternatives as possible.
The objectives become a set of specifications by which to develop alternative courses of action.

Step 5: Evaluate alternatives and select the best one.
Evaluate each alternative against the objectives and the selection criteria.

Step 6: Look for flaws in the choice.
Ask a lot of "what if" questions. Assess the possible adverse consequences of your choice. These may be so hazardous that other alternatives must be sought or special measures taken to avoid or minimize such undesired side effects.

Step 7: Develop an action plan.

Step 8: Implement the plan.

Step 9: Follow-up.
Follow-up has two purposes. The first is to ensure that the actions planned are implemented. The second is to prevent any adverse consequences. If what you are doing is not working well, take appropriate action.

THE INTUITIVE APPROACH TO PROBLEM SOLVING

Problem solving without creative thinking is a garden without seeds.[3]
    J. Conrath

Intuition (right brain function) is based largely on experiential material stored and reworked in the catacombs of our subconsciousness. Our subconscious minds serve as mainframe computers with almost unlimited memory storage capability. Unfortunately, what is filed in these cerebral banks cannot be readily recalled voluntarily by us. These files are a computer program for which we have lost the password. However, unlike computer-stored data, brain information is constantly and subconsciously analyzed, synthesized, and reformatted.

Innovative or creative people have greater insight or gut reactions. They visualize more than do their rational counterparts. They prefer diagrams to printouts. They often throw logic out of the window. Intuitive thought processes seldom can be flowcharted—they are hop-skip-and-jump. When intuitive managers interview job candidates, they visualize them in the work area surrounded by the rest of the team and sense if the fit seems good.

What flows up from our subconscious mind may be perfect. Mozart composed a note-perfect symphony, written in one flow of ideas.[3] What most of us get, however, is flawed or distorted. Like gossip, it must be checked out by our rational mind.

Techniques for Augmenting Individual Intuition

- **Concentrate on the problem.** Think hard and long about it. If a solution does not emerge, dismiss it from your mind and go to step 2.

- **Let it incubate.** Turn off conscious cerebration (left brain) and let your cerebrocortical energy flow into your subconscious mind (right brain cogitation). Daydreaming, relaxation, or meditation may help. Solitude can also be effective, particularly when enhanced by listening to ocean sounds (real or recorded) or background music.

- A popular strategy espoused by Joyce Brothers, the well-known psychologist, is to think about a problem just before dropping off to sleep. Before she falls asleep, Dr. Brothers makes a mental note of the three most important decisions she must make in the morning. She claims that the solutions come to her as soon as she awakens.[4]

- Use the mind-forcing technique. Document your problem at the top of a sheet of paper. Under the problem, number the lines 1 through 20. Now, force yourself to write down 20 solutions. The first few will come easy (these are usually the ones that you have already discarded). Subsequent alternatives surface with increasing difficulty and are more likely to have originated in the subconscious mind—and are more inspirational. This technique prevents you from stopping as soon as a promising lead materializes.

- Be sensitive to hunches. Pay attention to nagging doubts. We call this insight or gut reaction.

GROUP PROBLEM SOLVING

The Responsibilities of the Supervisor

The supervisor helps the team to identify the kinds of decisions they should and may make, and the kinds of problems they should solve. To assist them,

Table I
Basics of Consensus Decision Making

Ensure that each person expresses his or her viewpoint fully.

Look for areas of agreement.

Avoid hasty conclusions or hasty agreements.

Explore the positive features of each alternative.

Expose and analyze the negative features.

Resolve disagreement.

Avoid techniques of voting, averaging, or bargaining.

Insist that each member agree that he or she can live with the solution that is selected.

If any member balks, you do not have a consensus.

the supervisor provides access to needed information and time, leads some sessions in the early stage of team building, and provides both rational and intuitive techniques for each of these processes. He or she delegates the authority to make choices of increasing complexity. When new teams learn to solve easy problems before they tackle the tough ones, confidence and enthusiasm increase.

To be successful, some tolerance for mistakes is necessary. To fail to develop this early in the game quickly discourages the team from taking risks. The supervisor must also bend over backwards to support team decisions, even when the team's choice is not what the supervisor would recommend. Obviously, this has limits. Poor choices that could have serious adverse consequences must be avoided.

The Team Effort

A problem is like a beach ball. From any one spot, you cannot see all of the ball. No one person has an all-encompassing view. In groups, more ideas are generated, and the group is more likely to support the choice that is made by consensus. Small groups of about five to ten persons usually elicit more active participation than larger groups and are less likely to get sidetracked.

Seeking a Consensus

A group often makes decisions before all the opinions of the members have been explored. Participants who are not heard from may leave the meeting angry, balk at the group's decision, fail to support it, or even sabotage its implementation. A consensus prevents this. See Table I for a list of the rules of consensus decision making. See Chapter 23 for suggestions for getting the most out of meetings.

Table II
A Brainstorming Technique for Problem Solving

1. A problem is presented to the group.
2. Each member thinks about the problem and records ideas on a sheet of paper. No comments or discussion are permitted at this time.
3. Each member reads one item from the list, which is recorded on a flip chart. No comments or discussion are permitted at this time, but members may piggyback on ideas of others.
4. The sequence is repeated until all the ideas are displayed on the chart.
5. Each item is discussed, amplified, or modified. The originator of each item may be asked to leave the room when his or her idea is discussed. Criticism is now permitted and encouraged.
6. Each member ranks the items that are regarded as feasible.
7. The votes are recorded on the chart.

CREATIVE PROBLEM SOLVING GROUPS

Logical thinking often works best at problem-solving meetings. However, when creative solutions are needed, open-ended, nonlinear, intuitive thinking can often provide unexpected opportunities or upgrade compromises to solutions in which both parties get everything they want—win/win results. Deciding on the best instrument or job candidate calls for logical thinking. Finding a way to improve attendance at dull meetings may call for more creativity.

Unstructured Brainstorming Groups

Unstructured brainstorming groups are nothing more than informal discussion groups—lots of talk, lots of wandering off the topic, and not much achieved. Exceptions may occur when a group of entrepreneurs or creative people get together.

Structured Brainstorming Groups

Structured brainstorming groups generate ideas guided by certain rules. See Table II for a description of one technique. A typical meeting has two phases: the generation phase (steps 1 to 4 in Table II) and the evaluation phase (steps 5 to 7 in Table II).

To get the maximum benefits, alert the participants before the meeting about the subject matter, and set a good example by bringing a large packet of your own ideas, including some really wild ones to encourage free-wheeling suggestions. It is important that criticism of any kind be prohibited during the first phase.

In the evaluation phase, creativity gives way to judgment. Don't move to the negatives until all the positives of each proposal have been discussed. Don't defend your pet ideas, at least not at first. If your idea has merit, someone else will recognize this and support it. When evaluating, try to put a positive spin on what appears to be a weak alternative before discarding it. Look for a hidden gem in the idea. Some of the world's greatest achievements were based on decisions that were the objects of derision.

Don't let the negativists derail an idea. For example, if a member articulates a put-down like, "We tried that a long time ago and it flopped," respond with "What's different this time?"

Decision-Making Traps

1. The problem statement is too restrictive.
   Example, "We must explore how we can raise employee salaries and benefits because of the high personnel turnover rate." This directive restricts the number of options the team has for solving the retention problem. A better problem statement would be, "To investigate the high personnel turnover rate, seek the cause or causes, and make recommendations for correcting that situation." This approach opens the door to multiple possible solutions.

2. Biases
   Previous experience may affect the present decision. For example, in the above scenario, an across-the-board pay increase several years ago did slow down the rate of personnel turnover. However, the situation may be different at the present time. To make matters worse, members may not only press arguments in support of their pet theory, but insist that they have the only solution. They resist all attempts by others and may become emotional.

3. Confirmation traps
   Once an attractive suggestion is proffered, the group may look only for evidence that supports this premature proposal, thus overlooking its negative features or neglecting the search for better solutions.

4. Defensiveness
   One of the barriers to problem solving is the defensiveness of people whose ideas are criticized. Members and leaders must train themselves to avoid defensiveness. They concentrate on asking pertinent questions rather than conjuring up rebuttals or attacking the other person. Often it is best to fall silent and let other participants rise to your defense. If the latter does not take place, perhaps your suggestion lacks substance or support.

5. Procrastination
   Sound judgment of scientists and professionals is sometimes flawed because they procrastinate. Many problems must be solved quickly, but some people with scientific backgrounds tend to procrastinate

Table III
Pitfalls in Group Decision Making

Insufficient preparation

Failing to define the problem

Unclear objectives or expectations

Information deficit or overload

Relying excessively on anecdotal information, limited personal
  experience, assumptions, vague perceptions, or initial impressions

Jumping to solutions before the problem has been sufficiently clarified
  or before all options have been explored

Forgetting about the customers, users, or implementers

Stone-walling

Straying from the original objective

Poor listening

Domination by one or two players

Passive members who do not speak up

Constant aside conversations

Personal attacks on individual members

Poor follow-up

Unresolved roles, responsibilities, or authority in the implementation
  process

because they want all of the data available. When they worry too
much about "going off half-cocked," they fall prey to paralysis from
analysis—procrastination or inaction because of an endless pursuit
of more data—or the jigsaw puzzle fallacy—the false assumption that
only one solution is good and it must have four straight edges. Often
the problem has several equally satisfactory solutions, but the edges
of life's puzzles are seldom straight lines.

6. Inconsistency

   It is easier to make decisions when rules, values, and practices
   remain constant. When the game plan changes every week, people
   can never be sure that what was right last week will still be the way to
   go this week.

See Table III for additional pitfalls.

PROBLEM PREVENTION: THE PROACTIVE APPROACH

Health care workers know that in the practice of medicine, prevention is
always better than cure. Likewise, the best way to cope with problems is to
avoid having them in the first place. Looking for situations that can lead to
problems is problem prevention at its best. The manager who manages by

walking around is a safety inspector, not a firefighter. He or she spots physical or interpersonal situations that have potential adverse consequences. These can be as simple as observing a frayed electric cord or may involve more complicated matters such as noting growing discordance between team members during group meetings.

REFERENCES

1. Kepner CH, Tregoe BB. *The Rational Manager.* Princeton, NJ: Kepner-Tregoe Inc; 1965.
2. Conrath J. The imagination harvest: training people to solve problems creatively. *Supervis Manage.* 1985;30:7-10.
3. Tracy B. *The Psychology of Achievement.* Chicago, Ill: Nightingdale Conant; 1987 (audiocassettes).
4. Sullivan G. *Work Smart, Not Hard.* New York, NY: Facts on File; 1987.

23. Team Meetings That Work

MEETINGS USUALLY INVOLVE disagreement and conflict. An absence of contention and conflict signals nothing productive is happening.[1]
Michael Hammer

CHAPTER OBJECTIVES

- To comment on the weaknesses or abuses of team meetings
- To list the major purposes and components of meetings
- To suggest appropriate preparations for meetings
- To specify the primary responsibilities of facilitators, recorders, and timekeepers
- To recommend how to start a team meeting
- To offer ten effective ways to increase participation
- To describe the Abilene paradox
- To catalog important don'ts for chairpersons
- To depict important postmeeting activities
- To assist participants in improving their meeting skills and make use of visual aids
- To list five keys to negotiating at meetings

The meeting is a team's most valuable tool. The amount of information flowing out of computers has made meetings even more important, because more data need to be shared and discussed.[2] Ad hoc problem-solving meetings conducted in a brainstorming mode are usually the most valuable ones. Competent teams usually rotate meeting facilitators or chairpersons so team members develop a greater appreciation for the need to cooperate at the meeting. This practice also avoids the problem of holding meetings when the permanent chair is absent.

WEAKNESSES OR ABUSES OF TEAM MEETINGS

Meetings can be major time wasters if they are not needed, last too long, involve too many people, or are poorly run. When fast action is needed, meetings can impede progress. If a meeting is held only to make announcements, it may not be necessary because the information can be disseminated more effectively by other channels. Likewise, many decisions can be made and problems solved without group dialogues. If you are certain that you have the right solution, do not refer it to a committee.

Groups are seldom as effective in organizing data or writing reports than are individuals. Meetings are less appropriate when the subject is trivial.[3]

MAJOR PURPOSES OF TEAM MEETINGS

- To explain new policies, laws, services, protocols, systems, restructuring—anything involving change
- To introduce new personnel
- To report on things such as lab inspections or physical construction progress
- To accept reports or recommendations
- To get help in making decisions, solving problems, allocating resources, preparing plans, establishing priorities, generating ideas, or assigning tasks
- To persuade or obtain commitment for an idea, program, or proposal
- To teach, train, demonstrate, or explain tasks and procedures
- To identify people who are potential leaders or have some other previously unidentified talent
- To congratulate or reward

THE COMPONENTS OF A MEETING

Input

Leader, members, agendum, visual aids, handouts, meeting room facilities, objectives, facts, and opinions

Process

Presentation, discussion, consensus, voting, negotiation, information exchange, expression of feelings, planning, problem solving, and decision making

Product

Problems solved, decisions made, compromises, commitment obtained, schedules, assignments, priorities, resources allocated, action plans

Feedback and Follow-up

Actions taken as the result of the meeting with feedback to constituents and other people who are affected

SPECIAL MEMBER ROLES

Facilitators (Who Are Not the Chairperson)

Facilitators observe the dynamics of the group—what goes on between members. They provide guidance and support to the leader and the members. They suggest that the leader summarize when things get complicated.

Recorders

Recorders keep the minutes and record progress on flip charts. This responsibility is best rotated among the members.

Timekeepers

Timekeepers keep the group on schedule and may allocate time for each item on the agenda.

MEETING PREPARATIONS BY THE CHAIR

In addition to preparing an agenda and ensuring that meeting space and facilities are available, chairs can improve their effectiveness by getting input from others before the session. In some organizations, members jot down suggestions for topics in a special agenda book or on a clipboard attached to a door.

Campaign for your own proposals about which you feel strongly. Review them with members who are already in agreement to make it difficult for them to change their minds at the meeting. Getting support from leaders of the opposition is even more important.

A caveat: Since these behind the scenes maneuvers represent a form of manipulation, they should be reserved for special issues.

Sometimes getting input from members or enlightening them prior to the meeting eliminates the need for the meeting. This is also a technique of getting opinions from nonassertive members who may be reluctant to speak up at the meeting.

Determining Who Should Attend

The selection of members is important. Cost can be decreased and displeasure avoided if attendance is limited to people who are needed and who are willing to serve. The group should collectively have the necessary knowledge and experience, and should include people who can be depended on to show up and participate.

Keep the group small. The more people attending, the slower the meeting becomes and the harder it is to stick to the agenda. A group of five to eight people is ideal for action meetings. To help reduce meeting size, consider part-time attendance; that is, ask people to come when they are needed and encourage them to leave when they have made their contributions. Most busy people will appreciate this. Let the participants know what is expected of them. Designate who will be called on to discuss certain points. Tell them how detailed you expect their contribution to be.[4]

If your meetings tend to drag on, schedule them just before quitting time. Friday afternoons are preferred by many managers because the week's progress can be reviewed, and the premature departure of folks who like to slip out early on Fridays is prevented.

Setting the Agenda

The agenda is one of the two most powerful instruments in meeting management—the other is the minutes.[5] The agenda should be upbeat, reflecting opportunities and optimism. Use action phrases like "to recommend" or "to make a final decision" rather than "to discuss" or "to consider." Invite your team members to suggest agenda items. Distribute the agenda several days before the meeting.

Responsibilities of the Chair or Facilitator During the Meeting

- To explain the purpose or goal of the meeting
- To ensure participation of all members
- To set the tone, to clarify, and to maintain focus
- To review the ground rules of the meeting
- To confront members who try to dominate, intimidate, ridicule, or otherwise impede progress
- To encourage lively debates while avoiding hostility and preventing escalation of conflicts
- To maintain the pace of the deliberations and refocus when necessary

Getting Started

The meeting begins the moment you, the chair, enter the room. If you promise that your meetings will start and end on time, and you do not fulfill that promise, your leadership reputation suffers. Arrive early to ensure that everything is ready.

Seat members in a circle or around a table rather than in classroom style. For short sessions, hold stand-up meetings.

Have your opening statement memorized. It establishes direction for the meeting. Sound and look enthusiastic.

Review the highlights of the previous meeting and ask for any comments or corrections. Note any progress that has been made since that meeting. Provide an overview of the agenda.

Establishing Ground Rules

Here are some good ground rules to establish before discussions start:

■ We will listen to others without interrupting.

■ Everyone gets a chance to talk and is expected to do so.

■ We will seek consensus rather than majority voting.

■ There will be no hidden agendas.

■ Put-downs, sarcasm, ridicule, and intimidations are outlawed.

■ The meeting will start and end on time.

Encouraging Participation

Here are some great ways to get members to speak up:

■ Go around the table, calling on each member by name.

■ Respond enthusiastically to all suggestions.

■ Split team into "breakaway" groups.

■ Let other participants lead some of the questioning or chairing.

■ Reinforce input from passive members, eg, "Thanks, Erica, for speaking so candidly; that took courage."

■ Use nonthreatening open-ended questions, eg, "How do you think someone who was opposed to that idea would respond?"

■ Withhold your opinion until everyone else has spoken.

■ If a person's suggestion cannot be accepted, try using part of it.

■ Encourage members to build on the ideas of others.

■ Preserve the ego of all members.

Encourage Discussions, Not Arguments

A discussion is an exchange of views. An argument is the rigid stating and restating of a position. Objectivity is lost in favor of inflexibility and repetition. The way to end an argument is to become objective about the issue, eg, "Sally, I'm afraid we're starting to repeat. Let's get back to the original point that Jim made."

Maintain Control

Keep people from going off on a tangent. When they stray, say something like "James, that's interesting. We ought to look into that further. Now about...." Summarize progress periodically by using a flip chart or chalkboard. Call for a break when things stall.

Force Decisions

Ask if anyone needs more data before a decision is made. Ask a proponent to sum up his or her view. Do the same for an opponent. Go around the table and ask each person for his or her position, then try to achieve a unanimous decision. Only when a serious effort has failed should you call for a vote. When forcing a vote, try to make it unanimous.

Ensure that recommendations are phrased in specific terminology. This is especially important when dealing with customer service. For example, "To improve emergency department service" is too general; "To decrease waiting time in the pediatric clinic to an average of 15 minutes" is much more specific.

The Abilene Paradox: The Inability to Manage Agreement[6]

The Abilene paradox occurs when members approve an action that is contrary to what they really want because they fail to communicate their true opinions. This leads the group into misperceiving the collective reality. In other words, there is overt agreement, but silent disagreement. When the result turns out unfavorably, the members accuse each other.

This problem has two underlying causes. The first involves inaccurate assumptions about what the other members think. The second cause is individuals' unwillingness to express their true opinions.

The paradox can be prevented by frank and open discussion in which members are not afraid to offer opinions they think are contrary to those of the other members. The paradox is quickly nixed when a vocal devil's advocate is present.

Ending the Meeting

To avoid confusion, summarize the discussion and decisions. Indicate the areas still requiring consideration. Review assignments and select the date for the next meeting.

When you must leave a meeting that is still in progress and you are the leader, provide an explanation and turn the meeting over to an alternate. Before you do that, assign any special responsibilities or tasks to members.

Some Important Don'ts for Chairs

Do not:

Try to dominate the meeting.

State your opinion before others have given theirs.

Tell a participant that he or she is wrong.

Instruct or lecture unless that is the purpose of the meeting.

Argue (disagreeing is acceptable).

Ridicule, kid, or be sarcastic.

Take sides early in the discussion.

Fail to control problem members.

Allow the meeting to run overtime.

Try to accomplish too much at one meeting.

Postmeeting Activities

Send thank-you notes to individuals who agreed to perform postmeeting tasks or who made excellent presentations, clarified remarks, made outstanding efforts, or supported you.[5]

Prepare minutes without delay. Copies should be available within 24 to 48 hours and should state important facts briefly but thoroughly. Include:

Names of attendees and members who were absent

Statement that previous minutes were read and approved

Discussion or presentation of each item on the agenda

Record of agreement or disagreement

Record of vote or decisions made

Date, place, and time of next meeting

Time of start and adjournment

How to Be an Effective Participant

Effective participation begins when you receive an agenda. If you do not receive an agenda or if the purpose of the meeting and the need for your presence are unclear, contact the chair. That also gives you an opportunity to ask if you should bring any data with you.

Think about what you can contribute. Be prepared to ask pertinent questions and to answer queries in your area of expertise. If you cannot attend, notify the chair as soon as possible.

At the meeting, listen attentively. When you speak, make eye contact with the group leader, then with others. Return, move away again, and return. A smile helps put your eyes in the right mode of friendliness.

Be positive about what you say and how you say it. Know when to come on strong and when to be tentative. Modulate your voice speed and volume. Never whisper or shout.

Tips for Better Member Participation

Good members:

Ask themselves why they are there.

Come prepared to contribute their expertise.

Arrive on time.

Listen thoughtfully to others and try to understand their points of view.

Ask for clarifications.

Respect the opinions of those with whom they disagree.

Offer honest opinions, even when these are unpopular.

Try to separate facts from perceptions, assumptions, or opinions.

Have the courage to disagree without being disagreeable.

Remain rational and assertive, even when harassed.

Seek win/win solutions and are willing to compromise.

Accept special assignments such as searching the literature or serving as recorder.

Avoid being a problem member.

Special Advice for Nonassertive Members

Some individuals hesitate to speak up at meetings, thus depriving the group of their knowledge and opinions. Ideally, these people should obtain assertiveness training via seminars, workshops, or books.

To bolster such a person's courage to speak up, come prepared. Use escalating dialogue in which you break your silence by asking questions, starting with benign requests for information or clarification, followed by more challenging queries, and finally expressing comments and opinions. Another technique is to maintain a state of interest and active neutrality during controversies. Opposing members try to convince fence sitters, who then become centers of attention. Simply listening to both sides and asking appropriate questions provide the neutral observer with clout.

Use power language by avoiding discounters like "I know this sounds silly, but...." Do not use clichés like "It goes without saying...." Eliminate those dreadful fillers such as "ya know" or "uh."

Sound enthusiastic; speak clearly and forcefully. Do not tolerate interruptions. Say, "I wasn't finished, Lou," then go on without waiting for an apology.

Support your vocal expressions with appropriate body language. When a speaker looks at you, give a head signal that indicates your reaction. If you nod agreement or shake your head, the person will glance at you more frequently for feedback.

Five Keys to Better Negotiating at Meetings

1. State your case, then listen while others state theirs.
2. Articulate points of agreement.
3. Move to areas of disagreement, beginning with the one least vital to your interest.
4. Concede points that concern you least.
5. If what you offer is not met by like concession or if your offer is met by enhanced demands for more concessions, resist vigorously.

Find more on negotiating skills in Chapter 24.

Use of Visual Aids

A good visual should assist, not replace, the presenter. Visuals are like the headlines of a newspaper story. Use visuals to open presentations, channel thinking, emphasize key points, present financial or statistical data, make comparisons, simplify complex processes, and explain new concepts. Here are some design criteria used by the 3M Corporation.[2]

> Letters large enough to be seen by everyone (at least one-quarter inch, and readable at 20 feet)
>
> One idea per visual
>
> Maximum of seven words per line, seven lines per visual
>
> Short words

Handouts

Outlines of topics can be useful, but avoid giving out lengthy handouts before the meeting starts unless they are essential to the discussion. Let the participants pick up the detailed documents as they leave.

Problem Members

Numerous kinds of problem members include chronic objectors, speechmakers, ultraconservatives, risk takers, nitpickers, shoot-from-the-hip decision makers, cautious people who always need more information, and many others. In Chapter 14 of my book, *Coping With Difficult People in the Health Care Setting*, I discuss the different kinds of problem people at meetings and how to cope with them (Chicago, Ill: ASCP Press; 1994).

REFERENCES

1. Hammer M, Champy J. *Reengineering the Corporation*. New York, NY: Harper Business; 1993.

2. The 3M Meeting Management Team. *How to Run Better Business Meetings: A Reference Guide for Managers*. New York, NY: McGraw-Hill Publishers; 1987.

3. Jandt FE. People problems. *Boardroom Reports*. 1994;23:6-7.

4. Douglass ME, Douglass DN. *Time Management for Teams*. New York, NY: AMACOM; 1992.

5. Burleson CW. *Effective Meetings: The Complete Guide*. New York, NY: John Wiley & Sons; 1990.

6. Harvey JB. The Abilene paradox. *Organizational Dynamics*. 1988; 17:35-80.

24. Persuasion and Negotiating Skills

LL OF US ARE negotiators at various times in our lives, whether we know it or not and whether we like it or not.[1]

Karl Albrecht

CHAPTER OBJECTIVES

- To list and describe negotiating imperatives
- To advocate some preparatory actions
- To present a series of major steps in a negotiation
- To report some barriers to successful negotiation
- To caution against certain strategies that can backfire
- To focus on negotiation between teams
- To offer advice for coping with aggressive and devious opponents
- To offer a list of tips for negotiators
- To posit a series of verbal statements that enhance negotiating skill

Negotiation is a specialized communication process for reconciling known differences between people.[2] Supervisors and team members have always had to negotiate. They negotiate with superiors over raises, with vendors over prices, and with colleagues over special assignments or overtime. Now, because of more cross-functional activities, health care leaders deal less with superiors and subordinates and more with colleagues. In other words, horizontal negotiations are of paramount importance.

Traditional haggling, in which each side argues a position and either makes concessions to reach a compromise or refuses to budge, is not the most efficient and amicable way to reach a wise agreement.[3]

    R. Fisher

Negotiation ideally is based on the merits of what is at stake. Fortunately, most people want to end up not only with a good deal, but also with good feelings. If it were not for that, many work sites would be battlefields.

Persuasiveness is rapidly replacing authority as the principle leadership moving force. Employees who serve on autonomous teams, who are involved in cross-functional activities, or who are active in quality improvement movements must be skilled negotiators if they want to get action on their ideas. Putting it bluntly, they must know how to get what they and their team want without rocking the boat.

NEGOTIATING IMPERATIVES

Rewards

People will move in your direction only when they feel that it is in their best interest to do so.[4] While this appears to be a given, it often is overlooked as negotiators concentrate only on what they want from the other person. The power persuader looks for ways to make concessions to the other side by focusing on its interests. For example, Wendy needs someone to fill in for her at the safety committee meeting—usually a boring session. She asks John to go, pointing out that it will give him an opportunity to speak for his pet project, a crisis intervention team.

Information

Effective negotiators have the necessary data. These data may be copies of laws, policies, protocols, or other written and unwritten guidelines. Negotiators who know what their antagonists are going to propose and what cards they hold have an obvious advantage. They must have up-to-date information gleaned from formal and informal communication channels. Nothing will shoot down a proposal quicker than a valid document proving that what has been proposed violates a law or the organization's mission statement. Information alone is not enough. It must be presented in a concise, understandable fashion, which often requires handouts, graphs, charts, and other visual displays.

Empathy

If you have a sense of empathy with the other party, you can direct more of your energy toward the mechanics of a solution rather than dealing with hostility and personality clashes.[1] Empathy leads to persuasive bonding—the method of getting a person to commit to a position.[4] An example of a bonding expression is "I've always considered you to be a fair person, Louise."

Credibility

If you have not earned credibility, you will be perceived as a manipulator or devious person. To increase your credibility, support your arguments with like opinions of trusted people, and make certain that you are truthful about these statements.

Flexibility

Without some flexibility, compromises can rarely be achieved, much less win/win solutions. Some give and take is always needed.

Allied or Network Power

People who have the support of powerful allies, teams, or networks have more clout at the bargaining table. If they rank high in the organization or if they control vital resources, they have power. Professional and technical expertise and experience carries much weight in many situations. On the other hand, passive individuals and those with low self-esteem lack bargaining power.

To generate an effective support group requires active networking. As you expand your network you increase the number of allies and reduce the number of potential antagonists. Anyone who has a stake in what goes on in your work unit should be considered a candidate for your network, even your current opponents.

Networking is an exchange process like a bank account. If you want to make withdrawals, you must make deposits. When you call for help, you are much more likely to get responses from those people whom you have helped in the past. For more on networking, see Chapter 26.

Time

Time can be a powerful ally in situations in which one party can stall while the other party must meet a deadline. It is also important when additional information or approvals must be obtained. Skilled negotiators know when their opponents are vulnerable (eg, after having just experienced a financial setback or having been castigated in public by a senior executive).

PREPARATIONS FOR NEGOTIATION

Like any worthwhile activity, planning is essential to successful negotiations. Too often people walk into a negotiation unprepared. Since each person has different interests, being prepared helps in understanding the different interests. Here are the major activities that should precede any important confrontation:

- Evaluate the situation by asking:
  - What is it I want, and what is the least I will accept?
  - What are likely to be the points of agreement and disagreement?
  - What does the other person want?
  - What are the strengths and weaknesses of my stance?
  - What are the strengths and weaknesses of her stance?
  - If the need to compromise becomes evident, what am I willing to agree to?
- Do your homework and gather any support you need.
  - Think of your adversaries as potential allies rather than an antagonist.
  - Take inventory of what you have that they want and what they have that you want. Ponder over possible trades.
  - Decide which issues are negotiable and which are not.
  - Prepare the arguments you can make to maximize the value of positive aspects, to minimize the negatives, and to counter other persons' arguments.
- Pick the best time and place.
  - Do not meet when your self-esteem is low or when either party is upset.
- Rehearse your argument.

Major Steps in a Negotiation

The key is in combining three factors: empathy, fairness, and assertiveness.[1]
    Karl Albrecht

Step 1: Clarify the disagreement or problem. Ask the person how he or she views the situation and what is important to him or her? Paraphrase the message and ask if you have interpreted the opposing view correctly. Then state your view and ask the person to summarize what you said. Recognize the difference between "can't" and "won't." Do not proceed until these viewpoints and desired outcomes are crystal clear.

Watch your body language. Maintain eye contact, sit or stand up straight, and appear relaxed. Do not fidget or squirm. Avoid threatening gestures such as finger pointing, fist making, crossed arms, hands on hips, or scowling. Smile when you agree; remain expressionless when you disagree.

Step 2: State what you perceive as points of agreement. Focus first on a point of agreement and work from there, eg, "Well, I think we agree that the solution must be one that will be acceptable to your team and to mine, right?'"

Step 3: Develop a problem solution statement. For example, "If I..., that would satisfy you, right? I would be satisfied if we could agree on...."

Step 4: Go into a problem-solving mode. Listen actively, paying close attention and occasionally interrupting to make certain you understand what the other person means. Ask that ideas be repeated if any ambiguity or uncertainty remains. It is important to understand perceptions, needs, and negotiating constraints.[3] For example, the person may know that certain solutions would not be acceptable to the boss.

Focus on the mutual benefits of your proposal. Do not get stuck believing your solution is the only good one. Be gracious. If the person has a valid argument, say so.

Step 5: Select the best alternative. Delay the selection until several credible alternatives have been mentioned. Examine the alternatives against the interest of each party, focus on those that would be acceptable to both parties, then settle on the preferred choice.[1] If you cannot come up with a win/win solution, be willing to compromise, but not until you have engaged in a vigorous brainstorming session.

Step 6: If things stall, call for a break or a postponement. Psychologists report that 20 to 30 minutes of steady negotiating is the limit without an interruption.[2] In some situations it is best not to make a definite commitment. Each of you may need to obtain more information or to consult with other individuals. View the initial meeting as an exploratory session.

Step 7: When agreement is reached on the action to be taken, agree on exactly who is going to do what and when.

Step 8: End on a positive note. Do not cause your opponent to lose face. Do not threaten or issue ultimatums. Ensure that he or she leaves believing that something was won.

PRINCIPAL BARRIERS TO SUCCESSFUL NEGOTIATION

Fears

Negotiation may cause participants to fear the loss of friendship or future cooperation. Some people cave in quickly because they just do not have the stomach for any kind of disagreement, conflict, or disharmony. Some people may be inflexible or demanding because they fear others will take advantage of them. Insecure and passive people have great difficulty negotiating and should get surrogates to represent their interests.

Gunnysacking

Gunnysacking is gathering up all past conflicts with the other party, especially those episodes in which you thought you had been taken advantage of, and then dumping all those past hurts in the lap of your opponent. While you may take that person by surprise—even overwhelm him or her—you will elicit defensiveness that impedes the negotiating process and erodes any friendship and spirit of cooperation.

Secrecy

Some negotiators mistakenly think that they will win more often if they withhold information. They do not reveal their real interests, statistical data, or what they are willing to give up. Obviously these folks are looking for win/lose outcomes.

Ultimatums and Deadlines

Ultimatums are warnings that if a decision is not made or an action not taken by one party by a stated date, a disaster will strike or the other party will take an undesired unilateral action. Avoid making such threats yourself unless they are absolutely necessary. Admittedly, sometimes the threat to walk out of a bargaining session will get results.

Anger, Guilt Induction, Ridicule, or Tears

Such tactics are seldom indicated. Experienced negotiators are not moved by these gimmicks, but they may be effective when dealing with novices.

Flawed Techniques

Flawed negotiating techniques include asking for too little and lack of persistence, patience, data, planning, or assertiveness.

STRATEGIES AND TACTICS THAT OFTEN BACKFIRE

Bargaining Over Positions

Fisher and Ury[5] emphasize that in negotiations, the focus should be on interests, not on positions. In position bargaining, each side adopts a rigid stance, and then fights for concessions from the other party. In other words, a win/lose result is sought. For example, an employee may insist on attending a laboratory seminar in Hawaii. The supervisor or team leader says, "No way, we will be short-handed that week and the trip is too costly." Each person has taken a position, and each refuses to budge.

When interests rather than positions are discussed in this scenario, the focus of the employee is on learning a new procedure and the team leader wants minimal expense and avoidance of understaffing. When they brainstorm the problem, they agree that the employee can wait a couple of months and attend a similar seminar at a more convenient time and at a location that will minimize the cost of attending.

When negotiators bargain over positions, they become locked into defending those positions to save face. This makes it difficult to modify their stance, thus reducing the possibility of agreement. The negotiations become contests of will rather than problem-solving exercises.

Bringing Along a Team

While team efforts have some advantages, such as augmented expertise and mutual support, problems do occur. Showing up with a bevy of supporters may suggest that you lack the ability to handle the process by yourself. Sometimes one member of your group makes a remark that hurts the group's case or may even disclose disunity among the members. Additionally, the team approach takes longer and is more likely to end without a consensus being reached.

Statistics

Statistics are good if they are valid and not redundant. However, reliance on them backfires when the other party points out flaws or comes up with more recent or more impressive data.

Delaying Tactics

Never rush to agreements simply to agree. Be patient and hold your ground. Know when to be stubborn. Keep in mind, however, that repeated and unnecessary delays not only postpone needed action but also erode the spirit of cooperation and increase the level of frustration.

Manipulation

Manipulation consists of actions that would be less effective if the target knew your true intentions. It may consist of promising more than you know you will deliver, pretending you like something or somebody that you cannot stand, or exaggerating your requests so that you can settle for less. You try to discover the other side's weaknesses and not let them discover yours. You keep them guessing. This strategy sooner or later catches up with most manipulators.[6]

NEGOTIATION BETWEEN TEAMS

Negotiation between teams is sometimes necessary, especially when collective areas of expertise are needed. In other instances, you may want to review work flows and pinpoint cross-functional areas where cooperation or collaboration are needed. Focusing on symptoms and individual complaints is rarely effective when teams negotiate. This often leads to exchanges of incident reports, which bring discredit to both parties and indicate a lack of leadership. Avoid drawing in third parties except as arbitrators or mediators.

How to Deal with Aggressive or Angry Opponents

Some people try to overwhelm you by using a domineering style. They are inflexible and demanding. You must not be intimidated into acceding to these demands. Ignore the overt or implied threats and insist on negotiating on the basis of interests and facts. Ask questions about the basis of any claims. Insist that any element of value demanded be backed up by logical reasons for its inclusion.[1]

How to Deal with the Devious Negotiator

Some people are manipulators who rely on ambiguity, secrecy, and subterfuge to get what they want. Their tricks work best when you are caught unaware or do not have enough information to know better. The more you know, the more you can clear the air and neutralize attempts at trickery or deceit. Try to fathom their real intent or goal and seek the reasons behind their statements. Encourage more openness and compliance by modeling it yourself.[1]

General Tips for More Effective Negotiation

- Regard the other person not as an enemy but as a partner in problem solving and a potential ally. The other person is usually willing to accept a solution if you can make it sufficiently attractive.
- Listen carefully for what is said, what is not said, and the body language used.
- Be assertive but not aggressive. Short responses are more assertive; longer ones suggest either passivity or aggressiveness.
- Attack the problem, not the other person. If the other person attacks you, ask to return to the problem.
- Do not be sarcastic or critical.
- Avoid distortions, exaggerations, or falsehoods. Successful negotiation requires mutual trust, not power plays, dirty tricks, or other manipulative traps.
- Control your voice. Keep its volume, pitch, and rate under control. Stop if you find it growing louder, faster, or higher pitched.
- Never appear to be taken by surprise.

- Be diplomatic and tentative when facing firm resistance. Use words like "maybe," "perhaps," or "you may be right."
- Remember your veto power. You can always say no or walk away.
- Promise rewards and hint of more.
- When you give the other person something they want, it is appropriate to ask for something in return. This is nothing more than the old barter system we used as youngsters.[1]
- Do not rush. Beware of shortcuts.

VERBAL EXPRESSIONS THAT ADD POWER TO YOUR DELIVERY[4]

- "Don't you agree that we want to do what is best for our patients?" (forces an affirmative response)
- "What do you think would be fair?" (great persuasion in action)
- "Yes, I do take that remark personally." (shows you are not a patsy)
- "Why would you want to do that?" (response to a threat)
- "It sounds like you got burned when this came up before. Would you like to talk about it?" (person gets angry at your proposal)
- "I apologize from the bottom of my heart." (great way to admit that you goofed)
- "That has not been my experience." (instead of "you're wrong," which only aggravates the situation)

REFERENCES

1. Albrecht K, Albrecht S. *Added Value Negotiating: The Breakthrough Method for Building Balanced Deals*. Homewood, Ill: Business One Irwin; 1993.
2. Goddard RW. Negotiation: how to win by forgetting about winning. *Training*. 1984;21:37.
3. Fisher R. Since almost everything in life is a negotiation. *Bottom Line*. 1993;14:1.
4. Dawson R. *Secrets of Power Persuasion*. Englewood Cliffs, NJ: Prentice-Hall; 1992.
5. Fisher R, Ury W. *Getting to Yes: Negotiating Agreement Without Giving In*. New York, NY: Penguin Books; 1983.
6. Cohen AR, Bradford DL. *Influence Without Authority*. New York, NY: John Wiley & Sons; 1990.

25. Financial Management

S INCE MOST MANAGERS began their careers in non-financial areas, it is only natural that they find these new demands for financial decisions somewhat bewildering.[1]
   Ronald Spurga

CHAPTER OBJECTIVES

- To discuss the purchase and storage of supplies
- To delineate the parameters of statistical, revenue, and expense budgets
- To differentiate capital equipment from other resources
- To explore the three principal budgetary methods
- To describe the six steps in preparing a budget
- To offer a few tips on getting the budget approved
- To briefly mention forecasting and financial record keeping

The supervisor, team leader, or team members may be responsible for purchasing, inventory control, billing, and/or budgets, so we will touch this subject with a light brush. Readers are urged to obtain a copy of Sattler's book, *A Practical Guide to Financial Management of the Clinical Laboratory*,[2] which was used extensively for this chapter. Worthwhile additional fiscal information can also be found in the recommended readings at the end of this chapter.

Supplies

The purchasing functions include selecting the vendor who provides the best quality, price, and delivery service and purchasing the right amount at the right time. Most major medical facilities use a centralized system in which primary control is vested in the purchasing department. In a decentralized system, control resides within each department or unit.

Requisitions

Requisitions and purchase orders are different. A requisition is simply a request to purchase and is usually initiated by a supervisor or team leader. A purchase order is an order to buy and is usually acted on by the purchasing department after receipt of a requisition.[2] "Traveling" requisitions actually travel back and forth between units and purchasing or materials management. The traveling requisition assists in controlling inventory by reducing the amount of space necessary for storage. Because it speeds the entire ordering process, delivery time is reduced, so the unit may order more frequently.[2]

Standing Orders

Standing orders eliminate the need to initiate repetitive monthly orders. If volume requirements change, a telephone call to the purchasing department is usually sufficient.

Computerized Ordering

Supply ordering can be streamlined through a variety of computerized ordering systems made available by vendors.

Storage

A system must be in place for periodically checking inventories to determine when items should be reordered. Computerization and the use of bar codes have simplified this process and made it more efficient. Using just-in-time systems, the need for large storage areas is lessened, and inventory costs can be drastically reduced.

Materials Management

Materials management is the control and management of all supplies, services, and equipment from the time of ordering until the time the supplies have been used, the services have been completed, or the equipment has been disposed of. This system eliminates the fragmentation of purchasing functions among various departments.

INTERDEPARTMENTAL COORDINATION

In medium and large organizations, cooperation and coordination must exist among several departments: data processing, purchasing, business office, human resources, payroll, and administration. Leaders must establish friendly relationships with the personnel in each of these departments and familiarize themselves with the protocols each department uses. Learning the appropriate channels, forms, and systems is important.[2]

BUDGETS

A budget is a written financial plan that serves as an estimate of future operations and a means of monitoring, controlling, and directing these operations. It establishes the amount of allowable expenses for operating a department or unit over a limited time.

Budgets are a fact of life. The better their planning and preparation, the easier it is to get them accepted and stay within their limits. By keeping track of each section's costs and revenues, one does not have to play Sherlock Holmes when problems are encountered. All expense and revenue components must be documented to meet the standards and regulations of federal and state governments, accrediting agencies, and third-party payers.[2]

Operating Budget

The operating budget consists of three parts:

1. Statistical Budget. This projects the numbers for anticipated activities, eg, number of laboratory procedures or radiographs, meals served, or patient admissions. These projections are based on past activities, current trends, and new plans. This information is usually furnished by the accounting department.

2. Revenue Budget. The projection of revenue is usually prepared by the accounting department. Information needed includes the source of the revenue, why it is earned, and how the sources are changing.

3. Expense Budget. This attempts to account for the costs of operations (personnel and other costs). Preparing this budget is the major task of team leaders or supervisors. The expense budget is used to track costs on a monthly basis and institute remedial actions such as control of overtime before major variances take place. Costs are listed under three major classifications: type of expense (personnel, supplies, etc), department or function, and individual jobs. The break-even point is the point at which total income equals total costs. Break-even goals can best be demonstrated by a graph (Figure 25.1).

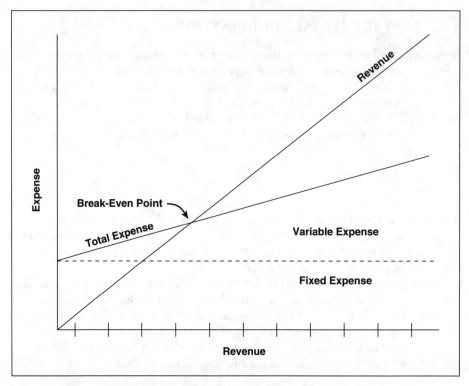

Figure 25.1   Break-Even Chart.

CASH BUDGET

The cash budget is prepared by the accounting department and is usually done last in the budgeting process. The objectives of a cash budget are to ensure enough cash on hand, to ensure that cash on hand is not excessive, and to safeguard the money against theft and mistakes. A cash budget has three parts: a beginning balance, identified cash disbursements, and sources (financing plans). The sources are internal (revenue, contributions, taxes, etc) and external (bank loans, bonds, etc). Cash budgets can also include credit sales, cash sales, inventory purchases, payroll, and other expenses of doing business.

CAPITAL EQUIPMENT

Capital items are different from other budget items because they are longer term, are more expensive, and their use and costs are spread over the life of the asset. Capital items affect both income statements and balance statements.

For practical purpose, capital equipment is usually defined as items that cost over a specific sum of money or have a useful life of a specified number of years. For example, your institution may decide that any item that costs more than $250 or has a useful life of more than 1 year will be regarded as a capital expenditure.

The acquisition of capital items is based on need. It is not necessarily enough to prove that the item will lighten the workload or increase efficiency and accuracy. These are important factors, but the primary consideration is whether the item is actually needed.[2] With today's shrinking budgets, approval usually depends on how the purchase will affect profitability or customer service.

To lease or to buy? The finance or materials management department can help to determine which decision is the proper one. Legal advice is often needed before contracts are signed.

Average Rate of Return (ARR)
    ARR = Savings or Revenue/Cost of Investment
Determination of Depreciation
    (Cost – Salvage Value)/Economic Life = Depreciation
        Example: An instrument costs $50,000, has a useful life of ten
        years and has a salvage value of $5,000.
        ($50,000 – $5,000)/10 = $4,500 depreciation/year

KINDS OF BUDGET METHODS

Fixed and Variable Costs

Fixed costs are not dependent on workload or other variable factors. Examples are charges for utilities, housekeeping, central purchasing, laundry and linen, maintenance service, equipment depreciation, education and in-service training, and administrative overhead based on amount of space occupied by department or unit. The annual total may simply be divided by 12 and the same number used each of the 12 months. These are called straight line items. Variable costs are all the others and vary from month to month depending on workload and other factors.

Continuous ("Rolling") Budget

These master budgets continually add one month to the future as the month ending is dropped, thus maintaining a continuous 12-month budget. As the year progresses, make notes pertaining to each item to project next year's occurrences.

Zero-Based Budgets

Instead of starting with last year's activities and modifying them, we start from scratch and justify every line item. This forces us to take a fresh look at what we are doing and helps to eliminate things that are no longer needed or have lower priorities. Usually only major line items are evaluated in depth.

Basic Budgeting Information

- The previous year's budget
- Management's objectives and plans for the next budget period
- Marketing or customer changes
- Policy on capital items, eg, any item that costs more than $1000 may be considered a capital expenditure
- When budget must be submitted; procedure and forms to be followed and used; when and how the budget is approved

Steps of a Budget Preparation

Teams should have sufficient information from management to be aware of changes that will affect the budget. Failure to provide this can have serious financial losses. For example, a team may purchase an expensive piece of equipment only to find out too late that the medical facility plans to discontinue the service that requires that piece of equipment.

A caveat: All too often, in the haste to prepare a budget, the manager takes the previous year's figure and simply adds or subtracts some percentage. This is immediately obvious to any alert financial officer and reflects badly on the manager's ability to consider departmental changes that affect inflow or outflow of resources.

Step 1: Consider your organization's mission, goals, and objectives. Formulate the mission for your work unit.

Step 2: Analyze specific needs. This should be a team effort with everyone contributing. Use "what if" analysis. If "A" increases or decreases, what things are likely to change? Also involved are value analyses and priorities. What items are absolutely essential (must have), what ones are important (should have), and what ones would be nice to have (wish list)?

Step 3: Set specific performance objectives—the what. Use brainstorming team sessions to identify all of the options. Evaluate the benefit/cost of each option.

Step 4: Plan the strategy—the how. Do not wait until a week before the budget is due. Instead, work on it continuously throughout the year. This involves considerations of what resources, kinds of equipment, and skills are needed, and also requires brainstorming sessions. Divide items into logical groupings, eg, function, supplies, equipment. For cost estimates, do not use the add-on percentage scheme, which is simply to take last year's budget and add a percentage increase. Use time lines and checklists, which are similar to "to do" lists, and include capital, salary, and nonsalary items. Consider the use of computer software to assist.

Step 5: Prepare your justification for each line item. "Load the justification with dollar signs and the quality of customer service—the ammunition that makes the loudest bang."[2]

Step 6: Negotiate for approval. Share information about needs, abilities, and decisions. Convince the approval group that you have not padded the budget.

TIPS FOR GETTING YOUR BUDGET APPROVED

Your request should be accompanied by the following:

- Convincing evidence of the need and urgency of each item. Include supporting statements from customers or users.

- Projections of costs and revenues. Items that affect the bottom line favorably are much more likely to be approved and assigned higher priority.

- Detailed descriptions of the item.

- Notation as to whether the item is a replacement or is new. If a replacement, is it because the old item is no longer satisfactory or because it represents an improvement? If it is an improvement, detail what is improved.

- If you meet with a budget official or committee, be prepared to justify every item in your proposal. Know what and who you want to bring with you.

FORECASTING

A business forecast or revenue projection is based on assumptions derived from past service volume, general economic and industry conditions, competition, advertising and other promotions, market research studies, and pricing policy. Work teams should have input into these projections.

RECORDS

Records of hours worked must be kept for each employee. The total hours should be broken down into regular hours, overtime, sick days, vacations, holidays, and others. These records highlight time abuses, such as excessive sick leave or overtime. Monthly differences become apparent. For example, while regular pay tends to be comparable with workload, total salary expense is usually higher during the summer when more employees are on vacation and temporary replacements are hired or more overtime is used.

A FINAL PIECE OF ADVICE

If you are responsible for the preparation of a budget, schedule meetings with your finance specialists to learn more about the process at your institution. These people will be happy to help you prepare your budget because it means less work for them in the long run. They will also be pleased to talk to your work unit and recommend reading materials.

REFERENCES

1. Spurga RC. *Balance Sheet Basics: Financial Management for Non-financial Managers*. New York, NY: Franklin Watts; 1986.
2. Sattler J. *A Practical Guide to Financial Management of the Clinical Laboratory*. Oradell, NJ: Medical Economics Co; 1980.

SUGGESTED READINGS

Barros A. Financial management is more than monitoring a budget. *MLO*. 1988;20:43-47.

Bennington JL. *Management and Cost Control Techniques for the Clinical Laboratory*. Baltimore, Md: University Park Press; 1977.

Berte LM. Finance skills for the non-financial manager. *MLO*. 1989;22:39-42.

Bittel LR. *Right on Time: The Complete Guide for Time-Pressured Managers*. New York, NY: McGraw-Hill; 1991.

Blackwell RD, Chapman JF. Inventory control: a microcomputer solution to an old problem. *MLO*. 1988;20:33-37.

Fantus J. The 10% solution to lab profitability. *MLO*. 1990;22:33-38.

Gore M. Financial management of the laboratory. *MLO*. 1988;20:24-32, 37-40.

Haughney JD. Test cost analysis: more vital than ever. In: Fitzgibbon RJ, Statland BE, eds. *DRG Survival Manual for the Clinical Laboratory*. Oradell, NJ: Medical Economics Books; 1985.

John M. A guide to cost accounting in the lab. *MLO*. 1991;23:53-54.

Johnson JL. A cost-cutting strategy. In: Fitzgibbon RJ, Statland BE, eds. *DRG Survival Manual for the Clinical Laboratory*. Oradell, NJ: Medical Economics Books; 1985.

Sharp JW. A cost-accounting system targeted to DRGs. *MLO*. 1985;17:34-41.

26. Networks, Mentors, and Organizational Politics

MANY OF US SUFFER from the Horatio Alger myth, the fairy tale that says if you work hard, make no waves, and are morally upright, you will rise to the top.[1]
Susan E. Ogborn

CHAPTER OBJECTIVES

- To define and characterize networks
- To list the many benefits of networking
- To present the potential negative aspects of and the barriers to networking
- To review the principal aspects of mentoring
- To advise on the selection and utilization of other potential network participants
- To offer a brief overview of computer networks
- To provide realistic advice on coping with workplace politics

WHAT NETWORKING IS ALL ABOUT

Developing outside relationships is largely a matter of networking. Supervisors who have shifted administrative and supervisory activities to delegates or self-directed teams have more time to network and to mentor.

Luebbert[2] defines a network as "...an informal group of contacts who share advice, facts, techniques, job leads, plans and dreams, and who lend each other moral support." We still hear the old (and true) cliché: "It's not what you know, but who you know that counts." Fortunately, in our culture abundant opportunity exists to get to know people who can help us, but this still requires some effort on our part.

Networking is building contacts with people who have information, expertise, and ideas, and who represent a wide spectrum of business, politics, and philosophy. A network is a subset of informal internal and external team building. Your network is your invisible team or your favor bank. Mastering networking is largely a matter of knowing how to be helpful to the people with whom you interface and how to ask them for help in return.

Benefits of Networking

No team can be highly successful using its own resources alone. To excel, teams and team members must look outward and see what is going on around them. They must regard these outside relationships as essential for mobilizing the trust, ideas, and active support of outsiders.

Networking is invaluable to teams for improving daily productivity, efficiency, and achievement. It is also a fast track to personal growth for individual members. People who build connections within and outside organizations are much more likely to succeed. Here are some of the many benefits that can derive from active networking:

- Obtain technical, professional, legal, or fiscal data or advice, eg, recommendations about relative value of new instruments or procedures.
- Acquire advance information about trends, new projects, or organizational changes.
- Receive feedback on proposals, ideas, speeches, or reports.
- Get moral support.
- Learn about job opportunities, since most good available jobs are never advertised.
- Become aware of the availability of candidates who are badly needed or who have unusual expertise.
- Solicit recommendations or support.
- Obtain mentoring or counseling services.
- Improve coordination and cooperation.
- Share experiences—successes and failures.

Potential Negative Aspects of Networking

- Colleagues may resent networking peers, and some managers perceive networkers as threats.
- Confusion may result from getting conflicting advice from different members of one's network—paralysis from analysis.

- Alliances may prolong or escalate inter- or intragroup conflicts. When the networks are political or activist groups, strong opposition may develop or the team splinters into squabbling factions.
- Relationships suffer when reciprocity falters, that is, when a team or a team member is a taker, someone who constantly makes requests of his or her contacts but rarely reciprocates.

BARRIERS TO NETWORKING

Many health care workers feel uneasy about reaching out to others. They may have been taught early in life that asking for help is a sign of weakness.[2] Autocratic and bureaucratic managers are less likely to participate in networks. People who are resistant to change tend to avoid outside contacts. Lack of goals or ambition is not conducive to networking. In rare instances, people find it difficult to make contacts outside their work units.

MENTORS: THE CROWN JEWELS OF NETWORKS

Mentoring is when an experienced or influential person guides and nurtures individual team members. Mentors teach mentees how to survive, thrive, and progress within an organization or a profession.

Mentoring may begin shortly after a new employee comes on board. During orientation, new hires have an excellent opportunity to spot a manager, senior team member, or trainer whom they would like to have as a mentor. In some organizations, each new hire is matched with a mentor through a formal program, but usually mentors and mentees just find each other.

The Mentor

A mentor can be someone on the same team, in another department, a retiree, or an outsider. He or she may be a senior manager or an expert in the same field. An employee's immediate supervisor is not the ideal mentor because the mentee will be more reluctant to ask questions for fear of appearing ignorant or irritating the supervisor.

- Mentors teach what textbooks and teachers cannot, namely, how to be successful in that particular organization or profession. They may suggest ways to cut bureaucratic red tape or to avoid troublesome people, policies, or practices. They describe how organizations function and how to recognize and use power. They point out the cultural sand traps and the rituals that must be followed. Mentors tell who has the clout, how decisions are made, and why one should not leave work until the chief does.[3]
- Mentors share visions of their protégés' future, perceive their potential, and pose challenges when this potential is not being

reached. They note real and potential handicaps of their mentees and recommend ways to eliminate or reduce these.

- Mentors regard their charges as extensions of themselves, and they are aware that the actions of their mentees reflect on the mentors' careers.[3]

- Mentors take an active interest in the employees' readings, work, and continuing education program. Readily available for questions, they are open, authentic, and receptive. They provide affirmation and offer feedback in a fashion that promotes the mentees' feelings of self-worth and competence.[4]

- The mentor is willing and able to select an individual and shape that person's career by removing obstacles, helping to develop team skills, advising on career development strategy, or serving as a role model. He or she may engage in one or more of the following activities: teaching, sponsoring, advising, coaching, counseling, hosting, guiding, motivating, and critiquing.

Mentor-Mentee Relationships

Mentees must respect their mentors and show some deference. The relationship is similar to that of doctor-patient or attorney-client. Mentor and mentee struggle with feelings of wanting to be autonomous and yet connected at the same time. Altering the relationship may prove stressful for both parties.[4]

Mentees must have a sincere desire to assimilate information and reconceptualize ideas. When they fail to take the advice of their mentors, they should apologize or explain, not avoid. The association may quickly or gradually end or change into a collegial relationship or a social friendship.

OTHER POTENTIAL NETWORK PARTICIPANTS

- External customers. Contact with patients, physicians, and other outside customers provides a constant source of suggestions for improving your service. If you satisfy these client needs, you will gain enthusiastic supporters. Try inviting some of these customers to your staff meetings. Members of your marketing and sales departments provide indirect consumer input.

- Internal customers include departments or individuals within your organization for whom you provide services.

- Peers include other teams or individual employees who precede or follow you in work flows and colleagues who serve with you on committees, task forces, or problem-solving groups.

- Former professors and teachers take pride in responding to your attempts to tap into their knowledge bank.

- Vendors and their representatives are loaded with valuable information and are willing to share it. For laboratory specialists, CLIA '88 will force closer cooperation regarding quality measures with suppliers of instruments and reagents.

- Members of support departments include materials management, data processing, environmental control, housekeeping, and engineering. Never underestimate the power of secretaries, security guards, or housekeeping personnel.

- In-house specialists, consultants, training specialists, researchers, and coordinators.

- Fellow members of civic, service, and social or religious organizations.

- Gatekeepers are the people inside and outside the organization who have access to important or useful people or knowledge.

- Competitors. Keep in touch with your friendly competitors. You can often teach each other how to save costs and avoid problems. If a cross-town competitor warns you against hiring one of her former employees who is a troublemaker, your friendly relationship has hit pay dirt.

How to Make and Maintain Contacts

Make use of your address book, files of correspondence and business cards, membership rosters of organizations, alumni associations, and computer databases. Professional contacts are made not only at meetings, seminars, workshops, committees, and other professional groups but also at churches or synagogues, schools, clubs, hobby groups, and in neighborhoods. The omnipresent lapel name tags on attendees are signs of networking in action. The networking at a meeting may be more valuable than the program offered. Raise your visibility by giving talks, holding office, becoming a spokesperson, and earning the reputation as a recognized expert in some professional or technical aspect of health care. Use your present network to get information about or contacts with people you would like to know.

Great Networkers in Action

Effective networkers set networking goals, eg, to meet one new person each week, to join a community association, or to visit another department each month. When they help get people promoted, the latter may join their network and return the favor. Expert networkers know that a network is like a bank account—depositors must put in as much as they take out. They build credit by being available, showing that they understand the outsider's situation and pressures, letting people know of demands on them well in advance, and explaining why they want things.[5]

How Great Networkers Get Help

- They know how to communicate with people. They ask good questions and listen attentively.
- They keep in touch with their contacts.
- They are great joiners.
- They circulate at parties and meetings where they introduce themselves rather than wait for someone else to do the honors.
- They are cordial and courteous to all, but are somewhat selective about the people with whom they develop special rapport.
- They use coffee breaks and lunch times to chat with different people.
- They develop friendly relationships with competitors and people who work for or service competitors.
- They accept invitations to sit in on meetings.
- They take advantage of corporate training sessions, seminars, and other functions to meet new people.
- They participate in extracurricular events.
- They invite visitors.

How Great Networkers Provide Help and Show Appreciation

- They volunteer for committees and other groups.
- They agree to help teach, to mentor, and to hold office.
- They quickly establish relationships with newcomers.
- They share clippings, reports, articles, and other information.
- They respond promptly and enthusiastically to questions and requests from others.
- They send out lots of thank-you notes and remember birthdays and other special occasions.
- They express their appreciation for big favors in special ways.

What Great Networkers Do Not Do

- They do not confuse networking with manipulating or posturing, eg, trying to get a request approved by inferring that they have the support of someone at the top.
- They do not use networking as an excuse for excessive socializing, neglecting their responsibilities, or dumping on others.

- They do not overuse people's time or take unfair advantage of alliances.
- They do not neglect old members of their networks.

COMPUTER NETWORKS

Computer networking is the sharing of computer resources among various users. These resources may be the computers themselves, databases, printers, or even human expertise. Messaging may be one-to-one electronic mail (E-mail) between individuals, message sending to a distribution list, and many-to-many communications when groups participate in electronic forums or conferences.

Document sharing, central databases, and computer forums now play a vital role in sharing knowledge and expertise. Electronic distribution lists enable managers and professionals to broadcast information or address concerns to numerous people.[6]

E-mail is rapidly replacing memos and has the advantage over telephone conversations in that the responder can look up information and get back to the sender when convenient. Computer networks enable employees to obtain information directly from sources without having to contact supervisors and middle managers. The widespread elimination of middle managers has been attributed in large part to this previously unavailable information channel.

Teams are learning through their computers how to do things for which they frequently depended on staff specialists or supporting departments. For example, teams now gather and process their own budgets, and find that they do not need the accounting department to do it for them. Greater access to accounts and files enables frontline employees to answer questions and serve their customers better—empowerment in action.

Personnel on after-hours shifts and those stationed in satellite facilities feel so much more in touch with each other and with their organization that loyalty is increased.[7]

Electronic meetings have distinct advantages over traditional ones. They are cost-effective when the participants would otherwise have to travel considerable distances to reach the meeting site. The lower cost permits larger numbers of people to participate. According to Sproull and Kiesler,[7] status tends to be negated in electronic meetings, whether they are conducted via E-mail or in real time. In face-to-face meetings, people with higher status tend to dominate the discussion. In electronic meetings, passive individuals are less reticent to speak up. Electronic communication tends to level the playing field.

Electronic networking also has its negatives, of course. People who spent lots of time in the break room or around the watercooler have moved their watercooler dialogues to computer stations. Others pump loads of unimportant information through the network. Some play computer games. Most users find that their computers have not decreased their paper flow or decreased the use of copiers, but massive amounts of information can now be stored on easily retrieved files.

POLITICS IN THE WORKPLACE

Organizational politics refers to the practice of using means other than merit or good performance for bettering your position or gaining favor in the organization.[8]

L.W. Rue

Despite all the team building and empowerment, negative politics is still alive and well. The original meaning of politics was to act in the service of society—a high form of public service. It has been reinterpreted to mean service to one's self.[9] This kind of self-empowerment usually carries a strong negative connotation.

Politics can and should be positive. What winners call interpersonal relationships, losers call politics. The losers make no effort to acquire mentors or to build personal networks. Instead, they grow resentful toward their employer, their superiors, and their colleagues. Often they become chronic complainers or shrill negativists.

If your political script is a positive one, you play the game fairly and ethically. Positive political behavior supplements professional competency. Leadership requires two sets of attributes: competence and political savoir faire. Political savoir-faire includes visibility, organizational sensitivity, presentation skills, and good judgment.[1] This kind of politics is beneficial not only to the practitioner but also to his or her associates, superiors, and employer.

Team and career failures can result from political as well as professional incompetence. Unwillingness to address the political components of a job has snuffed out many a promising career and inhibited cross-functional activities or reengineering of systems.

Negative Politics

Negative politics may be dysfunctional, unethical, or even illegal. It gets blamed for almost everything—bad communication, inappropriate behavior, unpopular promotions, discrimination, and favoritism. Often, when one is accused of playing politics, it is simply a matter of faulty communication that leads to false assumptions and distorted perceptions. In units where negative politics are rife, the situation can often be reversed when communication flaws are corrected.

Political Games That Stakeholders Play

- Taking advantage of being indispensable
- Abusing friendship
- Probing for weaknesses of others, then revealing those weaknesses

- Undermining operations or new services
- Starting unfounded rumors or providing misleading information
- Creating crises or discord
- Displaying undue emotional distress to achieve selfish gains
- Discrediting teammates in public or undermining in private
- Intimidating new employees and provoking sensitive people

Political Games That Managers Play

- Manipulating situations and people
- Managing information and plans to their own advantage[9]
- Stealing ideas or credit
- Excluding others from meetings or information
- Eliminating or downgrading the jobs of employees whom they dislike or distrust
- Assigning unpleasant tasks
- Delegating work that places delegates at risk or that prevents them from handling their regular work
- Pitting one employee against another
- Giving unfair or false performance appraisals
- Not hiring anyone who could be threatening

Manipulative Politics

Manipulation is the act of trying to control other people without their knowing it. Manipulators invoke the names of high-level people to get their way.[9] They curry favor of those who outrank them, sometimes to a degree of obsequiousness. They take advantage of friends and colleagues. Threats or even bribes may be part of their strategy. Their promises are quickly forgotten, and they say things they do not mean. You know you are being manipulated when someone leads off with something like "You owe me one," or "The boss will back me on this." Teams and team leaders can reduce manipulation by eliminating secrecy, status differences, and other trappings of bureaucracy.[9]

Unethical Politics

- Divulging confidential information
- Blaming others for one's mistakes or taking undeserved credit
- Authorizing subordinates to violate rules, policies, or laws
- Not reporting violations
- Placing personal interests above those of the organization, its stakeholders, or its employees

- Discriminating or showing favoritism
- Cutting corners, especially in matters of safety or quality
- Giving or receiving gifts or favors in exchange for preferential treatment

Positive Political Scripts

Healthy political scripts call for authentic attitudes, honest and open communication, networking and mentoring, coping honestly with superiors, and earning the support and respect of coworkers and subordinates. Positive political tactics benefit the organization, the work unit, and the employees. For example, a supervisor who is politically skilled and has a large supportive network is much more able to obtain the resources needed to improve services, products, and morale.

Positive political acts require trust in the people with whom we work and are especially difficult when our superiors are regarded as adversaries. The role of leaders is to resolve differences that arise between individuals and work units, to honestly represent the interests of those who report to them. These leaders reach decisions through consensus rather than through manipulation. They rarely use threats or power and always seek win/win solutions. They are skilled at persuasion, bargaining strategy, and compromise. They train their associates in political skills such as fact-finding, conciliation, mediation, negotiation, and representation.

Positive negotiating skill resolves sticky interpersonal conflicts and leads to win/win solutions. Negative political statements and unfulfilled promises lead to resentment, anger, and loss of trust.

Here are some other desirable political skills as listed by Fry[10]:

- Being able to deal with people tactfully
- Knowing whom to count on to get something
- Finding out what pleases your superiors and colleagues
- Knowing how to use what and whom you know in a positive way to reach your goal
- Being aware of what additional expertise you need

Rapport With Team Members

"One of the first things employees notice is whether 'the score' is being kept equitably."[11] *The score* refers to how individual achievement is evaluated, how each employee is treated, and how rules are enforced. Political power is short-circuited when employees feel that they are being manipulated or hoodwinked. On the other hand, if trust and respect are mutual, no political games will be played.

Educational Programs

Appropriate educational programs can help people develop political awareness and skill. These include a description of the organizational political structure, identification of political factions, and an explanation of workplace ethics. Skills in communication, fact-finding, conciliation, mediation, negotiation, and participative leadership are essential components. Participative leadership features problem solving, planning, and troubleshooting.[12]

Tips for Improving Political Skills

- Dress like the people you want to work with—usually conservatively, tastefully, and professionally.
- Offer your name first when meeting someone. It lessens the awkward "Have we met before?" query.[1]
- Do not abuse other people's time in person, on the phone, or in written communication.
- Use humor tactfully and tastefully.
- Keep your emotions under control.
- Take courses in interpersonal skills.
- Get involved socially.
- Build your network.
- Keep your eyes and ears open.
- Offer positive comments about management.
- Get all the facts before you make a presentation.
- Know when to push and when to back off.
- Prove yourself through your work.
- Be flexible in your thinking and expectations.[10]
- Do not take criticism personally.
- Document important transactions.
- Accept delegations but try to avoid being dumped on.
- Learn how to say no.
- Do not overuse alliances, mentors, or other members of your network.
- Do not let your alliances and network lapse.
- Learn negotiating skills (see Chapter 24).

REFERENCES

1. Ogborn SE. Positive politics: playing corporate games with personal integrity. *Health Care Supervis.* 1992;11:39-45.
2. Luebbert PP. Networking for survival and success. *MLO.* 1987;19:39-42.

3. Bernstein AJ, Rozen SC. *Dinosaur Brains*. New York, NY: John Wiley & Sons; 1989.

4. Liebler JG, Levine RE, Rothman J. *Management Principles for Health Professionals*. 2nd ed. Gaithersburg, Md: Aspen Publishers; 1992.

5. Hastings C, Bixby P, Chaudhry-Lawton R. *The Superteam Solution*. Aldershot, Hants, England: Gower Publishing Co; 1986.

6. Filipczak B. The ripple effect of computer networking. *Training*. 1994; 31:40-46.

7. Sproull L, Kiesler S. *Connections: New Ways of Working in the Networked Organization*. Cambridge, Mass: MIT Press; 1991.

8. Rue LW, Byars LL. *Supervision: Key Link to Productivity*. Homewood, Ill: Richard D. Irwin, Inc; 1982.

9. Block P. *The Empowered Manager: Positive Skills at Work*. San Francisco, Calif: Jossey-Bass; 1987.

10. Fry PL. How to be skillful at playing office politics. *Communication Briefings*. 1992;11:8a-8b.

11. Rendero T. Editorial. *Personnel*. 1990;67:2.

12. Young S. Politicking: the unsung managerial skill. *Personnel*. 1987; 64:62-68.

27. Innovation, Creativity, and Entrepreneurship

THE FAILURE TO PROMOTE innovation will lead to lower quality or more rationing of care—two equally undesirable results.[1]
  Elizabeth O. Teisberg

CHAPTER OBJECTIVES

- To describe the characteristics of creative people
- To compare and contrast corporate entrepreneurs and inventors
- To highlight the importance of being receptive to new ideas
- To delineate the major barriers to creative thinking
- To list 11 techniques for stimulating your creativity
- To suggest how to stimulate creativity in others

Teamwork requires trust, cooperation, communication, and creativity.[2] Quality improvement initiatives demand that all members of a team be thinking about ways to improve the performance of their unit.[1,3]

Creativity cannot be explained. It is like Mozart's music or Van Gogh's painting.[4] (Creative problem solving that requires tapping into the experiences tucked into the depths of our subconscious minds was discussed in Chapter 22.)

Intuitive judgment is affected by previous experiences that enable experienced health care workers to recognize patterns and cultural differences that escape the attention of novices.[5]

THE CORPORATE ENTREPRENEUR VS THE INVENTOR

Historically, the attitude of the U.S. health care system was, 'If it might work, try it.' Today the equally risky bias is, 'If we're not sure, don't do it.' This kind of thinking can only stifle innovation and erode quality.[1]
     Elizabeth O. Teisberg

Entrepreneurs are not the same as inventors. The latter are creative, but they may or may not convert their ideas into action.[6] In the 3M corporation, an employee discovered a glue that would cause paper to stick to paper but permitted the paper to be removed without tearing it. That invention was ignored until another 3M employee found that characteristic to be useful for attaching papers temporarily to his hymnal. This led to the development of "Post-it" notes. The first 3M employee was an inventor, the second was a corporate entrepreneur or intrapreneur, a term coined by Pinchot for individuals who act as entrepreneurs within the existing organizations.[7]

    Entrepreneurs may be a bit short on originality. Their bright ideas often come from others or from something they read or heard. They may just improve somebody else's work or flow chart. They are great adopters and adapters who can see the merit in ideas that others developed but have abandoned. What makes them unique, however, is their ability to put ideas to use and their willingness to accept full accountability for developing pet projects.[6] These folks can visualize complex steps from an idea to its actualization. They are willing to take risks, even put their careers on the line. Since they need the cooperation of others and the support of their superiors, effective entrepreneurs are skilled negotiators—something often lacking in inventors. They get their kicks from putting ideas into action rather than from creating them.

    In times of rapid change when new services and products are required to prevent stagnation and decline, the health care industry needs lots more inventors and intrapreneurs. When inventors and corporate entrepreneurs do not get the support they seek to do their good works, they either become disgruntled conformists or take their expertise elsewhere.

IMPORTANCE OF RECEPTIVITY TO CREATIVE IDEAS: THE PARADIGM EFFECT[8]

When data are presented, people see with clarity what matches their expectations and tend to ignore what is outside the boundaries of their personal paradigm or to distort the data to fit their expectations. These paradigms prevent individuals from accepting the suggestions of creative people who present data that fall outside the personal paradigm.

The Swiss failed to see the value of the quartz-movement watch and lost their watch industry. We all know office workers and laboratorians who resigned, took early retirement, or were forced to seek new positions because they were unwilling or unable to learn how to use computers. Each of us must recognize the limitations of our own personal paradigm and try to expand its limits.

Major Barriers to Creative Thinking

The need to solve things quickly puts a brake on creativity. We become impatient when we are presented with ideas that are complex or difficult to understand. We must learn to assign a higher priority to this activity. Saying yes too quickly can get supervisors into hot water, since bad ideas may be implemented. If a quick yes is followed by a reversal, its proponent gets discouraged or resentful. Premature rejections are even worse. Great ideas (often also the idea person) are lost, and creativity is suppressed.

Do not reject ideas on the basis of a person's status. We are all inclined to pay more attention to people whom we respect or who have fancy titles. Because of this selectivity, many great ideas are ignored.[9]

Other factors are:

- Restrictive policies, systems, rules, procedures, and practices
- Rigid controls, budgets, and group norms
- Insistence on consensus
- Monotonous tasks and boring meetings
- Excessive committee work
- Long chain of command
- Excessive specialization
- Disparaging remarks, skepticism, and cynicism
- Autocratic or bureaucratic leadership

Characteristics of Creative People

- They are more intuitive. They pay more attention to their insights, which they refer to as their gut reactions.
- They are chronically dissatisfied with status quo and routines. They are comfortable with change.
- They have enormous curiosity, enthusiasm, and persistence. They bombard others with whys and why nots.
- They produce a constant flow of suggestions, comments, and ideas, often regarded by others as impractical.

- They are optimistic risk takers who rarely use the word *failure*.
- They demand much of themselves and of others, but seldom are perfectionists.
- They are impatient, especially regarding red tape and bureaucratic interference. On the other hand, they are more tolerant of the existence of a problem and of ambiguity. Less creative people feel uncomfortable when faced with problems and tend to jump at the first solution.
- They are often nonconformists who cherish independence and autonomy.
- They frequently appear to be preoccupied or wasting time.
- They possess playfulness and humor. They play with ideas, often not for any immediate practical purpose but just for the joy of exploration.
- They rely more on pattern recognition than on words.[5]

Techniques for Stimulating Your Creativity

- Alter your daily routines: take a different route to work, eat with different people, use different-colored pens and paper.
- Engage in more personal and group brainstorming.
- Inject humor into situations. Some of the best ideas are proposed as jokes. Solemn people are less creative. Humor gets you into a playful creative mode. Laughter produces relaxation.
- Play the devil's advocate.
- Challenge rules, especially your own.
- Tolerate ambiguity. Avoid the jigsaw paradigm in which solutions must fit established boundaries, like the straight edges and perfect fits of puzzles.
- Spend more time with creative people. Creativity is to some extent a learned skill.
- Try to be less concerned about failure or criticism.
- Use relaxation techniques. Have an oasis of quiet that is free of interruptions. Ideally, you have a set time for such contemplation each day.
- Become more aware of what goes on around you. Make your senses more sensitive.
- Overcome ideonarcissism, which is the egotism of thinking that your idea is unique and because of your vast experience must be the best one.

How to Stimulate Creativity in Others

- Start the process during your orientation program for new employees. Spend less time telling and more time listening. All too often, indoctrination is a show-and-tell process with the theme "Do it our way, and you'll do just fine." These introductions to conformity and compliance snuff out innovativeness. New hires must be encouraged to express opinions, articulate disagreements, and make recommendations. When a trainee says "I think there is a better way," what kind of response is he or she likely to get in your unit?

- Provide challenges. Creative people thrive on challenges. Encourage a "what if" or "maybe we could" attitude. A pervasive dissatisfaction with current methods is conducive to idea generation.

- Ask colleagues what they would do differently if they owned their departments. Seek more input about resolving problems, satisfying customers, or attracting new business.

- Do not make employees dependent on you by solving all their problems. Insist that they bring in solutions with their problems.

- Involve employees in operational problem solving. Problem solving, especially of the brainstorming type, is relished by most idea people.

- Tolerate idiosyncrasies. Creative people are not the easiest ones with whom to get along. They can be trying at times. Their impulsiveness, constant questioning, and nonconforming habits induce supervisory headaches. Idea people must be given looser reins.

- Protect them. These folks are often not popular. They may be loners. Their ideas introduce change that is often unwelcome to their peers. They may be regarded with suspicion, even hostility.

- Provide idea sources. Idea pumps are primed by exposure to the works and thoughts of others. These sources include:

  seminars and professional meetings

  networks, consultants, and mentors

  publications

  client input

REFERENCES

1. Teisberg EO, Porter ME, Brown GB. Making competition in health care work. *Harvard Bus Rev.* 1994;72:131-141.

2. Frings CS. Setting a climate for motivating your staff. *MLO.* 1993;25:47-50.

3. Byham WC. *Zapp! The Lightning of Empowerment.* New York, NY: Harmony Books; 1988.

4. Cleese J. And now for something completely different. *Personnel*. 1991; 68:13-15.

5. Davidhizar R. Intuition and the nurse manager. *Health Care Supervis*. 1991;10:13-18.

6. Umiker WO. Do you have an 'intrapreneur' in your lab? *MLO*. 1986;18: 48-50.

7. Pinchot G III. *Intrapreneuring*. New York, NY: Harper & Row; 1985.

8. Barker JA. *The Business of Paradigms*. Burnsville, Minn: Chart House International Learning Corp; 1974.

9. Kepford C. Keeping up with employee ideas. *Supervis Manage*. 1993;38: 3-4.

28. Time Management for Individuals and Teams

T HERE IS ALWAYS a better way to do anything. It's up to you to find it.[1]
　　　Thomas Edison

Chapter Objectives

- To identify the six big time wasters
- To explore why most time management programs fail
- To identify and delineate intrinsic and extrinsic factors that waste time
- To recommend techniques for coping with people who waste your time
- To provide a few tips for saving time at meetings
- To urge the use of time logs
- To suggest ways to increase office or work station efficiency
- To list tips for better time control
- To discuss time thefts at work and how to reduce their incidence

Health care professionals are well aware of the importance of time. Their days are filled with deadlines, turnaround times, emergencies, unanticipated problems, and interruptions. There never seem to be enough hours in the day to complete their tasks. Cost cutbacks have resulted in staff shortages, thus further aggravating the time crunch.

Everyone has the same amount of time, and how that time is managed is, at least to a limited extent, up to the individual performer. The successful time manager takes time to think about how time is currently spent, which things waste time, and how time can be saved. Time, like money, can be spent wisely or foolishly. Finally, it is essential that we substantially improve the way we handle information, and electronic devices have made such improvements available to almost everyone.

THE SIX BIG TIME WASTERS

1. Doing things one need not do
2. Inefficient scheduling
3. Poor communication systems
4. Meetings
5. Interruptions
6. Incompetent workers who need help

WHY MOST TIME MANAGEMENT PROGRAMS FAIL

Time management programs, like weight reduction programs, succeed only when the participants are truly committed. To lose weight, people must give up things they like to eat. To gain time, they must give up some things they like to do or, incorrectly, feel compelled to do.

Another cause of failure is attempting to do too much too soon. Enthusiastic dieters start off with a bang, practically starving themselves for the first few days or weeks. They usually quit gradually or abruptly because it requires too much will power to continue that demanding routine. An employee attends a time management seminar or reads a book on the subject, then tries to do everything all at once instead of one step at a time. That effort is also too much for most people and usually ends in the abandonment of any change at all.

For the average team member, most time is dedicated to routine tasks. Other big chunks are demanded by superiors, customers, visitors, vendors, colleagues, and communication devices such as meetings, telephones, computers, and written documents. The little time that remains for planning, creating, studying, and other purposes is rarely assigned a high priority. Employees who do not carry out their compulsory functions efficiently, who cannot say no, or who waste precious time have little or no time left for nonurgent but still important personal activities.

INTERNAL FACTORS THAT WASTE TIME: WHAT YOU DO TO YOURSELF

- You fight fires instead of preventing them. When individuals and teams lack anticipatory strategies and only react to problems, they are problem fighters. Problem or fire fights take lots of time and are seldom completely reversible. The alternative approach, proactivity, requires fire or problem prevention, which includes doing things right the first time to avoid having to correct things done sloppily. Proactive people and teams avoid problems, or nip them in the bud, by planning and focusing on potential problem systems or areas. Proactivity is time efficient, more effective, and much less stressful.

■ You procrastinate. Procrastination results in inactivity or in spending time doing low priority tasks instead of the ones you should be doing. Here are some practical suggestions for avoiding or minimizing procrastination.

Develop the habit of saying "I want to" instead of "I should" or "I have to."

Use daily prioritized to-do lists.

Start the work day with high-priority or unpleasant tasks.

Avoid the temptation to stall. Do not get involved with trivia. Challenge your excuses. Psyche yourself up.

Block out enough time to complete time-consuming tasks.

Slice a big task into thin slices that are more easily completed.

Set a timer for five minutes and force yourself to start when it goes off.

Do not reward procrastination by permitting yourself to engage in pleasant activities while you delay action. Sit in a straight chair without coffee or conversation. Do reward yourself when you beat procrastination.

■ You are a perfectionist. Perfectionism can be more deadly than procrastination when it comes to wasted time, and it is harder to overcome. Go for excellence, but not perfection. Team members must learn which activities demand zero defects and which do not. It is one thing to fail to detect an incompatibility when cross-matching blood, another thing to fail to answer the phone within three rings. What is sometimes called perfectionism is really a lack of willingness to take responsibility or risk. For example, Denise, a chemistry technologist, insisted on repeating every test she ran, even though the repeats never showed any significant deviations. She had to be discharged because she was a major bottleneck to the work flow.

■ You fail to set boundaries on your availability. To avoid overcommitment of your time and other resources, you must be able to say no diplomatically and emphatically, but firmly. When requests come from associates or superiors, this is not easy, especially if you are susceptible to flattery or manipulation.

■ You erode your discretionary time. This is largely doing things that should be done by others, trivial things that could be eliminated, or possibly excessive socializing.

EXTERNAL FACTORS: WHAT OTHERS DO TO YOU

Interruptions by associates. Look for patterns among the interruptions. Analyze these in depth and take appropriate action. For example, a spouse might be making a daily call of minimal importance or at an inconvenient time. A colleague drops in several times a day on the way to the copy room.

Contact people in their offices or work stations rather than in yours. This gives you control over when the contact starts and ends.

Decrease the need of your associates for your help by showing them how they can help themselves. Offer alternatives. When a superior makes a request that creates a problem, nail down priorities, eg, "Should I stop working on the...?"

Come to work early or stay late. Shut your door when you need privacy.

A caveat: Each team member must realize that interruptions are part of the job, and it may be attitudes toward these interruptions that need adjusting.[1]

Advice for Team Members When Your Leader or Supervisor Makes Excessive Demands on Your Time

- If the supervisor delegates or assigns too much work to you, ask which of your routine tasks should be delayed or if you are to shift some of your work to another team member.

- If the supervisor sends for you several times a day or drops in too frequently, suggest a daily brief meeting at the start or the end of the day.

- Excuse yourself from group meetings in the supervisor's office when you sense that you are no longer needed.

- Make certain that you understand the supervisor's instructions.

- Give the supervisor positive strokes for not interrupting your work, eg, "Thanks for your perceptiveness. Yesterday when I had to finish my report, I know you diverted some interruptions. I appreciate that."

- Be assertive, say "I'm in the middle of a problem, can I get back to you?"

- Interruptions by visitors. Be firm with time, but gracious with visitors. Do not call visitors annoyances or time wasters. Most of them are external or internal customers and should be treated as such. Effective professionals save time elsewhere so they can devote more time to visitors.

Seven Techniques for Controlling Visitors Who Abuse Your Time

1. Train others to help visitors when you are not available. You may not even be needed.

2. In the case of the casual drop-in, say "I'm very busy right now, can we get together later?"

3. Intercept visitors outside your office—once people get in your office the transaction time increases. If you have kept them waiting, apologize.

4. Remain standing. Once visitors sit down, the visit time escalates.

5. Use nonverbal language to signal that you wish to end the meeting, eg, reduce eye contact, glance frequently at your watch, start shuffling papers, tapping a pencil, or drumming your fingers, or put your hand on the telephone.

6. Say "Could we continue this later, when I'm not so swamped?" or "I won't take any more of your time."

7. Stand up and extend your hand or come out from behind your desk and walk them toward the door.

The Terrible Interrupter: The Telephone

The telephone can be a great time-saver, especially when it substitutes for personal visits. Increasingly, the telephone is used for conference calls. However, the telephone is also a major interrupter. Here are some tips for saving telephone time:

- Minimize personal calls—incoming and outgoing.
- Use an answering machine.
- Allocate a time for receiving and returning calls.
- Have someone screen your calls.
- Plan what you are going to say before making calls.
- Have paper, pencil, and a list of frequently called numbers next to the phone.
- When calling others, start with business and end with social dialogue. Skip the latter if the person sounds busy.
- Make a special effort to be brief.
- Avoid phone tag (a sequence of missed phone connections). If a person is out, leave a message instead of having the person call back.

Meetings

Meetings are where minutes are kept and hours are wasted.
    An old apothegm

Meetings can be massive time wasters. Before suggesting a team meeting, make sure that it is really needed. Perhaps you can achieve what you need by talking to one or two other people. Memos, electronic mail, or a fax may be just as effective. Teleconferences can often substitute for face-to-face meetings.

If you are a leader, invite only the people you need, and excuse them after they have make their contributions. When you want specific individuals to discuss certain aspects of a topic, let them know ahead of time. Stand-up meetings are great time-savers. Do not condone lateness or delay a meeting by waiting for stragglers. Team leaders may arrange the agenda so that items of interest to habitual latecomers appears first. In some team meetings, the late arrivals get the least desirable assignments. (See Chapter 23 for tips on holding more efficient meetings.)

YOUR MASTER PLAN STARTS WITH FINDING OUT WHERE YOUR TIME GOES

Use time logs to determine how each team member spends time. This enables you to see how effectively time is utilized. where the time wasting is, where efforts are being duplicated, and how systems can be made more efficient.

Tasks Can Be Divided Into Five Categories

1. External customer tasks relate directly to external customers such as physicians, patients, and third-party payers. A simple criterion is that the customer would be willing to pay for what is being done, eg, collecting a specimen, running a test, interpreting a result, or preparing blood components. Conway[2] found that only 15% of the work hours of a typical organization are spent on necessary work. Lathrop[3] reported that only 16 cents of every health care dollar is spent on direct medical care.

2. Supplemental tasks are needed to get work done but do not provide direct patient service, eg, recording or reporting, dealing with internal customers and vendors, ordering supplies, taking inventory, training, filing, some meetings, performance reviews, interviewing candidates, and counseling sessions.

3. Fence-mending tasks would not have to be done if all work were done perfectly in the first place and to the customer's satisfaction. Most of this time is spent responding to complaints or redoing work. It includes the investigation of possible transfusion reactions, getting new specimens, and conferring with disgruntled customers and employees.

4. Unnecessary tasks are those that could be eliminated without any significant harm. These include some reports, some paperwork, some meetings, some traveling, and some phone calls.

5. Not working includes the authorized items like personal time, breaks, holidays, and vacations. Idle time may occur because of delays in blood collections, centrifugation, and other process steps when employees do not find other things to do during the waiting

periods. Unauthorized time wasters include self-imposed idle time, socializing, late arrivals and early departures, abuses of sick days, and sleeping on the job.

Recording of Time

Throughout the work day at predetermined intervals such as 15 minutes, each team member jots down brief descriptions of how time is spent. Keep the record for at least two weeks. Using the list of five kinds of tasks, team members individually categorize each time period and transfer the time totals to a chart (Table I).

To get the biggest bang for the buck, the team works first on the items classified as nonwork or unnecessary work. Little detailed study is required, but often much will power is needed to eliminate these factors because many of them are habits that some individuals are loath to give up. Some solutions require simple changes, such as assigning tasks to people who have been idle while waiting for others who precede them in the work flow, eg, technologists waiting for phlebotomy teams to return or people waiting for an automated apparatus or centrifuge to process specimens.

Most of the unnecessary tasks are qualified by the word *some*, and these same items are also found in the group labeled supplemental tasks. We all know that some meetings, reports, travel, and phone calls are necessary and some are a waste of time. The team must determine which of each of these requires attention.

For some of the tasks, especially those in the first two categories, process reengineering is required (see Chapters 17 and 18). Quality improvement studies help to identify procedures that often result in complaints or rework.

Use Charts to Help in This Process

Charts are helpful in displaying aspects of time management. For example, once you have timed various tasks that could be modified, use a Pareto chart to highlight the tasks that consume the largest time. Run charts with time marked on the horizontal axis and work hours on the vertical axis display the effectiveness of remedial efforts to reduce unnecessary work hours. Gantt charts and flow diagrams enable team members to ferret out the steps in a work process that could be eliminated or streamlined.

INCREASE THE EFFICIENCY OF YOUR OFFICE OR WORKSTATION

The best place to start a time management program is in your office or workstation, because this is where results can be observed quickly. Avoid what Peter and Hull[4] call *papyrophobia* (an abnormal desire for a clean desk). Organized clutter is OK. No one has yet proved the old cliché that "a messy

Table I
Task Time Analyzer

Kinds of Tasks	Time (hours)	Comments
External Customer Tasks		
Urinalysis dip sticks		
Centrifugation		
Microscopics		
Special tests		
Phone reports		
Supplemental Tasks		
Records/reports		
Training		
Meetings		
Quality control		
Study		
Fence-Mending Tasks		
Complaints from physicians		
Complaints from others		
Repeats		
Unnecessary Tasks		
Staff meeting		
Committee meeting		
Errands for supervisor		
Answering phone		
No Work Activity		
Breaks		
Waiting time for specialist		
No assignment		
Tardy/early departure		
Socializing/visitors		

desk indicates a messy mind," and a desk "cleared for action" is not always the sign of efficiency. If you can quickly find what you are looking for, and you have enough surface work space, let the mess stay and ignore the jibes from your associates.

Table II
Examples of Electronic Time Management Aids[5]

Calendar, to-do list, address and phone directory

Appointment schedule, prioritized task lists, address and phone directory

Rolodex-type cardfile directory and notepad, task manager, calendar, automatic phone dialer

Palmtop computer: Appointment book, to-do list, phone directory, memo pad, and financial calculator

An action-oriented filing system and paper flow includes the following:

- Arrange your filing cabinets to provide ready access. The average person spends an inordinate amount of time looking for things in his or her office. Periodically clean out drawers.

- Revise your filing system so you can find things quickly.

- Filing begins when you sort your incoming mail. Practice the 3-D concept: Do, Delegate, or Discard. When you hesitate to discard, ask yourself "What's the worst thing that could happen if I don't keep this?"

- Do not let your hold basket or folder get out of control. Try to handle each item only once. Review the items daily and act on as many as you can. Do feel uncomfortable when you find yourself handling the same piece of paper day after day. Do something with it!

- Place a throw-out date on major filed items.

- A tickler file is helpful. For a tickler file, you need folders numbered 1 to 31 for days of the month. File items on the day of the month when action is due. Put in reminder notes for starting projects, information needed when attending meetings, or to give you a few lead days for getting ready for something. If you are the team leader, use this same file for checking on the work assigned to others.

- Consider the use of a date book organizer. Many good ones are on the market. Make full use of electronic systems. Address books and Rolodexes become messy and illegible after crossing out and rewriting information that keeps changing. Computer software has the same advantages but eliminates the drawbacks of pencil and paper systems. These programs also enable you to transfer information directly to letters or reports in word processing or spreadsheet programs. Handheld portable information managers are also available.[5] Examples of these aids are listed in Table II. Electronic support systems (EPS) provide immediate answers to questions posed by workers and avoid waiting to contact superiors or specialists.

Planning and Scheduling

When you fail to plan, you are planning to fail.
    Source unknown

Most of our work time is fixed by outside events or people. Our discretionary time is usually limited and comes in bits and pieces—a few minutes at the start of the day, a few more right after lunch, and some more while waiting for an appointment to show up. We must make maximum use of this discretionary time.

Kanban, which is Japan's just-in-time inventory system, is an excellent example of how planning and scheduling not only improves time management but also lowers operational costs and increases efficiency.

- Establish goals, priorities, schedules, and deadlines for all major undertakings. The more time spent preparing for meetings, interviews, and instructional sessions, the less wasted time at these functions.

- Differentiate between real deadlines, like payroll data, and less stringent ones, like the minutes of a meeting.

- Avoid rigid schedules. Be flexible by allowing for the unexpected. Unanticipated problems always pop up when you least expect them.

- If possible, make an appointment with yourself to get something done that requires a large block of time. Even schedule it with your team leader and put it on your day calendar. This measure is also an effective way to avoid procrastination.

DAILY ACTION LISTS

Prepare a to-do list first thing each morning or the last thing before leaving. Some people list all of their daily tasks; others only those tasks that fall outside the routine responsibilities, such as critical phone calls, reports, appointments, or part of a special project. These lists not only organize your daily routine, they also help to avoid one of the major pitfalls of time management—procrastination.

A poorly prepared to-do list can be demotivating or frustrating if the list is too challenging and the person rarely accomplishes the important tasks. Individual tasks should be prioritized according to their importance. Some teams develop daily or weekly individual lists and plans, and then coordinate them with the other team members. This helps to avoid problems, allows better coordination, and prevents overcommitment or duplication of efforts.[1]

Delegation

Delegation is one of your most effective time-savers. See Chapter 4.

Tips for Better Time Management

- Be considerate of other people's time. Do not interrupt them unnecessarily.
- It takes 21 days to establish a habit. Select your top five time wasters and work on them for three weeks.
- Express as much appreciation to people for saving your time as you do to people who help you save money.
- Use margin replies for informal written notes.
- Use videotapes for repetitive teaching, such as orientation and training of new hires.
- Ask for help when you need it. Some people are stubborn about this and make every effort to avoid asking others to help. Be equally willing to help others.

Restrain the Time Bandits

Time theft may be America's biggest crime. Half[6] writes: "The average worker in the U.S.A. has an average of 7 to 12 unscheduled absences each year. He wastes 18% of the time he is supposed to be working. That equals nine 35-hour weeks...a 'vacation' of more than two months per year at work."

Major Time Thefts

Unjustified sick days
Tardiness or leaving early
Long breaks or meals
Leaving work station for personal trips, eg, shopping
Doing personal tasks on the job
Excessive socialization and idle conversation
Interrupting others
Wandering around the building
Excessive personal phone calls
Personal or family visitors
Daydreaming

Bad habits should be nipped in the bud by better coaching and counseling. However, remember that teammates should be treated with kindness and consideration. For example, a little compassion must be shown when dealing with employees who have children at home or other special situations.

The first step in eliminating or decreasing this time waste is to be aware of it. The strategy of managing-by-walking-around pays off handsomely. Merely appearing on the scene will squelch idle conversations and let people know that you are aware of their absences from the work area. Changes in work stations can often help. People accomplish more alone than in groups when the work is boring. Study your work flow patterns and other systems to see if greater efficiency can be achieved.

REFERENCES

1. Douglass ME, Douglass DN. *Time Management for Teams*. New York, NY: AMACOM; 1992.

2. Conway WE. *Waste Chasers*. Nashua, NH: Conway Quality, Inc.

3. Lathrop JP. The patient-focused hospital. *Healthcare Forum J*. 1991; 34:17-20.

4. Peter LJ, Hull R. *The Peter Principle: Why Things Always Go Wrong*. New York, NY: Bantam Books; 1969.

5. Mayer JJ. The new time management tool: your computer. *Boardroom Reports*. 1994;23:13-14.

6. Half R. Management roundup. *Manage Rev*. 1984;73:7.

SUGGESTED READINGS

Bittel R. *Right on Time: The Complete Guide for Time-Pressured Managers*. New York, NY: McGraw-Hill; 1991.

Scott D. *The Telephone and Time Management*. Los Altos, Calif: Crisp Co; 1988.

Sullivan G. *Work Smart, Not Hard*. New York, NY: Facts On File; 1987.

Index

Page numbers in **boldface** indicate figures and tables.

A

Abilene paradox, 256
Absenteeism, 138
  solutions for, 138
Acceptable behavior, 118
Accountability, team, 76
Action list, daily, 306
Action plan, 199–200, 243
Active listening, 104, 233
Active neutrality, 258
Adaptability, 24
Addicted employee, 142–144
Address book, 305
Administrative competency, 221, **222**
Adult learners, 104, 223
Affirmative action, 177
Age discrimination, 141
Agenda, for team meetings, 254
Aggressive people, 268
AIDS, 142
Alcoholism, chronic, 144
Allied power, 263
Alternative healing beliefs, 177
Analytical thinking, 241
Angry people, 268
  anger as barrier to negotiation, 266
Annual bonus, 167
Apprenticeship, 218
ARC, 142
Argument, discussion vs, 255–256
Assertiveness training, 258
Assigning process, 39
Attendance records, 138–139, 277–278
Attitude, 128–129. *See also* Unpleasant
    people
  "can'ts" and "won'ts," 137–138
  definition of, 128

Autonomous work team. *See* Self-direct-
    ed work team
Average rate of return, 275

B

Bad attitude, 128–129
Bar codes, 272
Bargaining power, 263
Behavioral modification, 128, 133
Benchmarking, 87, 196–197, 220
Bias, 176, 247
Bickering stage. *See* Confusion stage
Body language, 178, 234, 258, 264
Bottleneck, 111, 140, 154
Brainstorming, 104, 122, 198, 252, 295
  structured groups, 246–247, **246**
  unstructured groups, 246
Break-even point, 273, **274**
Broadbanding, 166
Budget, 273
  basic budgeting information, 276
  capital equipment, 274–275
  cash, 274
  continuous, 275
  fixed costs, 275
  getting approval for, 277
  kinds of budget methods, 275–276
  operating, 273
  preparation of, 276–277
  for process reengineering, 200
  zero-based, 275
Bystanders, 28

C

"Can'ts" (underperformers), 137–138
Capital equipment, 274–275
Career advancement, 91
  risk taking and, 15

Career development, 43–45, **45**
Career plan, 198
Cash budget, 274
Cause and effect charts, 242
Cautious people, 259
Celebrations, 164
Chair
  don'ts for meetings, 257
  preparation for team meeting, 253–254
  responsibilities during team meetings,
    254
Challenge, 295
Change
  acceptance of, 28
  achieving smooth and effective change,
    32
  adjusting to, 21–32
  anticipation of, 27–28
  competitive edge and, 22
  coping with cynics, 31
  in customer demand or expectations, 23
  employee commitment to, 24
  enlisting help from team, 26–27
  goals and objectives of implementing,
    25
  immediate response to (denial stage),
    27–28
  indicators for, 23–24
  kinds of, 22
  in laws, policies, and practices, 23
  motivating people to change, 24
  need for process reengineering,
    195–198
  new competitors or new challenges, 23
  in organizational culture, 174
  planning process, 25–26
  questions employees want answered
    about, **30**
  requirements to achieve, 24–25
  resistance to, 28, 132
    diversity of opinion, 30
    fear of loss of control, 28–29
    fear of unknown, 28
    mindsets and, 29
    overcoming of, 29–30
    reasons for, 28–29
  role of supervisor or team leader, 25
  stages of employee responses to, 27–28
  tips for agents of, 27

training of supervisor-in-transition,
    225–226
  during transition to self-directed work
    teams, 96–97
  using recognition and reward system,
    31, **32**
  in work force, 23–24
Change agent, coach as, 102
Change essentials, 24
Charts, 242
  charting methods, 104
  as project tools, 182
  time management, 303
Checkpoints, 40
Chronic alcoholism, 144
Chronic complainers, 50, 149–150, 286
Chronic objectors, 259
Cluster pitfall, 241
Coach, 95–105
  extradepartmental activities of, 103
  functions for, 97
  responsibilities of, 100, **101**
  roles of
    change agent, 102
    communicator, 98–99
    customer advocate, 98
    defender, 102
    facilitator, 99–100, **101**
    guide, 100–102
    liaison agent, 102
    mentor, 103
    model, 103
    persuader, 98
    visionary, 97–98
  team activities of, 103–104
  team leaders and, 95–96
  traditional supervisor vs, 97
  training of, 104
  what to do when team is acquired,
    104–105
Commitment, 118
Committee, 72, 183
Communality, 124
Communication, 229–238
  between culturally diverse people, 178
  by leaders, 230–232
  electronic, 237–238, 285–286
  team, 233
  interteam, 100–102
  organizational culture, 175

in process reengineering, 201
tips for better verbal communication, 234
written vs verbal, 235
Communication skills
as leadership trait, 65
of team leader, 109
of team members, 119
Communicator, coach as, 98–99
Competencies, of team members, 116–117
Competitive edge, 22
Competitors, networking with, 283
Complainers, chronic, 50, 149–150, 286
Complaints, 210–212, **212**
answering of, 235
role of supervisor or team leader, 211
Compromise, 265
Computer
communication via, 237–238, 285–286
as project tool, 182
Computerized ordering, 272
Computer network, 285–286
Concealers, 151–152
Condescending attitude, 149
Confirmation trap, 247
Confusion stage, of team building, 87–88
Consensus, 245, **245**
Contingency planning, 200
Continuous budget, 275
Continuous quality improvement (CQI), 4
Control, lack of, 50
Cooperation, 118
Coordinator. *See* Coach
Coping approach, to people problems, 134–135
Corporate reengineering, 185–186
CQI. *See* Continuous quality improvement
Creative problem solving, 246–247
Creativity, 24, 102, 291
barriers to, 293
characteristics of creative people, 293–294
effect of orientation program on, 227
receptivity to creative ideas, 292–293
stimulating in others, 295
stimulating in yourself, 294
Credibility
of coach, 105

of leader, 65
as negotiating imperative, 263
of team leader, 109
Criticism
constructive, 231–232
goal of, 231
Critics, 147–148
Cross-functional system, 100
Cross-functional team, 24, 40, 73, 190
Cross-training, 54, 67, 81, 85–86, 116, 131, 209, 225
advantages of, 225
Cultural diversity, 172–180
administrative programs for, 177
benefits and dangers of, 176
biases, prejudices, and stereotypes, 176
diversity awareness training, 177–178
in health care institution, 175
helping potential victims of harassment, 179
impact on medical care, 177
multicultural values, 178–179
tips for supervisors and team leaders, 179–180
Culture, 8
organizational. *See* Organizational culture
Culture survey, 177
Customer(s)
benefits of employee empowerment, 49
benefits of team concept, 74–75
networking with, 282
Customer advocate, coach as, 98
Customer satisfaction, 54
Customer service, 175
detecting situations needing improvement, 195–196
risk taking and, 14–15
Customer service committee, 184
Customer service team, 183
Customer tasks, 302
Customs, 178
Cynics, 149
resistance to change, 31

D

Daily action list, 306
Daily work plan, 198
Date book organizer, 305

Daydreaming, 244
Deadlines, as barrier to negotiation, 266
Decision making, 53–54, 239–249
  basics of consensus, 245, **245**
  group, **248**
  importance of, 240
  pitfalls in, 247–248, **248**
  problem solving vs, 241
  questions that assist, **18**
  risk taking and, 14
  in team meetings, 256
  triad for effective decisions, 240
Defender, coach as, 102
Defensiveness, 247
Delaying tactics, in negotiation, 267
Delegation, 4, 111, 306
  assigning process, 38–39
  benefits of
    to delegates, 34
    to delegators, 34
    to organization, 34
  "do" and "do not do" lists, 41
  "dumping," 35–36
  failures in, 40–41
  follow-up to, 40
  getting acceptance from delegate, 39
  "hopscotch," 36
  horizontal, 40
  inept, 36
  leaders who fail to delegate, 34–35
  problems with, 35–36
  risk taking and, 14
  selecting the delegate, 38–39
  selecting what to delegate, 37–38, **37**
  upward, 36
  what may not be delegated, 38
  what should not be delegated, 38
  in writing, 39
Depreciation, 275
Depression, 142
Desktop publishing, 230
Devious negotiator, 268
Difficult people, 127–135
  aggressive or angry people, 268
  attitudes of, 128–129
  high-tech professionals, 129–131
  nonconformists, 131–132
  people with difficulty serving on
    teams, 132
  at team meetings, 259
Diplomacy, as leadership trait, 65

Directive message, 230
Disbanding stage, of team, 89
Disbelievers, in participative manage-
  ment, 61
Discontentment, 206
Discretionary time, 299, 306
Discussion, argument vs, 255–256
Dissatisfaction stage. *See* Confusion
  stage
Distribution lists, electronic, 285
Diversity awareness training, 177–178
Domineering negotiator, 268
Downward communication, 230–232
"Dumping," 35–36

E

Egotists, 150–151
Electronic bulletin board, 230
Electronic forum, 285
Electronic meeting, 285
Electronic performance support system
  (EPS), 238, 305
Electronic time management aids, 305,
  305
E-mail, 237, 285
Emotional needs, unfulfilled, 128–129
Empathy, as negotiating imperative,
  262–263
Employee attitude survey, 118, 121–122,
  123
Employee empowerment. *See*
  Empowerment
Employee evaluation worksheet, 53
Employer, challenges faced by, 2–3
Empowered work team. *See* Self-direct-
  ed work team
Empowerment, 3–4
  barriers to
    lack of confidence in leaders, 52
    managers not wanting to share
      power, 52
    people who eschew empowerment,
      51–52
  benefits of
    to customers, 49
    to employees, 48–49
    to organization, 48
  empowering actions, 52–55
  group, 59–69
  leaders in, 52

problems and pitfalls surrounding, 56
risks of, 51
training of, 218
of work team, 55–56
Entrepreneur, 24
inventor vs, 292
EPS. *See* Electronic performance support system
Equal opportunity, 177
Equivocators, 16
Escalating dialogue, 258
Ethical issues, 156, 287–288
"Excel," 220
Executive summary, 200
Expediter. *See* Coach
Expense budget, 273
External customer tasks, 302

F

Facilitating skills, as leadership trait, 65
Facilitator, 85–88, 99–100, **101.** *See also* Coach
  role in team meeting, 253–254
Fake know-it-alls, 151
Faulty process, 187
Favoritism, 178
Fax, 237
Fears, as barrier to negotiation, 265
Feedback, constructive, 231–232
Fence-mending tasks, 302
Filing system, 305
Financial management, 271–278
Financial plan, 197
Firing. *See* Termination of employee
Fixed costs, 275
Flexibility, 24
  as negotiating imperative, 263
Flow-chart paradigm, 76
Flow diagram, 303
Focus group, 73, 122, 177, 183
Followership
  essential of, 118
  styles of, 117
Follow-up
  of delegate, 40
  to team meeting, 253
  to training program, 224–225
Food differences, 177
Force-field analysis, 104

Forecasting, 277
Formal control, 201–202
Formal recognition systems, 163–164
Foul language, 152–153
Functional plan, 197

G

Gainsharing, 168
Gantt chart, 303
Gatekeepers, 283
Generalist team members, 116
Goals, 198–199
Goof-off, 139
Gossips, 153
Grievances, 210–212, **212**
  handling of, 210–211
  records of, 211–212
  role of supervisor or team leader, 211
Ground rules, for team meetings, 255
Group decision making, **248**
Group empowerment, 59–69
Group problems, 132
Group risk taking, 17
"Groupthink," 17
Guide, coach as, 100–102
Guilt induction, 266
Gunnysacking, 133, 231, 266
Gut reactions, 244, 293

H

Hand-off plan, 86
Handouts, 259
Harassment, helping potential victims of, 179
Hard work, 175
Hierarchical pyramid, flattening of, 75
High-tech professionals, 129–131
  characteristics of, 130–131
  preventing problems with, 131
Honesty, 175
Honeymoon phase, of team building, 87
"Hopscotch" delegation, 36
Horizontal communication, 233
Horizontal delegation, 40
Horizontal negotiation, 262
Human resources matrix, 201, **202**
Humor, 120, 294
Hunch, 244

I

Ideonarcissism, 294
Idiosyncrasies, 295
Idle time, 302–303
"Ignore-zap" approach, 169
Illness, long-term or terminal, 142
Incentive. *See* Recognition and reward
systems
Incessant talkers, 154
Inconsistency, 248
Individual performance, recognition of,
162
Informal control, 202
Informal learning, 220
Informal recognition systems, 164–165,
164–165
Information, as negotiating imperative,
262
Information message, 230
In-house resume, 219–220
Innovation, 120
Integrity, 175
Interactive skills, 221, **222**
Interdepartmental coordination, 273
Interruptions, 300
by telephone calls, 301
by visitors, 300–301
Interteam communication, 100–102
Intoxication in workplace, 144
"Intrapreneur," 292
Intuitive thinking, 241, 243–244,
246–247, 291–293
Inventor, entrepreneur vs, 292
Inventory, 272

J

Jigsaw puzzle fallacy, 248, 294
Job analysis, 219
Job dimensions, 219
Job insecurity, 206
Job mismatch, 129
Job rotation, 54, 67, 116, 209, 218, 225
Just-in-time inventory system, 306
Just-in-time learning, 104, 238

K

Kanban, 306
Know-it-alls, 150–151
fake, 151

L

Laboratory information system (LIS),
190, 237
Leadership skills, 109, 168
Leadership training, 225–226
Learning style, 223–224
Leasing, 275
Legal issues, teams as labor organiza-
tions, 212–213
Letters, 235
tips for writing, 236–237
Liaison agent, coach as, 102
Liars, 154
LIS. *See* Laboratory information system
Listening skills, 104, 233–234
Longevity raise, 167
Long-term illness, 142
Loyalty
definition of, 122
of team members, 122, 124

M

Management
participative. *See* Participative management
of time. *See* Time management
training role, 219
union-management partnership,
205–213
Management-by-information, 98–99
Management information system (MIS),
237
Manager
challenges faced by, 2–3
in organizational politics, 287
team leader vs, 108
Managing-by-objectives, 60
Managing-by-policy, 60
Managing-by-principle, 60
Managing-by-walking-around, 60, 100,
112, 169, 248–249, 307
Manipulative politics, 287
Manipulators, 155–156
manipulation in negotiation, 267–268
Martyr syndrome, 142
Materials management, 272
Maturation stage, of team building,
88–89

Medically disadvantaged persons, 142
Meditation, 244
Meetings. *See also* Team meetings
  electronic, 285
  time management and, 301–302
Meeting skills, 104
Memo, 235
  tips for writing, 236–237
Mentally challenged individuals, 8
Mentor, 169, 220, 281–282
  coach as, 103
  developing successor, 45
  mentor-mentee relationship, 282
Merit pay, 167
Mind-forcing technique, 244
Minority groups, 172–180
Minutes, of team meetings, 257
MIS. *See* Management information system
Mission statement, 63, 76, 98, 104
Mobile laboratory unit, 189
Model, coach as, 103
Monetary reward systems, 166–167
  kinds of, 167–168
Moodiness, 142
Morale, 121–122, 206
Multicultural values, 178–179
Myers-Briggs Type Indicator, 220

N

Nagging doubts, 244
National Labor Relations Board
  (NLRB), 206
Negative politics, 286
Negativism, 148
Negativists, 50, 286
Negotiating skills, 259, 261–269
Negotiation
  aggressive or angry opponents, 268
  barriers to success, 265–266
  between teams, 267–268
  bringing along a team, 267
  with devious people, 268
  flawed techniques in, 266
  horizontal, 262
  negotiating imperatives, 262–263
  for pay raises for your team, 169–170
  preparations for, 263–264
  steps in, 264–265

strategies and tactics that backfire,
  266–267
  at team meetings, 259
  tips for effective, 268–269
  verbal expressions that add power,
  269
Networking
  barriers to, 281
  benefits of, 280
  computer, 285–286
  definition of, 279–280
  effective methods of, 283–285
  to increase bargaining power, 263
  making and maintaining contacts, 283
  negative aspects of, 280–281
  participants in, 282–283
Network power, 263
Neutral observer, 258
New employee, orientation program for,
  226–227
Nitpickers, 111, 259
NLRB. *See* National Labor Relations
  Board
Nonassertive people, 258
Nonconformists, 131–132, 294
Non-English speaking people, 8, 231,
  233, 236
Nonmonetary rewards, **164**, 168–169
Nonverbal messages, 234
Normalization stage. *See* Resolution
  stage
Norms, 175
  team, 86, 118
"Not working," 302–303
Nutritional variables, cultural, 177

O

Objectives, 198–199
  written, 199
Objectors, 259
Older workers, 141
One-minute praising, 112, 166
One-on-one peer training, 224
One-on-one recognition, 165–166
Operating budget, 273
Operational meeting, 99
Operational plan, 197
Operational team, 96
Optimism, 148

Ordering, 272
Organizational change, 22
Organizational culture, 173–180
  changes in, 174
  definition of, 174
  questions that reflect, **176**
  responsibility for, 174–175
  values and norms, 175
Organizational plan, 197
Organizational politics, 286–289
  educational programs about, 288–289
  games that managers play, 287
  games that stakeholders play, 286–287
  improving political skills, 289
  manipulative, 287
  negative, 286
  positive political scripts, 288
  rapport with team members, 288
  unethical, 287–288
Organized labor. *See* Union(s)
Orientation program, 168
  encouraging employee creativity, 227
  leader of, 227
  for new hires, 226–227, 295
  for new team member, 99
  presenting big picture, 227
  stimulating creativity during, 295
  for team leaders, 226, **226**
Outward-bound experience, 86, 218, 220

P

Paper flow, 305
Papyrophobia, 303
Paradigm effect, 292–293
"Paralysis from analysis," 248, 280
Pareto charts, 242, 303
Participative management, 3–5, 59–69
  applications of, 68
  assumptions predicated on, 4–5
  benefits of, 61
  commitment by management, 63
  commitment by supervisors, 64–65
  definition of, 59–61
  disbelievers in, 61
  employee responses to initiatives, 62
  failure of, 68
  feeling of ownership by participants, 62
  history of, 60–61

implementation of, 65–67
  monitoring and evaluation, 67
  organizing issues in, 67
  planning process, 66–67, **66**
leadership traits for, 65
prerequisites for, 4, 62–65
problems and pitfalls in, 67–68
union rights and, 68
Patience, as leadership trait, 65
Patient-focused care (PFC), 189, **190–191**
Pay-for-knowledge, 167–168
Pay-for-performance, 167
Pay-for-skills, 167–168
Pay raises, 166–167
  negotiating raises for your team, 169–170
  rejecting requests for, 170
Peer(s), networking with, 282
Peer feedback, 90
Peer review, 90
Peer training, 224
People problems, 128
  dealing with, 133–134
    coping approach, 134–135
    inability to solve problem, 135
    mistakes in, 133
Perfectionists, 16, 140, 299
Performance appraisal, 102, 124, 162. *See also* Team performance appraisal
Performance review, 118
Performance standards, 162
Personal appearance, 152–153
Personal problems, 129
Personnel resource audit, 104
Personnel selection criteria, 120–121, **121**
Persuasion, 261–269
  coach as persuader, 98
Pessimists, 148
PFC. *See* Patient-focused care
Physically challenged individuals, 8
Physical plan, 197
Pilot study, 85
Planning
  activity plans for team building, 85
  benefits of, 197
  for change, 25–26
  classification of plans, 197–198

contingency, 200
for implementing participative management, 66–67, **66**
for negotiation, 263–264
for process reengineering, 197–198
review of plan, 200–201
succession. *See* Succession planning
time management, 306
Playfulness, 294
Point-of-care testing, 189
Policy-making team, 73
Politics. *See* Organizational politics
Position bargaining, 266–267
Postmeeting activities, 257
Power communication. *See*
    Communication
Power language, 258
Powerlessness
    causal factors in, 50
    characteristics of powerless people,
        50–51
    effects of, 50
    feelings of, 49–50
Power persuader, 261–269
Praise master, 169
    team leader as, 111–112
Praising, one-minute, 112, 166
Prejudice, 176
Pride, 175
Prima donna complex, 130–131
Priorities, 201
Proactivity, 299
Problem fighters, 299
Problem prevention, 248–249, 299
Problem solving, 239–249, 295
    analytical approach to, 241
    basics of consensus, 245, **245**
    creative, 246–247
    decision making vs, 241
    formulation of objectives, 242–243
    group, 244–245
    intuitive approach to, 241, 243–244
    in process reengineering, 202
    steps in, 241–243
    by team members, 120
Problem statement, 241–242, 247
Process reengineering, 8, 83
    applications of, 188–189
    assigning tasks and responsibilities,
        201, **202**

barriers to, 191–192, **192**
definition of, 186
detecting situations that should be
    improved, 195–198
flawed systems, 187
health care results of, 189–190
making modification/adjustment in
    plan, 202
monitoring, controlling, and recording
    activities, 201–202
planning for, 197–200
practical aspects of, 195–202
principles of, 181–192
problem solving, 202
steps in project development, 198–202
traditional vs reengineered processes,
    186–187
visions, goals, and objectives, 198–199
Process reengineering team, 73
Procrastination, 16–17, 299
    in decision making, 247–248
Profanity, 152–153
Professional competencies, 221
Professional contacts, 283
Project, 182
    objectives of, 182
Project management, 8
    evaluation of, 185
    principles of, 181–192
Project management software, 182
Project proposal, 184–185
    components of, 184
    selling of, 185
Project results, 185
Project systems, 183
Project team, 73
Project tools, 182–183
Promotion, 25, 29
Proposal. *See* Project proposal
Purchase order, 272
Purchasing function, 272

Q

Quality circle, 5, 10, 60–61, 73, 183–185
    advantages and disadvantages of, 184
    anticipated results of, 183
    appropriate topics for, 183–185
    history of, 183
Quality improvement system, 183

Quality of work life (QWL), 108–109
QWL. *See* Quality of work life

R

Recognition and reward systems, 7–8,
    109, 161–170
  for behavioral modification, 133
  benefits of, 163
  changes associated with team building,
    161–162
  formal, 163–164
  goals of, 163
  individual differences in recognition
    sought, 163
  informal, 164–165, **164–165**
  measurement of goal achievement, 163
  monetary rewards, 166–167
  nonmonetary rewards, **164**, 168–169
  one-on-one recognition, 165–166
  payoff for change, 25, 31, **32**
  recognition of individual perfor-
    mances, **162**
  rewards as negotiating imperative, 262
  team leader as praise master, 111–112
  team recognition, **165**
  unions and, 209
Record(s)
  of grievances, 211–212
  of process reengineering, 201–202
  of team meetings, 253
  time, 303, **304**
Recorder, at team meeting, 253
Reengineering
  corporate, 185–186
  process. *See* Process reengineering
Reforming stage, of team building, 89
Relaxation techniques, 244, 294
Religious beliefs, 177
Requisition, 272
Resolution stage, of team building, 88
Respect, for team leader, 109
Resume, in-house, 219–220
Revenue budget, 273
Revenue projection, 277
Reward. *See* Recognition and reward
    systems
Ridicule, as barrier to negotiation, 266
Risk
  definition of, 14

of empowerment, 51
Risk avoiders, 15–17
Risk taking, 13–20
  career advancement and, 15
  change and, 24
  characteristics of risk takers, 17
  customer service and, 14–15
  decision making and, 14
  delegation and, 14
  encouraging others to take risks,
    19–20
  entrepreneurship, 292
  group, 17
  importance of, 14–15
  minimizing risks in risk taking, 18–19,
    18
  in succession planning, 42
  supervisory activities involving, 15, **15**
  at team meetings, 259
Rivalry
  between individuals, 132
  between teams, 132
Role clarification stage. *See* Resolution
    stage
Rolodex, 305
Roundabout phrases, 236, **237**
RUMBAS, 199
Run chart, 303

S

Sabotage, 132
Sacrifice, sense of, 51
Salary
  discussions with team member, 170
  monetary reward systems, 166–167
  negotiating pay raises for your team,
    169–170
  rejecting requests for increases, 170
Sarcastic attitude, 149
Scheduling
  in process reengineering, 200
  time management, 306
Secrecy, as barrier to negotiation, 266
Self-directed work team, 3, 6, 60. *See
    also* Team entries
  changes during transition to, 96–97
  characteristics of effective team, 76–77
  definitions of, 72
  establishment of, 83–91

features of, 77, **78**
members of, 7, 76
responsibilities of, 73, **73**
supervisor of, 77
supervisor-coach, 95–105
supervisors-in-transition, 6–7
traditional work groups vs, 73, **73**
Self-efficacy, 26, 47–48
Self-expression, denial of, 50
Sexist remarks, 152–153
Shared governance, 4
barriers to, 9–10
Sharpshooters, 17
Shoot-from-the-hip decision makers, 259
Silence, power of, 234
Simulations, 218
Situational leadership, 64, 109, 168
Skill-based pay, 167–168
Skills inventory, 104, 116–117, **117**,
219, 225
"Skunk Works," 6
Slow worker, 140
Snipers, 155
Socializers, 154
Specialists, 80–81, 116
Specimen transport, 190
Speechmakers, 259
Standing order, 272
Statistic(s), in negotiation, 267
Statistical budget, 273
Steering committee, in team establish-
ment, 84–85
Stereotypes, 176
Steward (union), 208–210
Storage area, 272
Storyboard, 183
Straight line items, 275
Strategic plan, 197
Substance abuse, 141–143
Succession planning, 41–45
benefits of, 42
database for, 43, **44**
grooming successor, 43–45, **45**
monitoring of, 45
risks in, 42
selection and training plan, 43–45,
44–45
Suicide, 142

Supersensitive people, 150
Supervisor
activities involving large risks, 15, **15**
benefits of teams, 74
coach vs, 97
commitment to participative management, 64–65
dealing with cultural diversity,
179–180
deficiencies causing team to fail,
77–79, **80**
fate when self-directed work teams
take over, 96
in group problem solving, 244–245
handling of complaints and grievances,
211
involvement in changes, 25
of self-directed work team, 77
union-management partnership,
205–213
Supervisor-in-transition, 6–7, 95–105
training of, 225–226
Supervisory competency, 221, **222**
Supplemental tasks, 302
Supplies
management of, 272
purchasing of, 272
SWOT analysis, 198

T

Tardiness, 138
solutions for, 139
Task force, 5, 73
Task identification, 200
Task sequencing, 200
Task time analyzer, 303, **304**
TAT. *See* Turnaround time
Team, 5–6
disadvantages of, 75
group problem solving, 244–245
illegal labor organizations, 212–213
implementing changes, 26–27
negotiation between teams, 267–268
rivalry between teams, 132
types of, 72–73
Team accountability, 76
Team behavior, 118
Team building, 6, 83–91

changes in recognition and reward systems, 161–162
examples of, 91
initial activity plans, 85
preimplementation phase of
information collection, 84
steering committee, 84–85
prerequisites to, 75–76
for process reengineering, 188
stages of
confusion stage, 87–88
maturation/unification stage, 88–89
reforming or disbanding stage, 89
resolution stage, 88
transition stage, 86–87
supervisor-coach in, 95–105
supervisors-in-transition, 6–7
union-management partnership in, 205–213
Team concept
barriers to shared governance, 9–10
benefits of
to customers, 74–75
to organization, 74–75
to supervisors, 74
to team members, 74
Team dynamics, 80–81, **81**
Team failure, reasons for
attitude or incompetence of managers, 77–79, **80**
dysfunctional dynamics, 80–81, **81**
lack of management support, 77, **78**
resistant or incompetent team members, 79–80
Team leader, 7, 77, 107–112
barriers to, 109–110
coach and, 95–96
dealing with cultural diversity, 179–180
handling of complaints and grievances, 211
involvement in changes, 25
leadership sins of, 110
leadership skills of, 109
manager vs, 108
orientation program for, 226, **226**
permanent, 108
as praise master, 111–112

relationship with union, 209
responsibilities of, 108–109
rotation of, 108
tips for, 110–111
Team meetings, 251–259
Abilene paradox, 256
agenda for, 254
better negotiating at, 259
components of, 252–253
decision making in, 256
discussions vs arguments, 255–256
don'ts for chair, 257
effective participation in, 257–258
encouraging participation in, 255
end of, 256
facilitator's role in, 253–254
follow-up to, 253
ground rules for, 255
handouts at, 259
latecomers to, 302
maintaining control in, 256
nonassertive people at, 258
postmeeting activities, 257
preparations by chair, 253–254
problem members at, 259
purposes of, 252
record of, 253, 257
responsibilities of chair, 254
selection of attendees, 254
start of, 255
timekeeper at, 253
tips for member participation, 258
visual aids at, 259
weaknesses or abuses of, 252
Team member(s), 7, 115–124
assigning specific tasks/responsibilities to, 124
benefits of belonging to team, 74
characteristics of great team players, 119–120
competencies of, 116–117
deficiencies of, 79–80
excessive demands on time, 300
followership styles of, 117
loyalty of, 122, 124
new. *See* Orientation program
people with difficulty serving on teams, 132
resistant or incompetent, 79–80

salary discussions, 170
selection of, 120–121, **121**
self-directed work team, 76
Team morale, 121–122
Team norms, 86, 118
Team performance appraisal, 89–90
  designing system for, 90
  peer feedback, 90
  selection of evaluator, 90
Team productivity, 108–109
Team publicist, 102
Team recognition, **165**
Team simulation games, 218
Team skills, 221, **222**
Team sports, 86
Team training. *See* Cross-training;
  Training
Teamwork, 5
Teamwork potential, 120–121, **121**
Tears, as barrier to negotiation, 266
Technical skills, 221
Technological change, 22
Teleconferencing, 301
Telephone calls, 301
Telephone tag, 301
Temper tantrum, 150, 154–155
Terminal illness, 142
Termination of employee, 135, 143
Thank you note, 112, 257
Tickler file, 305
Time, as negotiating imperative, 263
Timekeeper, at team meeting, 253
Time log, 302
Time management, 198, 200, 297–308
  categorization of tasks, 302–303
  charts to aid, 303
  controlling visitors, 300–301
  daily action lists, 306
  efficiency of office/workstation,
    303–305
  electronic aids, 305, **305**
  failure of time management programs,
    298
  meetings, 301–302
  planning and scheduling, 306
  telephone calls, 301
  time records, 303, **304**
  time thefts, 307–308
  tips for improving, 307

Time records, 303, **304**
Time theft, 307–308
Time wasters (underperforming individuals), 140–141
Time wasters (situations), 298
  external, 300–302
  internal, 298–299
Togetherness, 119
Total quality management (TQM), 4
TQM. *See* Total quality management
Training, 5, 9, 168. *See also* Cross-
  training
  adequacy of, 54
  apprenticeships, 218
  benefits of, 218
  choosing trainers, 223
  of coaches, 104
  determination of training needs, 219
  evaluation of program, 223, **223**
  follow-up to, 224–225
  group rules for formal sessions, 223
  guidelines for, 223
  leadership, 225–226
  management's role in, 219
  on organizational politics, 288–289
  for participative management, 66–67
  peer, 224
  succession planning, 43–45, **44–45**
  teaching sources and tools, 220
  of team members, 217–227
  timing of, 220
  topics covered in, 221
Training center, 220
Transition. *See* Change
Transition stage, of team building,
  86–87
Traveling requisition, 272
Troubled employee, 141–144
Turnaround time (TAT), reduced,
  189–190

U

Ultimatums, 266
Ultraconservatives, 259
Uncooperative people, 152
Underperformers, 137–144
  "can'ts" and "won'ts," 137–138
  goof-off, 139

older worker, 141
perfectionist, 140
slow worker, 140
tardiness and absenteeism, 138–139
time wasters, 140–141
troubled employee, 141–144
Unethical behavior, 156
Unethical politics, 287–288
Union(s), 8–9, 205–213
complaints and grievances, 210–212,
212
infringement of participative management on rights of, 68
organizing drives, 207–208
reasons that employees join, 206–207,
207
Union contract, 207–208
supervisory difficulty imposed by,
210
Union representative, 208–209
relations with supervisors, 209–210
Unnecessary tasks, 302–303
Unpleasant people, 147–156
bad appearance, 152–153
chronic complainers, 149–150
concealers, 151–152
critics, 147–148
cynics, 149
employees who bypass their leader,
153
explosive tempers, 154–155
fake know-it-alls, 151
foul language, 152–153
gossips, 153
incessant talkers and socializers, 154
know-it-alls, 150–151
liars, 154
manipulators, 155–156
pessimists, 148
snipers, 155
supersensitive people, 150
uncooperative types, 152
unethical types, 156
Upward delegation, 36

V

Values
multicultural, 178–179
organizational, 175
Variable costs, 275
Vendors, networking with, 283
Verbal communication
tips for improving, 234
written communication vs, 235
Verbal message, 230–231, 235
Victim mindset, 50–51
Vision(s), 76, 198
Visionary, coach as, 97–98
Vision statement, 63, 98
Visitors, interruptions by, 300–301
Visual aids
design criteria for, 259
at team meetings, 259
Voice mail, 230
Voice quality, 234

W

Weepers, 150
Whiners, 149
"Wild ducks," 130
"Won'ts" (underperformers), 137–138
Work circle, 91
Work ethic, 119
Workforce
change in, 23–24
stability of, 24
Work shifts, communication between, 99
Work station rotation. See Job rotation
Work team. See also Team
empowerment of, 55–56
self-directed. See Self-directed work
team
Writing skills, 235
Written communication, 235
verbal communication vs, 235
Written record, of grievances, 211–212

Z

Zero-based budget, 275